THE CHEMISTRY
OF SULFIDES

One of a Series of Collective Volumes Sponsored by

THE SULPHUR INSTITUTE
Washington, D.C.—London

THE CHEMISTRY
OF SULFIDES

EDITED BY

Arthur V. Tobolsky

Frick Chemical Laboratory
Princeton University
Princeton, New Jersey

INTERSCIENCE PUBLISHERS

A DIVISION OF JOHN WILEY & SONS

NEW YORK-LONDON-SYDNEY

CHEMISTRY

Library of Congress Catalog Card Number 67-29545

Printed in the United States of America

Foreword

Organic and inorganic sulfides are abundant and play a very important role in science and industry. Inorganic sulfides occur in large mineral deposits, and organic sulfides occur in minerals, in petroleum, and in all living organisms. In recent years, sulfides have been discovered to be most useful and interesting participants in polymer chemistry.

In view of their wide occurrence and great scientific and industrial importance, it is astonishing how little is known about the basic properties of sulfides. But research in all fields of sulfur chemistry is now rapidly gaining momentum. It is the purpose of The Sulphur Institute-sponsored conferences to highlight developments in new and expanding fields, and to give scientists an opportunity to review progress.

The Princeton University Conference on the Chemistry of Sulfides held at Princeton University, June 29–July 1, 1966, served to highlight three fields: Fundamental Chemistry of Sulfides, Sulfide-Containing Polymers, and Sulfides in Biological Systems.

In recent years, sulfur-containing polymers have attracted increasing attention. After many years of intensive basic research, industrially useful sulfur-containing polymers can now be formulated. As a result, sulfur polymers are entering the industrial world, and research in this field has been expanding quickly into developmental work. One of the aims of the Princeton Conference was to accentuate this transition from an exploratory basic science to a fully developed field, and to provide an opportunity for interested researchers to review part of this exciting field by looking back over the achievements in the basic chemistry, and to look forward toward new goals of better basic understanding, and possible goals in developing new commercial sulfur-containing polymers.

This conference also afforded an opportunity to celebrate the outstanding pioneering work in the polymer field by the excellent research group of Professor A. V. Tobolsky in Princeton. Professor Tobolsky's contribution opened completely new vistas in sulfur polymers, and in his teaching capacity, he provided and provides the chemical world with a whole generation of much needed sulfur chemists.

The dinner speaker of this conference, Professor A. I. Virtanen, Nobel laureate 1945, provided the conference with a unique and excellent opportunity to highlight progress in the biological field.

v

615

Scientists from all over the world gathered in Princeton to exchange information. In the spirit of earlier conferences sponsored by The Sulphur Institute, such as the meetings on Sulfur Allotropes in Berkeley, 1964, and the meeting on Organic Sulfur Chemistry in Groningen, Holland, 1966, an attempt was made to bring together specialists from different fields: Physical Chemistry, Polymer Chemistry, Organic Chemistry, Biochemistry, and Developmental Chemistry. In this way the topic could be covered in a very broad way, and the participants had a unique opportunity to hear about progress in fields far removed from their daily work.

It is our belief that the Princeton University Conference on the Chemistry of Sulfides was a great success. It proved again that interdisciplinary stimulation constitutes an important contribution toward progress. We wish to thank Professor A. V. Tobolsky for his outstanding work which made this conference possible, and the Princeton University Conference staff under Mr. Sapo, who provided a most stimulating location and organization.

Although the written word can hardly communicate the lively spirit of the conference, we are sure that the reader will find the chapters of this book full of new information. The interdisciplinary combination of articles is unique and should help the reader to survey readily the past and present work in this rapidly expanding field.

Beat Meyer
Director of Research
The Sulphur Institute
Washington, D.C. and London

Washington, D.C.
October 1967

Preface

The Princeton Conference on the Chemistry of Sulfides was held at Princeton University June 29–July 1, 1966. Nearly two hundred guests from industry, government, and universities attended the conference.

The Conference was divided into three sessions: Fundamental Chemistry of Sulfides, H. Gunning, Chairman; Sulfide-Containing Polymers, A. V. Tobolsky, Chairman; and Sulfides in Biological Systems, E. T. Kaiser, Chairman. We regret that some significant papers, especially in the biochemical area, were not available.

Most of the papers are concerned with substances containing the sulfide or polysulfide linkage. A few papers relating to higher oxidation states of sulfur were included because they seemed relevant to other papers in the program.

The chemistry of sulfides and polysulfides is of wide interest, including practical topics such as rubber vulcanization and hair curling, and vital topics such as muscle contraction. This compilation of articles does not cover the chemistry of sulfides in a very comprehensive or in a definitively organized manner. It rather presents recent research in a wide variety of fields. As such we hope it will stimulate the reader to further studies in this area.

The aid of The Sulphur Institute in organizing this conference is gratefully acknowledged, and specifically the help of Dr. Marion Barnes and Dr. Beat Meyer. We also acknowledge the assistance of the AROD in supporting our research in polysulfides.

Arthur V. Tobolsky

October, 1967

AUTHORS

M. B. BERENBAUM, Thiokol Chemical Corporation, Trenton, New Jersey

G. L. BRODE, Union Carbide Corporation, Bound Brook, New Jersey

R. E. DAVIS, Purdue University, West Lafayette, Indiana

J. A. EMPEN, Plastics Department, Experimental Station, E. I. du Pont de Nemours and Company, Wilmington, Delaware

R. H. GOBRAN, Thiokol Chemical Corporation, Trenton, New Jersey

J. W. GREIDANUS, Fundamental Sulphur Research Group, Alberta Sulphur Research Ltd., and Department of Chemistry, University of Calgary, Alberta, Canada

ERHARD GROSS, National Institute of Arthritis and Metabolic Diseases, National Institutes of Health, Bethesda, Maryland

M. C. GUENTHNER, Purdue University, West Lafayette, Indiana

H. E. GUNNING, Department of Chemistry, University of Alberta, Edmonton, Alberta, Canada

J. B. HYNE, Fundamental Sulphur Research Group, Alberta Sulphur Research Ltd., and Department of Chemistry, University of Calgary, Alberta, Canada

WILLIAM L. JOLLY, Department of Chemistry, University of California, and Inorganic Materials Research Division, Lawrence Radiation Laboratory, Berkeley, California

EMIL THOMAS KAISER, Department of Chemistry, The University of Chicago, Chicago, Illinois

NORMAN KHARASCH, University of Southern California, Los Angeles, California

AHMED I. KHODAIR, Department of Chemistry, Assuit University, Assuit, U.A.R.

C. G. KRESPAN, Central Research Department, Experimental Station, E. I. du Pont de Nemours and Company, Wilmington, Delaware

F. LAUTENSCHLAEGER, Dunlop Research Centre, Sheridan Park, Ontario, Canada

G. E. MEYER, Reactive Diene Rubbers Section, The Goodyear Tire and Rubber Company Research Laboratory, Akron, Ohio

J. A. MOORE, Institute of Polymer Research, Polytechnic Institute of Brooklyn, Brooklyn, New York

S. W. OSBORN, Thiokol Chemical Corporation, Trenton, New Jersey

C. G. OVERBERGER, Department of Chemistry, University of Michigan, Ann Arbor, Michigan

T. L. PICKERING, Plastics Division, Union Carbide Corporation, Bound Brook, New Jersey

M. PORTER, The Natural Rubber Producers' Research Association, Welwyn Garden City, Herts., England

LUDWIG REBENFELD, Textile Research Institute and Princeton University, Princeton, New Jersey

HIKOICHI SAKAI, Department of Biophysics and Biochemistry, Tokyo University, Bunkyo-Ku, Tokyo, Japan

K. J. SAUNDERS, National College of Rubber Technology, London, England

W. H. SHARKEY, Central Research Department, Experimental Station, E. I. du Pont de Nemours and Company, Wilmington, Delaware

GABRIEL STEIN, Department of Physical Chemistry, Hebrew University, Jerusalem, Israel

J. K. STILLE, Department of Chemistry, University of Iowa, Iowa City, Iowa

O. P. STRAUSZ, Department of Chemistry, University of Alberta, Alberta, Canada

A. V. TOBOLSKY, Princeton University, Princeton, New Jersey

F. J. TOURO, Freeport Sulphur Company, Belle Chasse, Louisiana

E. S. WAGNER, Purdue University, West Lafayette, Indiana

HANS-DIETRICH WEIGMANN, Textile Research Institute, Princeton, New Jersey

T. K. WIEWIOROWSKI, Freeport Sulphur Company, Belle Chasse, Louisiana

CONTENTS

PART I
Fundamental Chemistry of Sulfides

Recent Studies of Sulfur–Nitrogen Bonds. By WILLIAM L. JOLLY . . 3

The Sulfur–Hydrogen Sulfide System. By T. K. WIEWIOROWSKI AND F. J. TOURO 9

Synthesis of Sulfur Compounds by Singlet and Triplet Sulfur Atom Reactions. By O. P. STRAUSZ AND H. E. GUNNING . . . 23

Recent Advances in the Chemistry of the Sulfur–Sulfur Bond. By R. E. DAVIS, E. S. WAGNER, AND M. C. GUENTHNER . . . 45

Cleavage and Disproportionation Reactions in Organic Polysulfides. By T. L. PICKERING, K. J. SAUNDERS, AND A. V. TOBOLSKY . . 61

The Synthesis of Novel Bicyclic Sulfides from Sulfur Dichloride and Cyclic Diolefins. By F. LAUTENSCHLAEGER 73

Transmission of Electronic Effects in Certain Sulfides. By J. B. HYNE AND J. W. GREIDANUS 83

Photolysis of Organic Sulfides and of Related Substances. By NORMAN KHARASCH AND AHMED I. KHODAIR 105

PART II
Sulfide-Containing Polymers

Adduct Rubber—Elastomers Obtained by Reaction of Mercaptans with Diene Polymers and Copolymers. By G. E. MEYER . . . 113

Polymerization of Cyclic Sulfides. By J. K. STILLE AND J. A. EMPEN . 125

The Relationship of Thermal Stability and Molecular Structure in Sulfone Compounds and Polymers. By G. L. BRODE . . . 133

Some New Monosulfide Polymers. By R. H. GOBRAN, M. B. BERENBAUM, AND S. W. OSBORN 145

On the Oxidation of Polyvinyl Mercaptan. By C. G. OVERBERGER AND J. A. MOORE 157

The Chemistry of the Sulfur Vulcanization of Natural Rubber. By M. PORTER 165

The Role of Disulfide Interchange in Keratin Fiber Deformation. By HANS-DIETRICH WEIGMANN AND LUDWIG REBENFELD . . . 185

Polymerization of Fluorothiocarbonyl Compounds. By W. H. SHARKEY 205

Fluorinated Polysulfides. By C. G. KRESPAN 211

Interchange Reactions in Alkyl Polysulfide Polymers. By M. B. BERENBAUM 221

PART III
Sulfides in Biological Systems

Electron Exchange between Thiols and Disulfides during Cell Division.
    By HIKOICHI SAKAI   231
The Action of Cyanogen Bromide on Protein-Bound Sulfur-Containing
    Amino Acids. By ERHARD GROSS   235
Studies on Esters of Sulfur-Containing Acids. By EMIL THOMAS KAISER   257
The Reactivity of Some Sulfur-Containing Compounds of Biological
    Interest with One-Electron Equivalent Reagents. By GABRIEL STEIN   263

Author Index   265

Subject Index   275

PART I

Fundamental Chemistry of Sulfides

Recent Studies of Sulfur–Nitrogen Compounds*

WILLIAM L. JOLLY

*University of California and
Lawrence Radiation Laboratory,
Berkeley, California*

Sulfur–nitrogen chemistry is a fascinating area of study because it has not yet been systematized. With our present understanding, it is very difficult, or impossible, to predict the structures and reactions of sulfur–nitrogen compounds. In this chapter several examples of recent research aimed at determining the structures and systematizing the reactions of these compounds are discussed.

SULFUR–NITROGEN–CHLORINE COMPOUNDS

Who would have predicted that a solid compound of formula S_4N_3Cl would form upon heating S_4N_4 with S_2Cl_2?

$$3S_4N_4 + 2S_2Cl_2 \longrightarrow 4S_4N_3Cl$$

This is just one of many similar reactions (1,2) which defy rationalization. Perhaps even more remarkable than this synthesis is the structure of S_4N_3Cl. A large number of metathetical reactions carried out in solvents such as formic acid and sulfuric acid show that the compound is just one member of a series of salts of general formula $S_4N_3^+X^-$. Two x-ray diffraction studies of the nitrate, $S_4N_3NO_3$, have shown that the $S_4N_3^+$ cation is a nearly planar seven-membered ring (1) (3). Concurrent with the

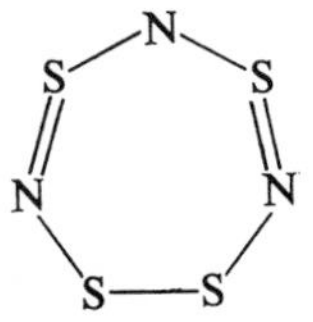

(1)

x-ray studies, we used ^{15}N NMR to study the structure of the $S_4N_3^+$ ion (4). Although the NMR method yielded nowhere near as much

* This work was supported by the United States Atomic Energy Commission.

structural information as the x-ray studies, this work will be discussed here because the method is relatively simple and is potentially applicable to a large number of nitrogen compounds.

Initially we tried ^{14}N NMR on a solution of normal S_4N_3Cl. However, the quadrupole broadening of the ^{14}N nuclei was so great that only an extremely broad, useless band was observed. It was clear that it would be necessary to use ^{15}N nuclei, which have spin $\frac{1}{2}$ and no quadrupole moment. Therefore we synthesized the ^{15}N-enriched compound, and ran the ^{15}N NMR spectrum. The spectrum consisted of two relatively sharp signals with intensities in a 1 : 2 ratio (see Fig. 1). The weaker signal was a triplet, as expected from coupling to two equivalent nitrogen atoms, and the stronger signal was a doublet, as expected from coupling to a unique nitrogen atom. The spectrum was thus entirely consistent with the structure shown above, and inconsistent with any structures having three equivalent nitrogens or three nonequivalent nitrogens.

The synthesis of the ^{15}N-enriched S_4N_3Cl presented some problem, because synthesis from S_4N_4 and S_2Cl_2 would require the preparation of ^{15}N-enriched S_4N_4, and preparation of the latter compound from S_2Cl_2 and ^{15}NH$_3$ would be very wasteful of NH$_3$. We developed a relatively efficient process for preparing S_4N_3Cl from ^{15}N-enriched NH$_4$Cl and S_2Cl_2. The first step of the procedure involved the refluxing of a mixture of the reagents, using an air condenser. NSCl vapor was evolved, and this

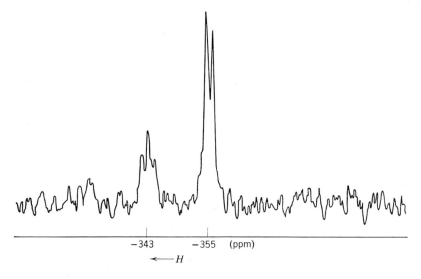

Fig. 1. The nitrogen-15 NMR Spectrum of $S_4{}^{15}N_3^+$. Reproduced from reference 4 by permission of the American Chemical Society.

combined with the cool S_2Cl_2 in the air condenser to form crystals of $S_3N_2Cl_2$.

$$NH_4Cl + 2S_2Cl_2 \longrightarrow NSCl + 3S + 4HCl$$

$$2NSCl + S_2Cl_2 \longrightarrow S_3N_2Cl_2 + SCl_2$$

The reaction pot was then replaced with a flask containing carbon tetrachloride and S_2Cl_2, and by refluxing this mixed solvent, the S_4N_3Cl crystals were converted to S_4N_3Cl.

$$3S_3N_2Cl_2 + S_2Cl_2 \longrightarrow 2S_4N_3Cl + 3SCl_2$$

By stopping the procedure after the initial refluxing of S_2Cl_2 with NH_4Cl, it was possible to isolate the crystalline $S_3N_2Cl_2$. Some of these crystals were submitted to Zalkin, Hopkins, and Templeton, who determined the crystal structure by x-ray diffraction (5). Here again the structure is quite remarkable and was completely unanticipated. The compound is a salt with an $S_3N_2Cl^+$ cation and a Cl^- anion. The cation contains a five-membered ring (2).

(2)

SULFUR NITRIDE–LEWIS ACID ADDUCTS

Sulfur nitride, S_4N_4, forms adducts with a wide variety of Lewis acids. The following empirical formulas have been reported: $S_4N_4 \cdot SbCl_5$ (6,7), $2S_4N_4 \cdot SnCl_4$ (6,7), $S_4N_4 \cdot TiCl_4$ (6,7), $S_4N_4 \cdot 2SO_3$ (8), $S_4N_4 \cdot 4SO_3$ (8), $S_4N_4 \cdot TeBr_4$ (9), $S_4N_4 \cdot 4SbF_5$ (10), and $4S_4N_4 \cdot BF_3$ (11). The unusual stoichiometry reported for the BF_3 adduct, and a lack of information regarding the other boron trihalide adducts, led us to a systematic study of the reaction of S_4N_4 with boron trihalides (12).

We found that S_4N_4 in methylene chloride reacts with BF_3 to form burgundy-colored crystals of $S_4N_4 \cdot BF_3$ and with BCl_3 to form red-orange needles of $S_4N_4 \cdot BCl_3$. The properties of the adducts are consistent with structures involving B—N bonds.

The $S_4N_4 \cdot BF_3$ adduct is fairly labile. It decomposes reversibly to S_4N_4 and BF_3 when heated, and the BF_3 in the adduct may be displaced by BCl_3 or $SbCl_5$. On the other hand, the $S_4N_4 \cdot BCl_3$ adduct is much less labile. This adduct, when heated, sublimes with slight decomposition. When we attempted to displace BCl_3 from $S_4N_4 \cdot BCl_3$ by treatment with $SbCl_5$, a completely unexpected result was obtained. Instead of obtaining $S_4N_4 \cdot SbCl_5$, we obtained the adduct $S_4N_4 \cdot BCl_3 \cdot SbCl_5$. This product is remarkable because no diadducts are found in the reaction of S_4N_4 with either excess BCl_3 or $SbCl_5$. Possibly the mixed adduct can be formulated as $S_4N_4BCl_2^+ \ SbCl_6^-$.

SULFUR NITRIDE PARAMAGNETIC ANIONS

Chapman and Massey (13) observed that a series of color changes is obtained when S_4N_4 is reduced with alkali metals in dimethoxyethane, and they observed a nine-line electron spin resonance spectrum, characteristic of a paramagnetic species containing four equivalent nitrogen atoms. They concluded that the spectrum was due to the $S_4N_4^-$ anion, in which the unpaired electron is delocalized over the entire S_4N_4 ring.

More recently, we have observed that several paramagnetic species are formed when a solution of S_4N_4 in tetrahydrofuran is titrated with sodium naphthaleneide (14). First both a five-line ESR signal and a three-line ESR signal are observed. The five-line signal is attributable to a species with two equivalent nitrogen atoms, and the three-line signal is due to a species with one nitrogen atom. These two signals disappear as more naphthaleneide is added, and are replaced by a weak nine-line spectrum identical to that observed by Chapman and Massey.

It was very difficult for us to understand how sulfur nitride fragment radicals could form *before* formation of an $S_4N_4^-$ radical. However, Meinzer and Myers (15) have recently completed an ESR study which clarifies this aspect of the problem. They have found that reduction of S_4N_4 in tetrahydrofuran below $0°$ yields a *new* nine-line spectrum, with a g value and splitting constant quite different from those of the spectrum first observed by Chapman and Massey. Above $0°$ this new radical decomposes to give the one- and two-nitrogen radicals and, with further reduction, the four-nitrogen radical of Chapman and Massey. It is believed that the new four-nitrogen species is the $S_4N_4^-$ ion, in which the odd electron is delocalized over the entire molecule, and that the other four-nitrogen species, $S_xN_4^-$, is somehow formed by the combination of smaller fragments.

The ESR parameters of all the sulfur nitride radicals which have been observed in tetrahydrofuran are presented in Table 1. The assignment of the new nine-line spectrum to $S_4N_4^-$ is supported by the following evidence: (*a*) The ESR spectrum of the new radical is broadened by the addition of S_4N_4, as would be expected for an electron-exchange reaction.

Table 1

Electron Spin Resonance Parameters of Sulfur
Nitride Radicals in Tetrahydrofuran

Radical	Number of lines	g	A (gauss)
$S_xN_2^-$	5	2.0101	5.13
S_xN	3	2.0053	11.2
$S_xN_4^-$	9	2.0065	3.13
e^- (free)		2.0023	
$S_4N_4^-$	9	2.0006	1.20

(b) The new radical is formed in high yields at low temperatures, and is a plausible precursor of the fragment radicals which form at higher temperatures. (c) The magnitudes of the A and g values are such as to put the new radical in a different class from the other radicals, indicating a different bonding type. It is suggested that the odd electron is essentially delocalized over all the atoms in $S_4N_4^-$, whereas it is relatively localized on nitrogen atoms in the other radicals.

References

1. E. Demarcay, *Compt. Rend.*, **91**, 854 (1880).
2. M. Goehring, *Ergebnisse und Probleme der Chemie der Schwefelstickstoffver-bindungen*, Akademie-Verlag, Berlin, 1957.
3. J. Weiss, *Z. Anorg. Allgem. Chem.*, **333**, 314 (1964); A. W. Cordes, R. F. Kruh, and E. K. Gordon, *Inorg. Chem.*, **4**, 681 (1965).
4. N. Logan and W. L. Jolly, *Inorg. Chem.*, **4**, 1508 (1965).
5. A. Zalkin, T. E. Hopkins, and D. H. Templeton, *Inorg. Chem.*, **5**, 1767 (1966).
6. O. C. M. Davis, *J. Chem. Soc.*, **89**, 1575 (1906).
7. H. Wölbling, *Z. Anorg. Chem.*, **57**, 281 (1908).
8. M. Goehring, H. Hohenschutz, and R. Appel, *Z. Naturforsch.*, **96**, 678 (1954).
9. E. E. Aynsley and W. A. Campbell, *J. Chem. Soc.*, **1957**, 832.
10. B. Cohen, T. R. Hooper, D. Hugell, and R. D. Peacock, *Nature*, **207**, 748 (1965).
11. O. Glemser and H. Lüdemann, *Angew. Chem.*, **70**, 190 (1958).
12. K. J. Wynne and W. L. Jolly, *Inorg. Chem.*, **6**, 107 (1967).
13. D. Chapman and A. G. Massey, *Trans. Faraday Soc.*, **58**, 1291 (1962).
14. W. L. Jolly, R. J. Myers, D. W. Pratt, and S. K. Ray, unpublished work.
15. R. A. Meinzer and R. J. Myers, *Am. Chem. Soc., Phys. Chem. Div.*, New York, Sept., 1966.

The Sulfur–Hydrogen Sulfide System

T. K. WIEWIOROWSKI and F. J. TOURO
Freeport Sulphur Company, Belle Chasse, Louisiana

INTRODUCTION

In recent years interest in liquid sulfur chemical equilibria has been increasing. The systems investigated include pure molten sulfur as well as a number of binary systems in which sulfur is the major component. Undoubtedly this interest in liquid sulfur systems originates from the element's unusual properties which can be interpreted in terms of changes in molecular composition occurring as a function of temperature.

This chapter reports on the chemical equilibria in the sulfur–hydrogen sulfide system. The solubility of hydrogen sulfide in molten sulfur has been investigated by Fanelli (1), who has shown that the system exhibits a curious temperature dependence. Hydrogen sulfide solubility increases sharply between 120 and 180°, proceeds through a broad maximum, and then decreases at temperatures above 385°. Fanelli qualitatively interpreted these observations by suggesting that a chemical interaction between hydrogen sulfide and sulfur takes place, resulting in the formation of hydrogen polysulfides in the system. No experimental means, however, were available for him to distinguish between the dissolved hydrogen monosulfide (H_2S) and polysulfide (H_2S_x).

In the course of our research on liquid sulfur systems, it has been found that their chemistry can be conveniently studied by direct infrared measurements. This experimental approach, when applied to hydrogen sulfide solutions in sulfur, provides a suitable method for determining the contributions of H_2S and H_2S_x to the total hydrogen sulfide solubility (2). The data obtained in this manner are presented in the following pages and interpreted in terms of a thermodynamic theory of chemical equilibria in this system.

EXPERIMENTAL

The application of infrared spectrometry to molten sulfur systems poses an experimental problem which originates from the necessity of employing temperatures above 119°C (the melting point of sulfur) during sample preparation and while the spectrum is scanned. The design of an infrared cell which facilitates the handling of molten sulfur samples is shown in Figure 1 (3). Essentially, the cell consists of two aluminum blocks equipped with rod heaters and separated by a Teflon spacer. The cell used in this work had a 6.4 mm light path. Sodium chloride crystals are used as window material, and the cell is equipped with a supporting plate which fits into most commercially available spectrophotometers. For dimensions and other details the reader is referred to reference 3. A Perkin-Elmer 221G infrared spectrophotometer was used in this investigation.

Sulfur purified by the method of Bacon and Fanelli (4) and hydrogen sulfide available in lecture bottles from the Matheson Company were used as reagents. Pure molten sulfur is free of infrared absorption bands over a wide spectral range (1400–4000 cm^{-1}) and can be considered a useful infrared solvent. Since there is no information in the literature on the exact location or intensity of absorption bands which one should observe on the hydrogen sulfide–sulfur system, several preliminary runs were carried out. In the first such run, an infrared cell maintained at 140° was filled with

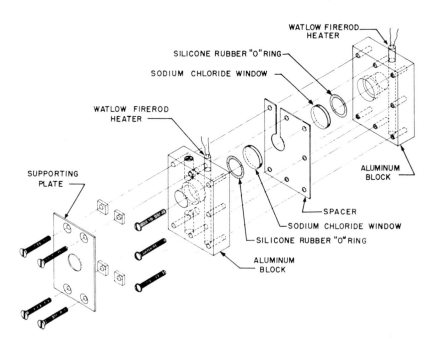

Fig. 1. Infrared cell.

molten sulfur and hydrogen sulfide was bubbled directly into it for a period of 24 hr. The mid-infrared spectrum was then scanned, and the appearance of two bands in the sulfur–hydrogen stretching region, at 2498 and 2570 cm^{-1}, was observed. Consequently, in all subsequent experiments only the 2300–2700 cm^{-1} region of the spectrum was scanned. Results obtained in the next run allowed for the assignment of the two bands to S—H stretching frequencies in hydrogen monosulfide and polysulfide, respectively. In this run, as illustrated in Figure 2a, hydrogen sulfide was again bubbled into molten sulfur contained in an infrared cell, and the spectrum was scanned periodically at predetermined intervals of time. It was observed that the two absorption bands are formed at different rates. The band at 2570 cm^{-1} is generated rapidly; it appeared within a few minutes and reached a constant intensity in less than 30 min. The other band, at 2498 cm^{-1}, is generated slowly; it appeared after 30 min and required about 20 hr to reach an equilibrium concentration. A reverse experiment gave rise to results illustrated in Figure 2b. In this case, nitrogen was passed through molten sulfur which had been previously saturated with hydrogen sulfide at 1 atm of H$_2$S overpressure. Both bands were present at the beginning of the experiment, but it soon became apparent that they not only form at different rates but also disappear at different rates. These observations provide sufficient justification to assign the 2570 cm^{-1} band to the volatile hydrogen monosulfide and the 2498 cm^{-1} band to sulfur–hydrogen stretching in hydrogen polysulfide

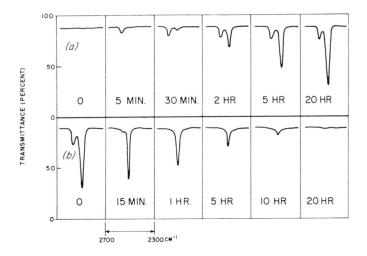

Fig. 2. (a) Generation of infrared bands in sulfur–hydrogen sulfide solutions vs. time at 138°. (b) Disappearance of these bands upon nitrogen blowing.

which is removed from the system as a result of slow conversion to hydrogen monosulfide.

From these preliminary tests, it was evident that infrared spectroscopy could be used to obtain quantitative information on chemical equilibria in the sulfur–hydrogen sulfide system. An experimental approach became available which enables one to break Fanelli's solubility curve down into its two components, namely, the contributions of H_2S and H_2S_x to the total hydrogen sulfide solubility. For this purpose, spectra were obtained on sulfur saturated at several temperatures with hydrogen sulfide at 1 atm of H_2S overpressure. Temperatures were measured by means of a thermocouple immersed in the sulfur, and a range from 125–181° was covered.

RESULTS

Experimental results presented in Table 1 illustrate the effect of temperature on the ratio of hydrogen monosulfide to polysulfide in the system. The

Table 1
Experimentally Observed Absorbance Values

Temp., °C	Observed absorbance		Absorbance corrected for temperature	
	2570 cm^{-1}	2498 cm^{-1}	2570 cm^{-1}	2498 cm^{-1}
125	0.056	0.107	0.050	0.102
132	0.049	0.160	0.049	0.160
148	0.043	0.415	0.048	0.453
156	0.039	0.688	0.047	0.777
162	0.038	0.790	0.046	0.908
181	0.037	0.940	0.045	1.130

band at 2570 cm^{-1}, assigned to S—H stretching in the monosulfide, decreases slowly with rising temperature. However, the intensity of the band at 2498 cm^{-1} increases as the temperature of the system is raised.

During the course of this investigation it has been noted that temperature affects the intensity of absorption bands in the S—H stretching region. Consequently, as shown in Table 1, the experimentally observed band intensities were corrected for temperature. To isolate the temperature effect, the band intensities were measured at constant concentration as a function of temperature. This was done on a sample containing both monosulfide and polysulfide which was repeatedly heated and cooled at high rates. The Lambert-Beer law was applied to the temperature-corrected absorbance values (A), normalized for 132° in order to calculate the relative absorption coefficients, K_{H_2S} and $K_{H_2S_x}$, for the monosulfide and polysulfide. Two equations with two unknowns (K_{H_2S} and $K_{H_2S_x}$) were set up.

$$\frac{A_{H_2S,T_1}}{K_{H_2S}} + \frac{A_{H_2S_x,T_1}}{K_{H_2S_x}} = C_{total\,H_2S,T_1} \tag{1a}$$

$$\frac{A_{H_2S,T_2}}{K_{H_2S}} + \frac{A_{H_2S_x,T_2}}{K_{H_2S_x}} = C_{total\,H_2S,T_2} \tag{1b}$$

To solve these equations, the total hydrogen sulfide concentrations, $C_{total\,H_2S}$, were taken from the data of Fanelli. The values of K_{H_2S} and $K_{H_2S_x}$ were found to be 1.11 and 10.8, respectively, for a 6.4 mm cell. With the use of these relative absorption coefficients, the temperature-corrected experimental absorbancies were converted to concentrations; the results are shown in Table 2. Figure 3 illustrates the contributions of hydrogen mono-

Table 2

The concentration of Hydrogen Monosulfide, Polysulfide, and Total Hydrogen Sulfide as a Function of Temperature

Temp., °C	% H_2S	% H_2S_x (as H_2S)	Total % H_2S	Reported by Fanelli
125	0.0450	0.0094	0.0544	0.056
132	0.0441	0.0149	0.0590	0.059
148	0.0432	0.0418	0.0850	0.082
156	0.0423	0.0718	0.114	0.108
162	0.0414	0.0838	0.125	0.124
181	0.0405	0.1045	0.145	0.145

sulfide and polysulfide to the total hydrogen sulfide concentration. It is apparent that the two components are characterized by a different temperature dependence and that the "unusual" solubility behavior is due to the formation of hydrogen polysulfide in molten sulfur. The solubility of hydrogen monosulfide decreases slowly with increasing temperature in accordance with the van't Hoff equation

$$\ln \frac{C_2}{C_1} = \frac{-\Delta H}{R} \left(\frac{1}{T_2} - \frac{1}{T_1} \right) \tag{2a}$$

where ΔH, representing the heat of solution of hydrogen monosulfide in molten sulfur, is equal to -818 cal/mole^{-1}. At 760 mm of partial H_2S pressure, the concentration of hydrogen monosulfide (in grams per 100 g of sulfur) is expressed by the following function of absolute temperature

$$\ln C_{H_2S} = (412/T) - 4.13 \tag{2b}$$

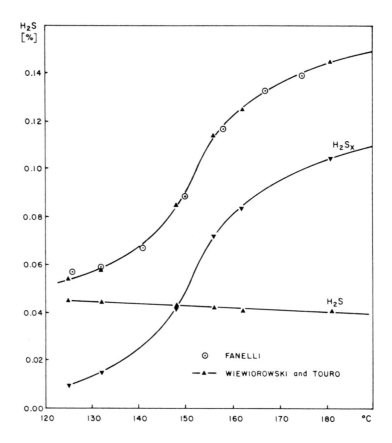

Fig. 3. Contribution of hydrogen monosulfide and polysulfide to the total hydrogen sulfide solubility at 760 mm of H_2S overpressure.

Although the values obtained for hydrogen monosulfide represent true solubilities at 760 mm of partial H_2S pressure, it is recognized that the values for hydrogen polysulfide should be referred to as concentrations which are at equilibrium with the system. Presumably, hydrogen polysulfides have a very high solubility in molten sulfur, but the experimentally determined values do not represent solubilities but rather equilibrium concentrations in molten sulfur with hydrogen sulfide at 760 mm of partial H_2S pressure. It will be shown in the next section that the "unusual" experimentally observed temperature dependence of hydrogen polysulfide concentrations is in agreement with thermodynamic requirements.

DISCUSSION

Chemical equilibria in pure molten sulfur have been the subject of several theoretical treatments. Of these, the theory developed by Tobolsky and Eisenberg (5) will be briefly reviewed here, since it serves as a suitable starting point for the discussion of chemical equilibria in the sulfur–hydrogen sulfide system. According to these workers, the equilibrium between octatomic sulfur rings S_8^R, and sulfur chains, S_x^{CH}, in pure molten sulfur* is defined by two equilibrium constants, K and K_3, pertaining to the following two types of reactions

Initiation:

$$S_8^R \xrightleftharpoons{K} S_8^{CH} \qquad [S_8^{CH}] = K[S_8^R]$$

Propagation:

$$S_8^R + S_8^{CH} \xrightleftharpoons{K_3} S_{2(8)}^{CH} \qquad [S_{2(8)}^{CH}] = K[S_8^R](K_3[S_8^R])$$

$$S_8^R + S_{16}^{CH} \xrightleftharpoons{K_3} S_{3(8)}^{CH} \qquad [S_{3(8)}^{CH}] = K[S_8^R](K_3[S_8^R])^2$$

$$[S_{n(8)}^{CH}] = K[S_8^R](K_3[S_8^R])^{n-1} \qquad (3)$$

On the basis of these assumptions the following equations describing chemical equilibria in pure molten sulfur are obtained:

$$N = \frac{K[S_8^R]}{1 - K_3[S_8^R]} \qquad (4)$$

$$W = \frac{K[S_8^R]}{(1 - K_3[S_8^R])^2} \qquad (5)$$

$$P = \frac{1}{1 - K_3[S_8^R]} \qquad (6)$$

$$M_0 = [S_8^R] + W \qquad (7)$$

where N is the total concentration of polymeric sulfur ($N = [S_8^{CH}] + [S_{2\times 8}^{CH}] + \cdots$), W is the concentration of S_8 units incorporated into the polymer ($W = [S_8^{CH}] + 2[S_{2\times 8}^{CH}] + 3[S_{3\times 8}^{CH}] + \cdots$), P is the number-average degree of polymerization ($P = W/N$), and M_0 is the total concentration of S_8 units in molten sulfur. These relationships, derived by Tobolsky and Eisenberg, are valid in the entire temperature range of liquid sulfur. They account very well for the changes which occur in liquid sulfur at 159°. The dramatic increase in the viscosity of sulfur at that temperature is a theoretically predictable consequence of the ring–chain equilibrium. It is a direct result of a sudden increase in the number-average chain length (P) and molar-chain concentration (N).

* The symbolism of molecular sulfur species adopted throughout this chapter has been proposed and discussed in reference 6.

This treatment of the sulfur system will now be expanded to develop a theory of chemical equilibria in the sulfur–hydrogen sulfide system. The theory should account for the unusual solubility pattern of hydrogen sulfide in sulfur as well as for other properties of the system, such as its low viscosity above 159° compared to the viscosity of pure sulfur. In addition to the initiation and propagation reactions, in the presence of hydrogen sulfide one must consider a set of chain-termination equilibria, in which a series of hydrogen polysulfides (H—S—S···S—S—H) are formed.

Termination:

$$H_2S + S_8^{CH} \underset{\longleftarrow}{\overset{K_4}{\rightleftharpoons}} H_2S_{8+1} \qquad [H_2S_{8+1}] = K_4[H_2S]K[S_8^R]$$

$$H_2S + S_{2(8)}^{CH} \underset{\longleftarrow}{\overset{K_4}{\rightleftharpoons}} H_2S_{2(8)+1} \qquad [H_2S_{2(8)+1}] = K_4[H_2S]K[S_8^R]K_3[S_8^R]$$

$$[H_2S_{n(8)+1}] = K_4[H_2S]K[S_8^R](K_3[S_8^R]^n)^{-1} \qquad (8)$$

Summation of polysulfide concentration terms leads to an expression for the total hydrogen polysulfide concentration, N', in the system.

$$N' = \sum_{n=1}^{\infty} [H_2S_{n(8)+1}] = K_4[H_2S]K[S_8^R]\{1 + K_3[S_8^R] + (K_3[S_8^R])^2 + \cdots\}$$

$$N' = \frac{K_4[H_2S]K[S_8^R]}{1 - K_3S_8^R} \qquad (9)$$

This expression for N' differs from equation 4 for N only by the factor $K_4[H_2S]$. Since K_4, as will be shown later, is very large, N' is much greater than N, particularly in the low-temperature range and at relatively high hydrogen sulfide concentrations. This implies that the chain termination equilibrium is effectively shifted toward the right under these conditions. However, at low H_2S concentrations another set of equilibria must be considered, namely, the termination of sulfur chains at only one end by an S—H group. Equations governing the system under these conditions have been derived by Teter (7). Equation 9 also implies that the ratio of hydrogen polysulfide concentration (N') to the monosulfide [H_2S] is not independent of the concentration of H_2S since this concentration affects the value [S_8^R] which appears in the equation.

The total concentration of octatomic sulfur units incorporated into hydrogen polysulfide, W', can be expressed as

$$W' = \sum_{n=1}^{\infty} n[H_2S_{n(8)+1}] = K_4[H_2S]K[S_8^R]$$

$$\times \{1 + 2K_3[S_8^R] + 3(K_3[S_8^R])^2 + \cdots\}$$

$$W' = \frac{K_4[H_2S]K[S_8^R]}{(1 - K_3[S_8^R])^2} \qquad (10)$$

The number-average chain length for the system as expressed in S_8 units is

$$P' = \frac{1}{1 - K_3[S_8^R]} \tag{11}$$

This expression for P' is formally identical with equation 6, but it is again recognized that although in pure molten sulfur the concentration of oct-atomic sulfur rings is a function of temperature alone, in the sulfur–hydrogen sulfide system $[S_8^R]$ is affected by the H_2S concentration. Instead of equation 7, the following relationship holds:

$$M_0 = [S_8^R] + W + W' \tag{12}$$

Equation 12 can be simplified considerably for systems with appreciable H_2S concentrations. From equations 5 and 10 it follows that

$$W' = K_4[H_2S]W \tag{13}$$

Since the equilibrium constant, K_4, is very large, W is small compared to W' in the presence of appreciable H_2S concentrations, and the following approximation can be made:

$$M_0 \approx [S_8^R] + W' \tag{14}$$

From equations 9 and 10 it is evident that

$$W' = N' \frac{1}{1 - K_3[S_8^R]} \tag{15}$$

Expressions 14 and 15 constitute a set of equations with two unknowns, W' and $[S_8^R]$, which were evaluated using the experimental data as a source of N' values and reference 5 as a source of K_3. Results of these calculations are condensed in Table 3, which also includes values of P' calculated from equation 11 and values of K_4 computed from equation 9.

Let us consider the temperature dependence of K_4. In Figure 4, $\log K_4$ is plotted versus the reciprocal of absolute temperature, yielding a straight line. This lends support for the experimental N' and H_2S concentrations which were employed in calculating K_4. Assuming that K_4 obeys van't Hoff's law over the entire liquid sulfur range, one can calculate ΔH and ΔS of the termination reaction.

$$\ln K_4 = \frac{-\Delta H}{RT} + \frac{\Delta S}{R} \tag{16}$$

$$\Delta H = -30,900 \text{ cal/mole}^{-1}$$

$$\Delta S = -25.7 \text{ cal/mole}^{-1}$$

It is also of interest to compare the values of $[S_8^R]$ in Table 3 with those calculated by Tobolsky and Eisenberg for the pure sulfur system. As

Table 3

The Values of K_4, S_8^R W', and P' versus Temperature for Sulfur Saturated with Hydrogen Sulfide at 760 mm of H_2S Overpressure

Temp., °K	Total % H_2S	% H_2S	% H_2S_x (as H_2S)	S_8^R	W'	K_4	P'
400	0.056[a]	0.0450[b]	0.011	3.89	0.01	1.70×10^{11}	3.33
410	0.062	0.0439	0.018	3.87	0.03	8.18×10^{10}	4.84
420	0.079	0.0428	0.036	3.82	0.08	3.09×10^{10}	8.06
425	0.096	0.0423	0.054	3.74	0.16	1.83×10^{10}	9.95
428	0.108	0.0421	0.066	3.68	0.22	1.94×10^{10}	11.0
430	0.114	0.0418	0.072	3.64	0.26	1.69×10^{10}	12.4
440	0.131	0.0409	0.090	3.44	0.46	7.49×10^{9}	17.0
450	0.141	0.0402	0.101	3.22	0.68	2.80×10^{9}	22.9
460	0.150	0.0394	0.111	3.02	0.88	1.28×10^{9}	27.0
470	0.157	0.0386	0.118	2.80	1.10	5.66×10^{8}	31.7
490	0.169	0.0372	0.132	2.45	1.45	1.50×10^{8}	37.4
510	0.175	0.0360	0.139	2.16	1.74	4.45×10^{7}	42.5
540	0.185	0.0345	0.151	1.82	2.08	9.02×10^{6}	46.8
580	0.187	0.0327	0.154	1.50	2.40	2.19×10^{6}	53.0

[a] Total hydrogen sulfide concentrations taken from reference 1.
[b] H_2S concentrations calculated from equation 2b.

expected, these values are smaller for the sulfur–hydrogen sulfide system and, although the difference may not appear to be significant, it results in a very drastic reduction in the number-average degree of polymerization. For example, at 450°K in pure sulfur P is equal to 113,900 S_8 units, while in sulfur saturated with hydrogen sulfide at 1 atm of H_2S, P' is 22.9. These phenomena are directly related to the viscosities of the system under consideration. Pure molten sulfur undergoes significant and reversible viscosity changes with temperature (8). Near its melting point (119°) it is a moderately mobile liquid, when heated, its viscosity initially decreases, proceeding through a minimum at about 157°, and then rises rapidly, reaching a maximum at $\sim 187°$. Further heating results in a slow viscosity decrease. This behavior is a reflection of ring–chain equilibria in the system. A quantitative relationship between viscosity and the concentration and length of chains (9) in sulfur systems has been derived. The model used in this derivation implies that pure molten sulfur is a pseudo solution consisting of octatomic sulfur rings behaving as the pseudo solvent with sulfur chains assuming the role of the pseudo solute. With this assumption the following equation can be derived

$$P = \left[\frac{\eta - \eta_0}{\eta_0 W} \right]^{1.1} \tag{18}$$

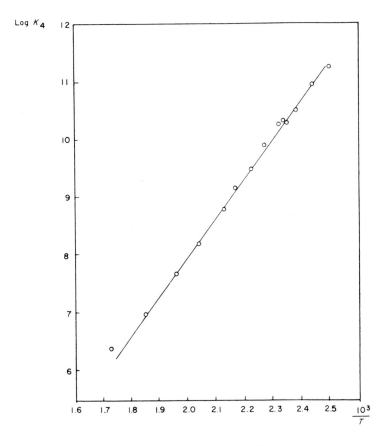

Fig. 4. Log K_4 vs. $1/T$.

where P is the chain length, W is the chain concentration, η is the viscosity of the pseudo solution and η_0 is the viscosity of the pseudo solvent which can be expressed as a function of temperature in terms of the following equation

$$\ln \eta_0 = 42.64 - 6.74 \ln T \tag{19}$$

If equation 18 is applied to the sulfur–hydrogen sulfide system, the hydrogen polysulfide chain length can be calculated and the values obtained are in close agreement with those presented in Table 2. This verifies that the pronounced viscosity reducing effect which hydrogen sulfide has on sulfur (10) is a direct consequence of the termination equilibrium which causes a reduction in the number-average chain length in the system.

Recently the formation of hydrogen polysulfides in the sulfur–hydrogen sulfide system was confirmed by NMR measurements (11). The NMR evidence can be discussed with reference to Figure 5. Curve *a* represents a spectrum obtained on a 5% solution in CS_2 of a synthetic hydrogen polysulfide mixture prepared by reacting an aqueous solution of sodium polysulfides with 6*N* hydrochloric acid. The assignment of the bands is based on the work of Schmidbaur et al. (12). The spectrum shown on Figure 5*b* was obtained on molten sulfur through which hydrogen sulfide was bubbled for a period of 24 hr. Only two bands, assigned to H_2S and

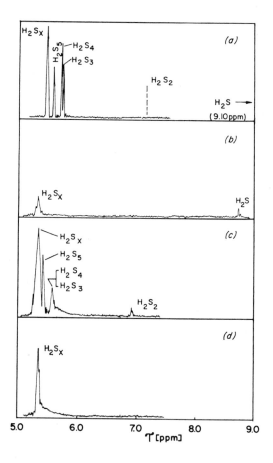

Fig. 5. NMR spectra of hydrogen polysulfides. (*a*) Hydrogen polysulfides in CS_2. (*b*) Hydrogen polysulfides formed by H_2S + S(liq.) in molten sulfur. (*c*) Hydrogen polysulfides added to molten sulfur after 3 min. (*d*) Same as (*c*) but after 100 min at 130°C.

H_2S_x ($x \geq 6$) appear. Bands which could be assigned to H_2S_2, H_2S_3, H_2S_4, and H_2S_5 are notably absent. When the synthetic mixture described above was dissolved in molten sulfur at 130°, the spectrum shown in Figure 5c was obtained. The presence of the lower homologs of hydrogen poly-sulfides is clearly evident, but upon equilibration, significant changes in the spectrum occur as shown in curve d. The bands assigned to H_2S_n ($S \leq x \leq 5$) disappear, indicating that in addition to H_2S, the molten sulfur contains only H_2S_x ($x \geq 6$). These spectra lend support to the results of thermodynamic calculations shown in Table 3. The number-average chain length of hydrogen polysulfides in this system is about $3.5\,S_8$ units at 130°C and consequently the existence of the lower members of the poly-sulfide series should not be expected.

In summary, this chapter reviews experimental evidence on chemical equilibria in the sulfur–hydrogen sulfide system and presents an inter-pretation of these equilibria.

References

1. R. Fanelli, *Ind. Eng. Chem.* (*Intern. Ed.*), **41**, 2031 (1949).
2. T. K. Wiewiorowski and F. J. Touro, *J. Phys. Chem.*, **70**, 234 (1966).
3. T. K. Wiewiorowski, R. F. Matson, and C. T. Hodges, *Anal. Chem.*, **37**, 1080 (1965).
4. R. F. Bacon and R. Fanelli, *Ind. Eng. Chem.* (*Intern. Ed.*), **34**, 1043 (1942).
5. A. V. Tobolsky and A. Eisenberg, *J. Am. Chem. Soc.*, **81**, 780 (1959).
6. T. K. Wiewiorowski and F. J. Touro, *J. Phys. Chem.*, **70**, 3528 (1966).
7. L. A. Teter, Ph.D. dissertation, University of California at Los Angeles, 1966.
8. R. F. Bacon and R. Fanelli, *J. Am. Chem. Soc.*, **65**, 639 (1943).
9. F. J. Touro and T. K. Wiewiorowski, *J. Phys. Chem.*, **70**, 239 (1966).
10. P. A. Rubero, *J. Chem. Eng. Data*, **9**, 481 (1964).
11. J. B. Hyne, E. Muller, and T. K. Wiewiorowski, *J. Phys. Chem.*, **70**, 3733 (1966).
12. H. Schmidbaur, M. Schmidt, and W. Siebert, *Chem. Ber.*, **97**, 3374 (1964).

Synthesis of Sulfur Compounds by Singlet and Triplet Sulfur Atom Reactions

O. P. STRAUSZ and H. E. GUNNING

Department of Chemistry, University of Alberta,
Edmonton, Alberta, Canada

INTRODUCTION

The first studies on the chemistry of the sulfur atom began some five years ago. Since that time not only have many new reactions of inherent interest been brought to light through such investigations, but also a number of important new chemical structures have been synthesized.

Among the group VI elements, the atomic reactions of oxygen have received the most attention (1–3). Thus, although experiments with oxygen atoms using electrical discharges started in the early 1930's, it was not until photochemical oxygen atom sources had become available that reliable quantitative information was obtained on the nature and rate of oxygen atom reactions with a large variety of organic molecules.

Studies on selenium atom reactions have been reported only in the past few years (4,5).

As comparative data accumulated, a marked similarity became increasingly evident among the chemical reactivities of the oxygen-group elements. Here the most interesting feature is the fact that all three atoms, when excited to their lowest metastable singlet level, undergo insertion reactions, that is a concerted-type addition process, with hydrogen-containing saturated compounds. On the other hand, in their ground, triplet, electronic states, these atoms exhibit entirely different behaviors in that they either attack C—H bonds abstractively or are unreactive. Their reactions with unsaturated compounds, such as olefins and acetylenes, are characterized by the initial formation of cyclic adducts which in some cases are readily stabilized collisionally and in others are inherently unstable.

From the foregoing it is evident that these divalent atoms possess chemical reactivity closely resembling that of the large variety of methylenes and other polyatomic biradicals. Consequently it is to be expected that their kinetic–mechanistic studies will effectively contribute to a deeper understanding of the elementary reactions of divalently unsatisfied reagents in

23

general, and perhaps help to realize some of the potentialities these reagents may have for synthetic–preparative applications. This latter aspect of sulfur (and selenium) atom chemistry is the one to which special emphasis will be given in the present article.

SOURCES OF TRIPLET AND SINGLET STATE SULFUR ATOMS

The general electronic configuration common to the oxygen group elements is [closed shell] ns^2np^4, from which three spectroscopic states $^3P_{0,1,2}$, $^1D_2$, and $^1S_0$ result. Transitions among these states are forbidden by optical selection rules. The excited $^1D_2$ and $^1S_0$ states are metastable, with long radiative lifetimes, and consequently may undergo bimolecular reactions. The ground state is the triplet (^3P) and the lowest lying excited level is the $^1D_2$ which in the case of sulfur is located 26.4 kcal above the ground state. Only these two states have significance in current studies.

The only useful sources of atomic sulfur are all photochemical, though recoil sulfur atoms from nuclear reaction have also been reported. Thermal sources are of no particular value since at the temperature required to generate the atoms the sulfur-containing products would be too unstable.

At present, the most valuable S-atom source (6,7) is the ultraviolet photolysis of carbonyl sulfide, COS. The first moderately intense absorption band ($\epsilon_{max} = 4000$ torr^{-1} cm^{-1}) of this molecule extends from ca. 2600 Å to 1800 Å, with a maximum at 2225 Å. In the gas-phase spectrum, vibrational structure is apparent and at subtorr pressures the spectrum breaks up into a number of diffuse bands indicating different electronic transitions. From molecular orbital calculations the lowest energy transition is of the $\pi'-\pi^*$ type. The absorption is temperature dependent with an apparent activation energy of 2.5 kcal, which closely coincides with the CS stretching fundamental of the linear OCS molecule. From the integrated absorption coefficient the radiative lifetime is $\sim 10^{-9}$ sec.

In the liquid phase, the absorption spectrum extends to ca. 3000 Å. Photolysis, though slow, is possible even in Pyrex vessels. The boiling point of COS is $-50°$ and the vapor pressure near room temperature is roughly numerically equal in atmosphere to 0.6 times the temperature in °C. A critical temperature of 105°C and a critical pressure of 61 atm have been reported (8). Thus, it is readily possible to carry out photolysis around 20° or in a 0° water bath in sealed-off quartz, Vycor, or Pyrex tubes.

Photolyses at 2139 Å (Zn resonance lamp), 2288 Å (Cd resonance lamp), or in the range 2290–2550 Å (medium pressure Hg arc) give rise to carbon monoxide and elemental sulfur. The quantum yield of CO formation in the gas phase is 1.8. It is well established that the primary photolytic step involves scission into carbon monoxide and a $^1D_2$ excited sulfur atom

$$COS + h\nu \longrightarrow CO + S(^1D_2) \tag{1}$$

to the extent of at least 74%. The remaining fraction may give a ground-state atom

$$COS + h\nu \longrightarrow CO + S(^3P) \tag{2}$$

The quantum yield of nearly 2 dictates that sulfur atoms produced in reactions 1 and 2 abstractively attack COS

$$S(^1D) + COS \longrightarrow S_2 + CO \tag{3}$$

$$S(^3P) + COS \longrightarrow S_2 + CO \tag{4}$$

Steps 3 and 4 are exothermic, respectively, to 55 and 29 kcal for ground-state products. The ground state of S_2, like that of O_2 and Se_2, is a triplet ($^3\Sigma_g^-$). However, there are two low-lying metastable singlet levels within the energy range available—a $^1\Delta_g$ at ~ 13, and a $^1\Sigma_g$ at ~ 24 kcal. There is strong evidence to suggest that the S_2 in reaction 3 is formed in the $^1\Delta_g$ excited state and in reaction 4 in its ground triplet state. Triplet abstraction via equation 4, is orders of magnitude slower than singlet abstraction via equation 3. At high light intensities, and in the presence of inert gases, the third-order recombination of triplet atoms

$$S(^3P) + S(^3P) + M \longrightarrow S_2(X^3\Sigma_g^-) + M \tag{5}$$

may become competitive.

Concomitant with reaction 3, electronic deactivation,

$$S(^1D) + COS \longrightarrow S(^3P) + COS^* \tag{6}$$

also occurs at a rate ca. 20% of that of reaction 3. This process may also be brought about by other quenching gases, such as perfluorocyclobutene, paraffins, or carbon dioxide. Carbon dioxide is chemically completely inert with respect to S atoms, and the rate of relaxation is very much the same as with COS. Through such deactivation it is possible to produce triplet atoms conveniently if the photolysis is carried out in the presence of a large excess of CO_2. An alternative method for generating triplet S atoms is the $Hg(^3P_1)$ photosensitization of COS itself.

$$Hg + h\nu(2537 \text{ Å}) \longrightarrow Hg(^3P_1) \tag{7}$$

$$Hg(^3P_1) + COS \longrightarrow CO + Hg + S(^3P) \tag{8}$$

The quantum efficiency of this process is the same as that of the direct photolysis. In both cases the carbon monoxide produced is an excellent monitor of atomic sulfur production.

The photolysis of carbonyl sulfide has also been studied under flash conditions with kinetic optical spectroscopy and kinetic mass spectrometry. The relevant conclusion may be summarized by stating that none of the intermediates of atomic sulfur polymerization show any detectable reactivity with respect to organic molecules. This appears to be an interesting distinction of S_2 (singlet excited) or S_3 from the corresponding oxygen analogs which both O_2 (singlet excited) and ozone are reactive entities with respect to olefins.

Among other sources of sulfur atoms are the photolysis of carbon disulfide at wavelengths shorter than 2100 Å, and the photolysis of ethylene episulfide (2200–2600 Å) and of SPF_3 (2100–2300 Å). The first two reactions afford triplet atoms and the latter, singlet atoms.

REACTIONS OF SULFUR ATOMS WITH PARAFFINS

When the photolysis of carbonyl sulfide (or SPF_3) is carried out in the presence of an added paraffin (9–11) (which in no way interferes with the photolysis of COS) such as ethane, propane, isobutane, cyclopropane, cyclobutane, or cyclopentane, one and only one additional type of product, the mercaptan, is formed. Mercaptan formation is accompanied by a decline in the carbon monoxide yield. A kinetic plot representative of the paraffin reactions is shown in Figure 1 for the isobutane reaction. The following features will be noted: The CO yield reaches a minimum as the mercaptan yield increases to a maximum with increasing paraffin pressure,

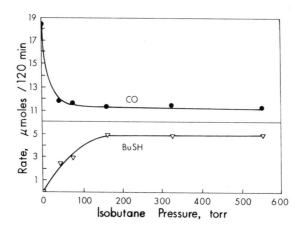

Fig. 1. Rates of products formation vs. isobutane pressure in the reaction of $S(^1D)$ atoms with isobutane: ($\bullet$) CO; ($\triangledown$) butyl mercaptan.

but CO suppression never reaches the theoretical 50%, nor does the mercaptan yield equal the CO yield as would be expected if the paraffin could scavenge all the sulfur atoms. The isomeric distribution of products is statistical (from isobutane sec-butyl/tert-butyl ~9, and from propane, n-propyl/isopropyl ~3). What is more, the H/D kinetic isotope effect is unity. These facts, taken in conjunction with the observation that the addition of a large excess of CO_2 completely suppresses mercaptan formation, lead to the conclusion that the attack of a sulfur atom is restricted entirely to the C—H bond. In fact, the mechanism is a concerted single-step insertion process with the sulfur atom reactive only in its excited singlet state. The ground state is inert to paraffins. Furthermore, in addition to insertion the $S(^1D)$ atoms suffer electronic deactivation by the paraffin in the ground state.

The reaction mechanism can be adequately accounted for by the following sequence of elementary steps

$$S(^1D) + RH \longrightarrow RSH \tag{9}$$
$$\longrightarrow RH^* + S(^3P) \tag{10}$$
$$S(^1D) + COS \longrightarrow CO + S_2 \tag{3}$$
$$S(^3P) + COS \longrightarrow CO + S_2 \tag{4}$$
$$2S(^3P) + M \longrightarrow S_2 + M \tag{5}$$

Steady-state treatment permits the estimation of relative rate constants; these are in the ratio $k_9 : k_3 : k_{10} = 2.2\text{--}1.1 : 1.0 : 0.71\text{--}0.16$, for the six paraffins mentioned above. The rate constant values vary slightly with the experimental conditions. With decreasing wavelength of the photolytic light a portion of the excess energy appears as translational energy over the Boltzmann distribution of the $S(^1D)$ atoms. At 2500 Å this excess translational energy may be as high as 6 kcal and at 2288 Å about 12 kcal. From temperature studies it is known that the insertion reaction, equation 9, has an activation energy about 1 kcal higher than the abstraction reaction (eq. 3). Consequently, translationally hot singlet atoms insert somewhat more readily than thermalized atoms relative to abstraction from COS.

Insertion reactions, like addition reactions, in general, are characterized by large enthalpy increases since their net result is formation of an additional bond. In $S(^1D)$ atom insertions, the enthalpy increase amounts to 85–90 kcal, which is sufficient to cause rupture of the weaker bonds of the molecule. Therefore, secondary fragmentation of the hot mercaptan initially formed may take place with small molecules where the number of internal degrees of freedom is inadequate to accommodate the excess energy, and ensure a lifetime sufficiently long for bimolecular removal of the energy. This is indeed the case with methane and hydrogen (9,12).

The chemically activated methyl mercaptan from the methane reaction may undergo four types of cleavage reactions

$$[CH_3SH]^* \longrightarrow CH_3S + H \tag{6}$$
$$\longrightarrow CH_3 + SH \tag{7}$$
$$\longrightarrow CH_2 + H_2S \tag{8}$$
$$\longrightarrow CH_2S + H_2 \tag{9}$$

In the case of the initially formed hydrogen sulfide molecule in the H_2 reaction, there is only one possible mode of decomposition

$$[H_2S]^* \longrightarrow H + SH \tag{10}$$

The reaction of sulfur atoms with the Si—H and B—H bonds have also been briefly investigated. Here again, only the excited singlet atom is reactive.

Methyl silane gives predominantly CH_3SiH_2SH along with smaller amounts of SiH_3CH_2SH and some secondary cracking products. From trimethylsilane the trimethyl silyl mercaptan results as the major product. The rate ratio, as estimated from product yields, for Si—H to C—H insertion is about 50.

Tetramethylsilane gives only one product, the trimethylsilylmethyl mercaptan, $(CH_3)_3SiCH_2SH$.

Diborane also yields one product in relatively high yield in its reaction with $S(^1D)$ atoms. It is an adduct with empirical formula B_2H_6S and its probable structure is

$$H_2B \overset{\displaystyle H}{\underset{\displaystyle H}{\diagup\!\!\!\diagdown}} BHSH$$

Thus far only gas-phase reactions have been considered, but the insertion reaction also proceeds in the liquid phase. For example, irradiation of a 1 : 10 solution by volume of COS in n-butane at room temperature gives n-butyl and isobutyl mercaptans in a relative yield of 1.25. But in the low temperature ($-196°$) solid phase photolysis of the same mixture, no mercaptan forms, although the photolysis of COS proceeds quite readily.

To illustrate the quantities and rates involved in the gas-phase synthesis we give some typical conditions for the synthesis of cyclopropyl mercaptan. Using a 4-liter quartz bulb, filled to 1500 torr pressure with a 1 : 5 mixture of COS and cyclopropane, a rate of a few millimoles of mercaptan formation per hour could be obtained by irradiation with two 140-watt mercury arcs. The rate of this process is admittedly slow from the standpoint of preparative organic chemistry. However, the technique requires no monitoring and in certain cases may provide unique synthetic routes. (This reaction was the first reported synthesis of cyclopropyl mercaptan.)

REACTIONS OF SULFUR ATOMS WITH OLEFINS

Gas-Phase Reactions

Sulfur (^1D) atoms, from the photolysis of COS, lead to three types of isomeric products with olefins: episulfides, alkenyl mercaptans, and vinylic mercaptans ($R_1R_2C{=}CR_3SH$). In the case of ethylene, the first synthesis of vinyl mercaptan, $CH_2 : CHSH$, was achieved by this method. By analogy with vinyl alcohol, this molecule was hitherto assumed not to exist. For such highly reactive compounds, product-handling and analytical techniques require special care in these systems.

With ethylene, two products—ethylene episulfide and vinyl mercaptan—result (11,13). Their relative yields are dependent on the conditions of the experiment. At a few hundred torr pressure and at $\lambda = 2500$ Å, they form in nearly equal quantities. The plot of product yields as a function of ethylene pressure, given in Figure 2, illustrates the kinetic behavior of this system. It is seen that with increasing pressure of ethylene the yields of the C_2H_4S products rise to a maximum and the yield of CO decreases to very nearly half of that found in the absence of ethylene. Thus, unlike paraffins, ethylene is capable of scavenging sulfur atoms nearly quantitatively. The optimum yield of the C_2H_4S products, in terms of the decrease in the carbon monoxide yield, is over 90%.

Addition of carbon dioxide to the system has a very marked effect on the product distribution. Vinyl mercaptan gradually diminishes with increasing CO_2 pressure with a concomitant and equivalent increase in the ethylene episulfide yield. Thus, it is clear that vinyl mercaptan forms exclusively

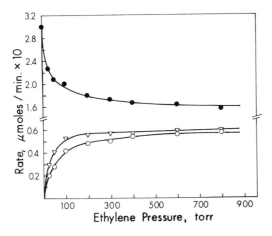

Fig. 2. Rates of product formation vs. ethylene pressure in the reaction of $S(^1D)$ atoms with ethylene: ($\bullet$) CO; ($\triangledown$) ethylene episulfide; ($\bigcirc$) vinyl mercaptan.

from $S(^1D)$ atom reactions, while episulfide arises from the addition to ethylene of triplet and possibly singlet atoms. This latter process is exothermic to 86 kcal, and the enthalpy change of the mercaptan-forming reaction should be very nearly the same. At low pressures, therefore, some fragmentation would be expected. From the fact that the ratio of vinyl mercaptan to episulfide exhibits an increasing trend with rising pressure, it appears that the vinyl mercaptan product undergoes secondary fragmentation more readily since it requires higher pressures for collisional stabilization than does the episulfide.

From the propylene reaction, four gas chromatographically separable products—propylene episulfide, propene-3-thiol, and the *cis* and *trans* isomers of propene-1-thiol—result in relative yields, respectively, of 1.0 : 0.25 : 0.20. Significantly, propene-2-thiol is absent. This is a general result: No vinylic mercaptan forms on the substituted carbon atom of the double bond (with the exception of cyclopentene; see below).

For the butenes, all four isomers have been investigated (14). 1-Butene gives episulfide, 1-butene-4-thiol, and 1-butene-3-thiol in the ratio of 1.0 : 0.22 : 0.18, respectively. Small quantities of a fourth product, C_4H_8S, were also found which could only partially be separated from the 3-thiol; it is probably the vinylic 1-butene-1-thiol. Isobutylene gives episulfide, 2-methyl-1-propene-3-thiol, and 2-methyl-1-propene-1-thiol in a ratio of 1.0 : 0.56 : 0.22.

The 2-butene reactions are particularly interesting. Reactions of singlet atoms, from the photolysis of COS, with *cis*- and *trans*-2-butene result, in both cases, in three products: 2-butene-1-thiol and *cis*- and *trans*-2-butene episulfide. The ratio of mercaptan to total episulfide yield is ~0.5. Under favorable conditions and after allowance is made for small secondary reactions, the episulfide consists of over 90% *cis* isomer from *cis*-2-butene and 98% *trans* isomer from *trans*-2-butene. By analogy with methylene chemistry, this result is an expected one if the reacting atoms are in their singlet state. It was, therefore, of considerable interest to examine the behavior of triplet state atoms under similar conditions.

To this end triplet atoms were generated by the photolysis of COS in the presence of a large excess of CO_2, and in other experiments, by the triplet mercury photosensitization of COS. With both sources, the absence of singlet state atoms was indicated by the fact that no mercaptans were found among the products. In both sets of experiments the same results were obtained, namely that triplet atom addition to *cis*-2-butene is over 95% stereospecific and in the *trans*-2-butene case, the stereospecificity exceeded 99%.

The reaction of $S(^3P)$ atoms with the 2-butenes is probably the first reported stereospecific triplet state addition reaction. From these findings it is clear that caution must be exercised in generalizing stereospecificity as a criterion for spin-state identification.

For 1,3-butadiene three products are found with sulfur atoms: vinyl-thiacyclopropane, thiophene, and a sulfur-containing product with a molecular weight of 88, presumably tetrahydrothiophene. The principal product is the vinylthiacyclopropane in a fractional yield of $>90\%$. Thiophene, at least in part, is a secondary product; the upper limit for the fraction which could have formed in a primary reaction is 9%. This result refers to both the singlet and the triplet atom reaction; therefore, in both cases the addition is at least 91% in the 1,2 position.

$$S(^1D) \text{ or } S(^3P) + \quad\nearrow\!\!\!\!\diagup\!\!\!\!\searrow \quad\longrightarrow\quad \nearrow\!\!\!\!\diagup\!\!\!\!\searrow_S \qquad (\geqslant 91\%) \qquad (11)$$

$$\longrightarrow\quad \left[\!\!\!\begin{array}{c} \\ S \end{array}\!\!\!\right] + H_2 \text{ (or 2H)} \qquad (<9\%) \qquad (12)$$

The H_2 yield is always smaller than the thiophene yield, indicating that thiophene may also be formed in some process involving loss of atomic hydrogen, in consonance with the appearance of the minor hydrogenated product of molecular weight 88. One peculiar feature of the reaction is the rapid decline in vinylthiacyclopropane with increasing butadiene pressure (at higher pressures). A similar, but much less pronounced trend, is also apparent in all monoolefin reactions and may be explained by the interaction of the thiatrimethylene biradical intermediate with the olefin, ultimately leading to polymerization

$$\cdot S\text{---}C\text{---}C\cdot + \begin{array}{c} \\ \end{array}\!\!C\text{==}C\!\!\begin{array}{c} \\ \end{array} \longrightarrow \cdot S\text{---}C\text{---}C\text{---}C\text{---}C\cdot \xrightarrow{\text{Olefin}} \text{polymer} \qquad (13)$$

Support for this also comes from studies on the photolysis of ethylene episulfide. When the episulfide photolysis is carried out in the presence of an olefin fairly good yields of a higher 1-olefin are found

$$\cdot S\text{---}C\text{---}C\cdot + CH_2\text{==}CHR \longrightarrow S(^3P) + CH_2\text{==}CH\text{---}CH_2\text{---}CH_2\text{---}R \qquad (14)$$

Although butadiene pressure has a suppressing effect on the vinyl-thiacyclopropane yield, no similar effect is found with CO_2. In the latter case, the thiophene yield is suppressed, indicating an energetic precursor for its formation.

In summary, the overall mechanism of sulfur atom addition to buta-diene is similar to that of CH_2 and $O(^3P)$, both of which have been shown to add mainly or entirely by the 1,2 mode.

Among the cyclic olefins, cyclopentene, cyclohexene, and perfluoro-cyclobutene have been studied.

Cyclopentene gives cyclopentene episulfide, a mercaptan which, according to NMR analysis, is a $1:1.5$ mixture of two isomers, very likely the cyclopentene-4-thiol and the cyclopentene-3-thiol, together with smaller yields of the cyclopentene-1-thiol. Product yields as a function of cyclo-pentene pressure are plotted in Figure 3. The tautomeric equilibrium be-tween the 1-thiol and thioketone is known to proceed spontaneously at room temperature. However, the equilibrium is strongly on the thiol side.

The effect of CO_2 on the reaction is shown in Figure 4. It is explained by the efficient electronic deactivation of the excited singlet atoms to the ground state prior to reaction with cyclopentene. If we take the relative mercaptan yield as a measure of the $S(^1D)$ atom concentration in the sys-tem, it is found that at a ca. 25-fold excess of CO_2 (over olefin) well over 90% of the $S(^1D)$ atoms are quenched.

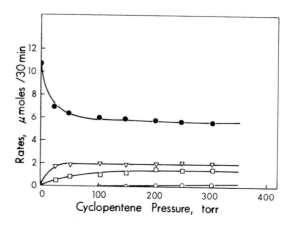

Fig. 3. Rates of products formation in the reaction of $S(^1D)$ atoms with cyclopentene as a function of cyclopentene pressure: (●) CO; (▽) cyclopentene episulfide; (□) cyclopentene-2-thiol and cyclopentene-3-thiol; (○) cyclopentene-1-thiol.

Cyclohexene behaves in a manner similar to cyclopentene, except that, owing to the larger number of CH_2 groups in the molecule, the relative mercaptan yield is somewhat higher.

Perfluorocyclobutene reacts slowly with sulfur atoms. The episulfide is inherently unstable at room temperature and could only be detected in flash photolysis with kinetic mass spectrometry. This lack of reactivity is most likely associated with the strong electron-withdrawing effect of fluorine. It is consistent with the electrophilic nature of the addition process (see below).

Trimethylethylene and tetramethylethylene give the expected products. With the former, in addition to episulfide, three isomeric mercaptans, from insertion into the three nonequivalent methyl groups, are formed in a combined yield of 42%. With tetramethylethylene only one mercaptan could be detected, in a yield of ca. 50%.

In addition to perfluorocyclobutene the following halogenated olefins have also been studied: vinyl chloride, *cis*-1,2- and *trans*-1,2-dichloro-ethylene, and the four fluorinated ethylenes. With vinyl fluoride, the epi-sulfide is found together with the *cis*- and *trans*-1-fluoroethylene-2-thiol in a ratio, respectively, of 1.0 : 0.28 : 0.23.

cis- and *trans*-1,2-Difluoroethylene produce only the *cis* and *trans* episulfides. The reaction, as with 2-butene, is highly stereospecific with both $S(^1D)$ and $S(^3P)$ atoms. The *cis* reaction is 99% stereospecific and the *trans* reaction over 80% stereospecific with $S(^1D)$ atoms. The stereospecificity in the $S(^3P)$ atom reactions is even higher at 100 and 87%, respectively.

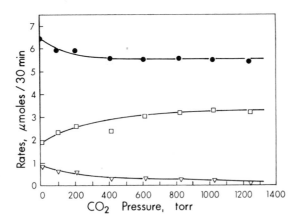

Fig. 4. Rates of products formation as a function of added CO_2 pressure in the reaction of sulfur atoms with cyclopentene: (●) CO; (□) cyclopentene episulfide; (▽) cyclopentene–thiol.

The reactions of the chlorinated counterparts of the above compounds are entirely analogous; the stereospecificity with $S(^3P)$ atoms of the *cis* isomer is 80% and of the *trans*, 90%.

These results emphasize the generality of the stereospecific nature of sulfur atom reactions irrespective of the multiplicity of the electronic state.

It may be of interest to point out that with 1,2-difluoroethylene the *cis* episulfide is formed in preference to the *trans*, while with 2-butene and 1,2-dichloroethylene the *trans* reaction is the more stereospecific. This may be taken as evidence that in 1,2-difluoroethylene episulfide the stability of the geometrical isomers is inverted, with the *cis* form being more stable than the *trans*.

The products from the 1,1-difluoroethylene reaction are the 1,1-difluoro-ethylene-2-thiol and the episulfide in a ratio of 0.45 : 1.0. Trifluoroethylene gives only the episulfide.

No volatile product could be recovered from the reaction of sulfur atoms with tetrafluoroethylene. Tetrafluoroethylene episulfide is apparently unstable and participates in the polymerization of the tetrafluoroethylene substrate. However, the episulfide could readily be detected in flashed $COS–C_2F_4$ mixtures by kinetic mass spectrometry and showed no significant decay in 50 msec (at low pressures).

Thus, halogenated ethylenes give mercaptan only when an unsubstituted CH_2 group is present in the molecule. The stability of the episulfide is reflected in the yield of the products (Table 1) which shows a gradual decline with an increasing number of halogen atoms in the molecule.

Table 1

Percentage Product Yields from the Halogenated Ethylenes

Olefin	Yield of products,[a] %	
	Pure COS	COS + CO_2
C_2H_3F	60	60
$C_2H_2F_2$	60	60
C_2HF_3	30	60
C_2F_4	nil	nil
C_2H_3Cl	80	80
cis-CHClCHCl	nil	20
trans-CHClCHCl	nil	80

[a] In terms of S atoms produced.

To reveal the nature of the attack of sulfur atoms on the olefinic π-bond a series of relative-rate measurements were carried out with triplet atoms and a representative set of olefins together with a few rather preliminary experiments with singlet atoms. A competitive system for these relative-rate measurements was used containing pairs of olefins and the relative-rate constant values were deduced from the ratios of product yields.

The data for triplet S-atom addition (15) are compared with the corresponding data reported in the literature for the other members of the oxygen group elements, oxygen (1) and selenium (4), in Table 2. A parallel trend is apparent for all three atoms: With increasing substitution on the doubly bonded carbon atom of the olefin molecule, the rate of addition increases, clearly showing the electrophilic nature of the attack. Also, a fairly regular

Table 2

Relative Rates of Addition of $S(^3P)$, $O(^3P)$, and $Se(^3P)$ Atoms to Olefins.

Olefin	$O(^3P)^a$	$Se(^3P)^b$	$S(^3P)$
Ethylene	1.00	1.00	1.00
Propylene	5.75	2.6	6.8
trans-2-Butene	28.3	56	19
cis-2-Butene	23.8	23.9	16
1-Butene	5.75	7.1	9.8
Isobutylene	25.0	44.7	52
1-Pentene	—	5.0	9.8
2-Methyl-1-butene	—	—	56
Cyclopentene	29.8	—	19
Vinyl chloride	—	1.3	1.4

[a] From reference 1.
[b] From reference 4.

relation exists between rate of addition and the ionization potential of the parent olefin. The logarithm of the rate-constant values increases nearly linearly with decreasing ionization potential (for a given type of substituent). Presumably a strongly polar transition state with some partial charge transfer is involved.

For singlet sulfur addition to the π-bond the following values were obtained: ethylene : propylene : isobutylene = 1.0 : 2.0 : 7.5. Thus, while $S(^1D)$ atoms also exhibit electrophilic character, they are less sensitive to changing electron density at the π-bond than $S(^3P)$ atoms.

For the effect of temperature on the S-atom addition reactions only fragmentary, preliminary data are available. For $O(^3P)$ and $Se(^3P)$ addition it has been shown that the variation in rate with olefin structure is almost entirely due to the variation in the activation energy, which has a value of about 2–3 kcal for ethylene. The preexponential factor remains nearly invariant. In view of the great similarity among the three atoms in these systems it appears justified to assume that similar factors are operative for $S(^3P)$ atom reactions.

For $S(^1D)$ atom reactions, the mercaptan-forming step (with C_2H_4, C_3H_6 and CF_2CH_2) has an activation energy some 0.5 kcal larger than the episulfide-forming step. The existence of this small activation energy difference for both the formation of allyl mercaptan and propene-1-thiol in the propylene reaction would indicate that the same type of process, namely the direct insertion of $S(^1D)$ atom into the C—H bond, is responsible for both types of mercaptans. Nevertheless, for vinylic mercaptans the possibility of an alternative route, involving the isomerization of the hot episulfide molecule

$$\left[\begin{matrix} CH_2\text{—}CH_2 \\ \diagdown \ S \ \diagup \end{matrix} \right]^{*} \longrightarrow CH_2\text{=}CHSH \qquad (15)$$

cannot be eliminated.

As for the paraffin reactions, the excess translational energy of the $S(^1D)$ atoms has a slight influence on the olefinic reactions as well. Since mercaptan formation has a higher activation energy than the episulfide-forming step, in shorter wavelength photolysis the mercaptan-to-episulfide ratio is somewhat increased. For example, with ethylene the mercaptan/episulfide ratio is ~1.0 at 2500 Å and ~1.4 at 2288 Å.

On the basis of the preceding discussion it is now possible to choose optimum conditions for the gas-phase synthesis of olefinic mercaptans and episulfides. If the aim of the experiment is the production of mercaptans, it is advantageous to use the unfiltered radiation of a medium-pressure mercury arc and to carry out the synthesis at elevated temperature (100–150°). The total pressure in the system should be kept as high as possible and an excess of olefin over COS should be maintained ([olefin]/[COS] should be ca. ~3 for reactive olefins and correspondingly larger for less reactive olefins).

If, on the other hand, the experiment is to be designed for the synthesis of episulfides, the reaction should be performed at room temperature in the presence of carbon dioxide diluent.

For the butadiene episulfide synthesis we used a circulatory system. It consisted of a quartz reaction vessel connected to a large ballast reservoir via an internally operated magnetic stirrer and a U-trap, with the latter kept at −80° to condense out the products and prevent secondary decomposition.

Condensed-Phase Reactions

The reactions of only two olefins, ethylene and propylene, have been studied in the condensed phase. From the data in Table 3 it is seen that the overall yields at room temperature are about the same in the gas- and liquid-phase reactions of ethylene. The relative importance of vinyl mercaptan formation, however, is decreased by about a factor of 2 in the liquid. At −196° the overall yield falls to ca. 3%, and the relative mercaptan yield again declines by a factor of 2.

Similar trends appear for the propylene reaction. The relative yields of mercaptans decrease in the order: gas, liquid, solid phase. However, the overall yield in the low temperature solid remains relatively high, at about 70%.

Table 3

Product Yields in the Reaction of Sulfur Atoms with Ethylene and Propylene in the Gas, Liquid, and Solid Phases

Olefin	Phase	[Olefin]/[COS]	Overall yield,[a] %	Mercaptan/ episulfide
C_2H_4	Gas	2.8	~80	0.85
	Liquid	2.8	~80	0.45
	Solid[b]	13	3	0.20
C_3H_6	Gas	5	~80	0.50
	Liquid	5.5	~80	0.33
	Solid[b]	10	~70	0.13

[a] In terms of S atoms produced.
[b] At −196°.

These results indicate that the liquid-phase photolysis at room temperature (or more conveniently at 0°C to reduce excess pressure) may be a useful synthetic process for the preparation of episulfides or olefinic mercaptans.

REACTIONS OF SULFUR ATOMS WITH ACETYLENES

The gas-phase reactions of sulfur atoms with acetylenes are more complex than are those of paraffins or olefins. The yield of volatile products is low and large amounts of solid materials form in conventional photolysis experiments.

With acetylene the volatile product amounts to ca. 10% of the scavenged S atoms. It is comprised of CS_2, thiophene, and benzene. In flash photolysis experiments, kinetic spectroscopy shows no absorbing transient. With kinetic mass spectrometry, however, the primary adduct C_2H_2S could be readily detected (Fig. 5). The adduct is relatively stable and shows no significant decay over several seconds. Only two structures appear reasonable, namely thioketone and thiacyclopropene:

$$H_2C{=}C{=}S \quad \text{and} \quad \underset{S}{\triangledown}$$

The thioketene, being the product of an isomerization reaction involving hydrogen migration, should decrease drastically in importance with increasing methylation. On the other hand, if the adduct has the ring structure, its yield would presumably rise with methylation because the rate of addition is faster with methylated acetylenes and the stability of the products should also be higher by analogy with the cyclopropenes.

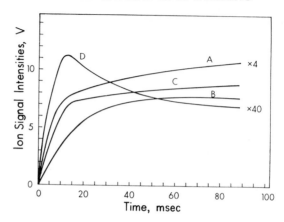

Fig. 5. Parent adduct ion signal intensities as a function of reaction time in the reaction of sulfur atoms with (*A*) acetylene (C_2H_2S); (*B*) methylacetylene (C_3H_4S); (*C*) dimethylacetylene (C_4H_6S); (*D*) perfluorodimethylacetylene (C_4F_6S).

Experiments were subsequently carried out with methyl acetylene and dimethyl acetylene. The mass intensities for the parent peaks of the adduct products were observed to increase markedly (Fig. 5). Furthermore, the adduct products showed no appreciable decay up to 5 sec. These findings strongly suggest that the primary product of the addition of $S(^1D)$ atom to acetylenes is the thiacyclopropane. The alternative possibility that $S(^1D)$ atoms insert into the methyl C—H bonds to give a stable mercaptan can be eliminated since essentially the same results were obtained using ethylene episulfide as the S-atom source, which is known to produce only triplet S atoms.

Perfluoro-2-butyne also reacts with sulfur atoms to yield a thiacyclopropene, although its reactivity is considerably less than that of 2-butyne itself, as is the stability of the perfluoro-1,2-dimethylthiacyclopropene product, which shows significant decay within 4 sec.

Cyclopropene itself is a known compound (16). It is relatively stable at room temperature in the gas phase but has a strong tendency to polymerize. Synthesis from the addition of methylene to ethylene, however, has not yet been achieved: The adduct gives allene (even at 4°K) and methyl acetylene (17). The methylated homologs are more stable and dimethyl cyclopropene has, in fact, been obtained from the addition of methylene to dimethyl acetylene.

The oxygenated analogs of the cyclopropenes, i.e., the oxirenes, have not been isolated to date (18), despite the fact that they have been predicted to be thermodynamically more stable than the cyclopropenes (19).

The present studies on the reactions of S atoms with the acetylenes appear to be the first synthesis of the thiacyclopropenes.

The final volatile products of conventional photolysis experiments on $COS-CH_3C{\equiv}CH$ systems are dimethyl thiophene and trimethyl benzene in a combined yield of ca. 20%. With dimethyl acetylene, tetramethyl thiophene and hexamethylbenzene are formed in a combined yield of ca. 20%. In the case of perfluorodimethylacetylene, perfluorotetramethyl-thiophene is produced in a yield of over 60%.

A tentative mechanism may be suggested

$$S + RC{\equiv}CR \longrightarrow \left[\begin{array}{c} S \\ \triangle \\ RC{=\!=\!=}CR \end{array}\right]^* \tag{16}$$

$$\left[\begin{array}{c} RC{=\!=\!=}CR \\ \diagdown\diagup \\ S \end{array}\right]^* + M \longrightarrow \begin{array}{c} RC{=\!=\!=}CR \\ \diagdown\diagup \\ S \end{array} + M \tag{17}$$

$$\left[\begin{array}{c} RC{=\!=\!=}CR \\ \diagdown\diagup \\ S \end{array}\right]^* \longrightarrow \text{free radicals} + CS_2 + \text{polymer} \tag{18}$$

$$\begin{array}{c} RC{=\!=\!=}CR \\ \diagdown\diagup \\ S \end{array} + RC{\equiv}CR \longrightarrow \begin{array}{c} RC{-}\!{-}CR \\ \| \quad \| \\ RC \quad CR \\ \diagdown\diagup \\ S \end{array} \tag{19}$$

$$\begin{array}{c} RC{=\!=\!=}CR \\ \diagdown\diagup \\ S \end{array} \xrightarrow{\text{slow}} \text{free radicals} + CS_2 + \text{polymer} \tag{20}$$

$$\text{free radicals} + RC{\equiv}CR \longrightarrow \text{benzene} + \text{acetylenic polymer} \tag{21}$$

This scheme is supported by a number of additional experimental observations. Thus, for example, when mixtures of 700-torr C_2H_2 and 700-torr COS were flashed and immediately frozen to $-196°$, upon slow rewarming, after removal of excess reactants, only CS_2 was found to form (in addition of a brown solid) in a much higher yield (60%) than in the conventional experiments. The reaction apparently proceeds according to equation 20. Furthermore, in conventional photolysis experiments, with mixed acetylenes for example, 700-torr C_2H_2 and 700-torr $C_2(CF_3)_2$, two products were obtained in good yields, perfluorotetramethylthiophene and di(trifluoromethyl)thiophene. The precise structure of the latter product is currently under investigation. It will have a decisive role in establishing the exact mechanism of the reaction and the nature of the primary transient adduct.

In conclusion, from the standpoint of synthetic applications, the reaction of atomic sulfur with acetylenes may have some use in the preparation of thiophene derivatives and perhaps also in the synthesis of some stable thiacyclopropene derivatives. As mentioned above, the photolysis of a

6 : 1 mixture of perfluoro-2-butyne with COS at a 1000–2000 torr total pressure produces pure perfluorotetramethylthiophene in a yield exceeding 60%.

THE ADDITION AND INSERTION REACTIONS OF SINGLET AND TRIPLET STATE SELENIUM ATOMS

The great similarity between selenium-atom and sulfur-atom chemistry and possible synthetic applications will perhaps justify a brief discussion here of the chemistry of reactions involving selenium atoms.

Reactions of selenium atoms with olefins have been reported in the literature (4). In flash-photolyzed CSe_2–olefin mixtures, transient spectra were observed and tentatively assigned to episelenides. Since authentic samples have not been available, these spectral assignments could not be confirmed.

From the time dependence of the spectral intensities it was possible to obtain absolute rate constants for a series of olefins. Preliminary experiments were also reported on COSe, and it was concluded, by analogy with COS, that selenium atoms in the $^1D_2$ state were formed in the photolysis of COS.

Conventional experiments carried out in our laboratory have indicated that reaction occurs between selenium atoms and olefins. However, the yield of organoselenium compounds was low, 2–3%, and of low reproducibility. In fast-flow experiments, with rapid cooling, it was possible to demonstrate that the initial reaction between selenium atoms and olefins is rapid and the low yields in the static photolysis experiments were largely attributable to the rapid decomposition of the initial product to the parent olefin. The products of the flow experiments were oily materials, containing selenium, but no further characterization could be achieved.

In further studies the reactions were investigated in flash photolysis by the recently developed kinetic mass spectrometry technique. The following olefins were examined: ethylene, propylene, allene, 1,3-butadiene, vinyl fluoride, di-, tri-, and tetrafluoroethylene, 2-fluoropropene, pentafluoro-1-butene, 2-(trifluoromethyl)-1-propene, vinyl chloride, *cis*- and *trans*-2-dichloroethylene, and vinyltrifluorosilane. In all cases, a more or less intense signal was obtained at *m/e* values corresponding to the adduct of (olefin + Se). Some representative oscillogram traces are reproduced in Figures 6 and 7. It is seen that most episelenides are inherently unstable and undergo decomposition with half-lives ranging from ca. 20 msec to over 5 sec.

Allene appears to be the only olefin which gives products having molecular weight higher than the episelenide [$(C_3H_4)_2Se$]. The allene episelen-

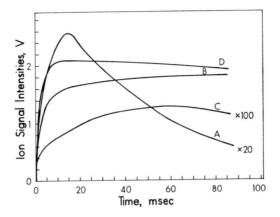

Fig. 6. Parent adduct ion signal intensities as a function of reaction time in the reaction of selenium atoms with: (*A*) vinyl fluoride (C_2H_3FSe); (*B*) difluoroethylene ($C_2H_2F_2Se$); (*C*) tetrafluoroethylene (C_2F_4Se); (*D*) ethylene (C_2H_4Se).

ide and butadiene episelenide are more stable than the episelenides of the simple olefins, such as ethylene. Their decomposition is very likely bimolecular:

$$\triangleright\!Se + Se\!\triangleleft \longrightarrow Se_2 + 2\ \text{olefins}$$

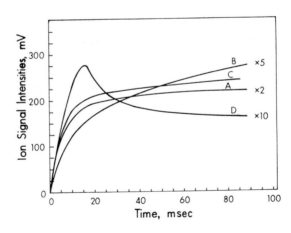

Fig. 7. Parent adduct ion signal intensities as a function of reaction time in the reaction of selenium atoms with: (*A*) allene (C_3H_4Se); (*B*) ($C_3H_4)_2Se$ from allene; (*C*) butadiene (C_4H_6Se); (*D*) dichloroethylene ($C_2H_2Cl_2Se$).

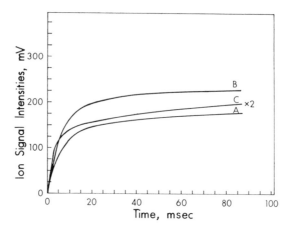

Fig. 8. Parent adduct ion signal intensities as a function of reaction time in the insertion reactions of $Se(^1D_2)$ atom with: (A) propane (C_3H_8Se); (B) isobutane ($C_4H_{10}Se$); (C) methylsilane (CH_3SiH_3).

The reaction of $Se(^1D)$ atoms, from the photolysis of COSe with paraffins, has also been examined. Experiments with propane, cyclopropane, cyclobutane, ethane, methylsilane, Si_2D_6, isobutane, etc., demonstrated insertion of excited selenium atoms into C—H and Si—H bonds (Fig. 8). As with sulfur, only the excited singlet atoms are reactive. By addition of the chemically inert CO_2 to the system, mercaptan formation could be completely suppressed.

Further experiments in a conventional system have led to the isolation of the stable products of the isobutane reaction, *sec*-butyl selenomercaptan and *tert*-butyl selenomercaptan. This is the first reported synthesis of *tert*-butyl selenomercaptan. An earlier attempt at synthesizing it by preparative organic methods was unsuccessful (20). The cyclopropyl, cyclobutyl, and silyl selenomercaptans are also novel structures.

CONCLUDING REMARKS

Although in most of the studies on atomic reactions described in this article, synthetic–preparative applications were not the primary objective, the number of new compounds synthesized by this program suggests that atomic reactions from photochemical sources can be successfully exploited for synthetic–preparative use. The quantities of product materials involved in most cases barely exceeded the minimum amounts required for reliable structural identifications. However, there is no reason why larger quantities could not have been produced. Photochemical processes, as a general rule, are too expensive for the industrial production of low-priced chemicals (except when the light energy is used as an initiator for long-chain reactions). On a laboratory scale, however, photochemically initiated atomic reactions could be advantageously incorporated into the general repertoire of preparative organic chemistry.

Acknowledgments

The authors are deeply indebted to many of their colleagues at the Photochemistry Laboratory at the University of Alberta for generously consenting to the use of their unpublished data in this article.

References

1. R. J. Cvetanovic, in *Advances in Photochemistry*, Vol. 1, W. A. Noyes, Jr., G. S. Hammond, and J. N. Pitts, Jr., Eds., Interscience, New York, 1963, p. 115.
2. L. I. Avramenko and R. V. Kolesnikova, in *Advances in Photochemistry*, Vol. 2, W. A. Noyes, Jr., G. S. Hammond, and J. N. Pitts, Jr., Eds., Interscience, New York, 1964, p. 25.
3. F. Kaufman, in *Progress in Reaction Kinetics*, Vol. 1, G. Porter, Ed., Pergamon, Oxford, 1961, p. 1.
4. A. B. Callear and W. J. R. Tyerman, *Proc. Chem. Soc.*, **1964**, 296; *Trans. Faraday Soc.*, **61**, 2395 (1965); **62**, 371 (1966).
5. W. J. R. Tyerman, W. B. O'Callaghan, P. Kebarle, O. P. Strausz, and H. E. Gunning, *J. Am. Chem. Soc.*, **88**, 4277 (1966).
6. O. P. Strausz and H. E. Gunning, *J. Am. Chem. Soc.*, **84**, 4080 (1962).
7. K. S. Sidhu, I. G. Csizmadia, O. P. Strausz, and H. E. Gunning, *J. Am. Chem. Soc.*, **88**, 2412 (1966).
8. R. J. Ferm, *Chem. Rev.*, **57**, 621 (1957).
9. A. R. Knight, O. P. Strausz, and H. E. Gunning, *J. Am. Chem. Soc.*, **85**, 1207 and 2349 (1963).
10. A. R. Knight, O. P. Strausz, S. M. Malm, and H. E. Gunning, *J. Am. Chem. Soc.*, **86**, 4243 (1964).
11. H. A. Wiebe, A. R. Knight, O. P. Strausz, and H. E. Gunning, *J. Am. Chem. Soc.*, **87**, 1443 (1965).
12. P. Fowles, M. de Sorgo, A. J. Yarwood, O. P. Strausz, and H. E. Gunning, *J.Am. Chem. Soc.*, **89**, 1056 (1967).
13. O. P. Strausz, T. Hikida, and H. E. Gunning, *Can. J. Chem.*, **43**, 717 (1965).
14. K. S. Sidhu, E. M. Lown, O. P. Strausz, and H. E. Gunning, *J. Am. Chem. Soc.*, **88**, 254 (1966).
15. E. M. Lown, E. L. Dedio, O. P. Strausz, and H. E. Gunning, *J. Am. Chem. Soc.*, **89**, 1056 (1967).
16. F. L. Carter and V. L. Frampton, *Chem. Rev.*, **64**, 497 (1964).
17. M. E. Jacox and D. F. Milligan, *J. Am. Chem. Soc.*, **85**, 278 (1963); T. Terao, N. Sakai, and S. Shida, *ibid.*, **85**, 3919 (1963); see also ref. 15.
18. R. N. McDonald and P. A. Schwab, *J. Am. Chem. Soc.*, **86**, 4866 (1964); V. Franzen, *Chem. Ber.*, **87**, 1479 (1954); J. K. Stille and D. D. Whitehurst, *J. Am. Chem. Soc.*, **86**, 4871 (1964).
19. R. A. Nelson and R. S. Jessup, *Chem. Abstr.*, **46**, 8505i (1952).
20. E. E. Reid, *Organic Chemistry of Bivalent Sulfur*, Chemical Publication Co., New York, 1958.

Recent Advances in the Chemistry of the Sulfur–Sulfur Bond

R. E. DAVIS, E. S. WAGNER, and M. C. GUENTHNER*

Purdue University, West Lafayette, Indiana

To be accurate and also apologetic, the title of this article should carry a subtitle indicating that the work to be discussed was performed at Purdue, because the work of numerous other chemists (particularly on the new and exciting heterocyclic compounds containing S—S bonds) cannot be covered or reviewed in this paper.

While surveying the literature during preparation of a thesis (1), it was noted that numerous x-ray determinations had been made on polythio compounds. In a thesis statement, a vague comment was made concerning the possible relationship between reactivities and the sulfur–sulfur single bond lengths. Work of the research group and of numerous others has in part clarified, supplied new data, and left or created new research problems. Some of these topics will be discussed in this article.

RELATIONSHIP BETWEEN ACTIVATION ENERGY AND THE LENGTH OF THE S—S BOND

Figure 1 is a plot of the activation energy, E_a kcal/mole in water near 25°C, versus the inverse cube (r^{-3}) of the sulfur–sulfur bond distance.

$$\text{NC}^- + \overset{\text{X}}{\underset{\underset{r}{\longleftrightarrow}}{\text{S}}}\overset{\text{X}}{-\text{S}} \xrightarrow{k} \text{NC}\overset{\text{X}}{\text{S}} + {}^-\text{SX} \tag{1}$$

$$\text{rate} = k(\text{CN}^-)(\text{XSSX}) \tag{2}$$

$$k = A \exp\left(-E_a/RT\right) \tag{3}$$

$$E_{a_{\text{CN}^-}} = 99/r^3 \text{ kcal/mole Å}^3 \qquad \text{for cyanide ion} \tag{4}$$

The data are unusual in several respects:

(a) The data on the reaction of the cyanide ion fall on one line (4) and those of the sulfite fall on another line (5).

---

* The work described herein was carried out while the senior author was an Alfred P. Sloan Fellow, 1962–1966.

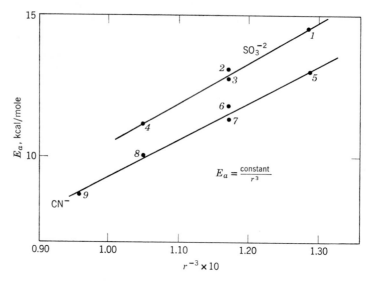

Fig. 1. Plot of E_a versus r^{-3} for the reactions of cyanide ion and of sulfite ion in water near 25°C with numerous compounds containing an S—S bond. The S—S length varies from 1.97 to 2.25 Å in this plot.

Point (1) $SO_3^{-2} + S_2O_3^{-2}$ (refs. 6, 14, 17), (2) $SO_3^{-2} + N,N'$-diacetyl cystine (ref. 16), (3) SO_3^{-2} + cystine (ref. 16), (4) $SO_3^{-2} + S_3O_6^{-2}$ (refs. 12, 15), (5) $CN^- + S_2O_3$ (refs. 5–7), (6) $CN^- + S_8$ (refs. 8, 9), (7) $CN^- + S_4O_6^{-2}$ (refs. 8, 10, 11), (8) $CN^- + S_3O_6^{-2}$ (refs. 12, 13), (9) $CN^- + S_2^{-2}$ (refs. 10, 13).

$$E_{a_{SO_3^{-2}}} = 110/r^3 \qquad \text{for sulfite ion} \tag{5}$$

$$SO_3^{-2} + XSSX \longrightarrow XSSO_3^- + XS^-$$

(b) Although all the reactions are in water near 25°C, almost all of the charge types are reactions with dinegative substrates. Thus

$$NC^- + S—SO_3^{-2} \longrightarrow NCS^- + SO_3^{-2} \tag{6}$$

$$NC^- + S—S^{-2} \longrightarrow NCS^- + S^{-2} \tag{7}$$

$$SO_3^{-2} + S—\overset{*}{S}O_3^{-2} \xrightarrow[\text{label } S^{35}]{} SSO_3^{-2} + \overset{*}{S}O_3^{-2} \tag{8}$$

$$SO_3^{-2} + RSSR^{-2} \xrightarrow[\substack{\text{cystine} \\ \text{dianion}}]{} {}^-RSSO_3^- + {}^-RS^- \tag{9}$$

$$SO_3^{-2} + {}^-O_3S—S—SO_3^- \longrightarrow {}^-O_3S—S—SO_3^- + SO_3^{-2} \tag{10}$$

Only the reaction of the cyanide ion with elemental sulfur has a charge

$$^-CN + S_8 \xrightarrow[\text{rate-determining step}]{} {}^-S_8CN \tag{11}$$

product of zero [(-1) times (0)]. Yet reaction 11 has a point (6) near the lower line in Figure 1.

(c) All the reactions are bimolecular (2) and presumably have similar mechanisms.

In the papers reporting this correlation (2,3), the reasons for the correlation being inverse cubic were discussed. While most of these reasons are completely *a posteriori* arguments, the best was the appeal by analogy to the relationship of bond energy of the S—S bond and its length (4).

Glockler found that the bond energy, E, was also related to the inverse cube of r_{ss} (and also of other bonds as C—H, C—C, etc).

$$E = C/r^3{}_{ss} \qquad C \text{ (constant)} = 520 \qquad (12)$$

Thus (3) it can be noted that the activation energies of equations 1 and 5 are about one-fifth of the total bond energies of the S—S bond.

$$E_{a_{CN^-}} = 0.19 \, E_{ss} \qquad (13)$$

$$E_{a_{SO_3^{-2}}} = 0.21 \, E_{ss} \qquad (14)$$

However, there is one datum point that falls far off the plot in Figure 1. The reaction is that of cyanide anion with the amino acid disulfide dianion, cystine (eq. 15). Now the sulfite data of Cecil and McPhee (16) fit (point 3);

$$NC^- + \quad \begin{matrix} ^-OOC & CH_2 & CH_2 & COO^- \\ \diagdown\diagup & \diagdown\diagup & \diagup\diagdown & \diagup\diagdown \\ CH & S\!-\!S & CH \\ | & & | \\ NH_2 & & NH_2 \end{matrix} \qquad (15)$$

see reaction 9. Three theories could explain reaction 15. (a) The theory (3) is all wrong. (b) The data of Gawron (19) on the activation energy of reaction 15 are wrong. (c) Something else is happening in reaction 15 that does not happen in reaction 9.

Reexamination and repetition of the work of Gawron by Wagner (22) shows that the original work was essentially correct. Thus either the theory is wrong or else something else is happening in reaction 15.

If we write out the products of reaction 9 and the deviant reaction 15, the reader can note that the final products are quite different.

$$O_3S^{-2} + \quad \begin{matrix} ^-OOC & CH_2 & CH_2 & COO^- \\ \diagdown\diagup & \diagdown\diagup & \diagup\diagdown & \diagup\diagdown \\ CH & S\!-\!S & CH \\ | & & | \\ NH_2 & & NH_2 \end{matrix} \longrightarrow$$

$$\begin{matrix} ^-OOC & CH_2 & & CH_2 & COO^- \\ \diagdown\diagup & \diagdown\diagup & & \diagup\diagdown & \diagup\diagdown \\ CH & S\!-\!SO_3^- + \, ^-S & CH \\ | & & | \\ NH_2 & & NH_2 \end{matrix} \qquad (16)$$

Sulfite forms the Bunte salt and cysteine (eq. 16). This is presumably the result of a simple S_N2 displacement of sulfite ion on one of the sulfur atoms. Cyanide ion reacts and the final products are cysteine and a heterocycle (eq. 17).

from eq. 15 ⟶

$$
\underset{\text{final products}}{
\begin{array}{c}
{}^-\text{OOC}\diagdown \quad \diagup\text{CH}_2 \\
\text{HC} \qquad \text{S} \\
\mid \\
\text{HN}\!-\!\!-\!\!-\!\text{C}\!=\!\text{NH}
\end{array}
\;+\;
\begin{array}{c}
\text{CH}_2 \diagdown \quad \diagup\text{COO}^- \\
{}^-\text{S} \qquad \text{CH} \\
\mid \\
\text{NH}_2
\end{array}
}
\tag{17}
$$

Reaction 15 has been interpreted in terms of two separate steps (19). The

from eq. 15 $\xrightarrow{\text{r.d.s.}}$

$$
\begin{array}{c}
{}^-\text{OOC}\diagdown \quad \diagup\text{CH}_2 \\
\text{CH} \qquad \text{S}\!-\!\text{C}\!\equiv\!\text{N} \\
\mid \\
\text{NH}_2
\end{array}
\;+\;
\begin{array}{c}
\text{CH}_2 \diagdown \quad \diagup\text{COO}^- \\
{}^-\text{S} \qquad \text{CH} \\
\mid \\
\text{NH}_2
\end{array}
\tag{18}
$$

first is the simple S_N2 displacement of cyanide ion forming the thiocyanate (eq. 18). Cyanide will do this with certain disulfides (eq. 19).

$$
\text{NC}^- + \text{RSSR} \longrightarrow \text{RSCN} + \text{RS}^-
\tag{19}
$$

Then the postulate (19) is reasonably made that the thiocyanate reacts with the amino group (eq. 20). All attempts (19) to prepare **1** lead to **2**.

$$
\begin{array}{c}
\text{OOC}\diagdown \quad \diagup\text{CH}_2 \\
\text{HC} \qquad \text{S} \\
\mid \qquad \mid \\
\text{H}_2\text{N} \qquad \text{C} \\
\quad \parallel\!\!\parallel \\
\quad \text{N}
\end{array}
\xrightarrow{\text{fast}}
\begin{array}{c}
{}^-\text{OOC}\diagdown \quad \diagup\text{CH}_2 \\
\text{HC} \qquad \text{S} \\
\mid \qquad \mid \\
\text{HN}\!-\!\!-\!\text{C} \\
\qquad \parallel \\
\qquad \text{NH}
\end{array}
\tag{20}
$$

(1)   (2)

If the theory is correct, the rate-determining step (eq. 18) ought to correlate with equation 4. Therefore it was postulated (21) and then proved (20) that equation 18 is not rate determining (20).

The evidence provided by Wagner (20,22) included the determination of the amino-nitrogen kinetic isotope effect. The kinetic isotope effect k_{14}/k_{15}

$$
\begin{array}{c}
{}^-\text{OOC}\diagdown \quad \diagup\text{CH}_2 \\
\text{CH} \qquad \text{S}\!-\!\text{SR} \xrightarrow{\text{CN}^-} \text{products} \\
\mid \\
\text{H}_2\text{N}^{15}
\end{array}
\tag{21}
$$

$$
\begin{array}{c}
{}^-\text{OOC}\diagdown \quad \diagup\text{CH}_2 \\
\text{CH} \qquad \text{S}\!-\!\text{SR} \xrightarrow{\text{CN}^-} \text{products} \\
\mid \\
\text{H}_2\text{N}^{14}
\end{array}
\tag{22}
$$

(ratio of reaction 22 to 21) was determined to be 1.0094 ± 0.0005. The 0.0005 is the experimental error measurement. Thus the amino nitrogen is moving and changing its bonding characteristics during the rate-determining step (r.d.s.). Thus we postulated product character (20) (of **2**) in the rate-determining step.

An effect of 1.0094 is small and the isotope effect in the sulfite reaction has been recently investigated (20) as a control experiment.

After a round of frustrations (see below) the isotope effect (23) with sulfite has been determined to be 1.0000 ± 0.0005. There is no isotope effect. Thus it is again postulated that cyanide ion reacts differently than sulfite (eq. 23). The data are given in the Appendix.

$$(23)$$

In equation 24 the amino nitrogen remains in the form of amino nitrogen while in equation 23 it becomes amide-type nitrogen.

$$(24)$$

But before the amino nitrogen isotope effect of reaction 16 can be measured, a means had to be found that would allow the reaction to be run nearly to completion. Therefore, a discussion of the oxibase scale is given.

The Oxibase Scale

Only a select group of nucleophiles can rupture a sulfur–sulfur single bond. This can be easily seen by considering the reactions of two nucleophiles. Sulfite ion displaces methyl bromide in water

$$SO_3^{-2} + CH_3Br \longrightarrow CH_3SO_3^- + Br^- \tag{25}$$

almost at the same rate as does thiosulfate.

$$SSO_3^{-2} + CH_3Br \longrightarrow CH_3SSO_3^- + Br^- \tag{26}$$

Thus the "carbon nucleophilicity" (24) of these two anions is about the same. Yet, only one of these will dissolve elemental sulfur. Therefore the

$$SO_3^{-2} \xrightarrow{\frac{1}{8}S_8} SSO_3^{-2} \tag{27}$$

$$S_2O_3^{-2} \xrightarrow{\frac{1}{8}S_8} {}^-SSSO_3^- \tag{28}$$

"sulfur nucleophilicity" or thiophilicity (25) of these two anions differ greatly.

Cyanide ion is a good thiophile (25); it forms thiocyanate. However, if we compare the reverse reactions of equations 27 and 29 in acidic media,

$$CN^- \xrightarrow{\frac{1}{8}S_8} SCN^- \tag{29}$$

only thiosulfate forms mainly elemental sulfur and sulfur dioxide. Thiocyanate does not decompose to the volatile HCN and elemental sulfur.

$$SCN^- \xrightarrow{H^+} HCN \uparrow + \tfrac{1}{8}S_8 \downarrow \tag{30}$$

$$SSO_3^{-2} \xrightarrow{H^+} H_2O + SO_2 \uparrow + \tfrac{1}{8}S_8 \downarrow \tag{31}$$

The reasons for reactions 25, 26, 27, 29, and 31 proceeding are thermodynamic. The free energy values, ΔG, of these reactions are negative and favorable. Reactions 28 and 30 are not thermodynamically favorable; ΔG is positive in both cases.

A method which can qualitatively (and semiquantitatively) predict these ΔG values and also estimate the *relative rates*, ($\Delta\Delta G\ddagger$), is called by the author the *oxibase scale* (26–28). Foss (29) used *oxi*dation potentials in a qualitative manner in sulfur chemistry. Edwards (30–32) used oxidation potentials (and unfortunately later changed to the less useful polarizability (31,32)) and *basi*cities to form his double basicity scale which we have renamed the *oxibase* scale.

If we write the oxidation dimerization potential relative to water under the nucleophile (26) and under the legate anion (28) (leaving group) and the two relative pK_a values ($H \equiv pK_a + 1.74$), then a *great deal* (but not all) of the thermodynamics of the system has been described. For example, writing equations 27 and 29, the E values (27) decrease ($\Delta G' < 0$) and the H values decrease ($\Delta G'' < 0$). The treatment (eqs. 32 and 33) is rather

$$SO_3^{-2} \xrightarrow{\frac{1}{8}S_8} SSO_3^{-2} \tag{32}$$

$$2.57 = E \longrightarrow E = 2.52$$

$$9.00 = H \longrightarrow H = 3.60$$

$$CN^- \xrightarrow{\frac{1}{8}S_8} SCN^- \tag{33}$$

$$2.79 = E \longrightarrow E = 1.83$$

$$10.88 = H \longrightarrow H = 0$$

exact because sulfur is an element with a ΔG_f° defined as zero at 25°C.

The process shown in equation 28 is unfavorable as seen with increasing E and H values.

$$SSO_3^{-2} \xrightarrow{\frac{1}{8}S_8} {}^-SSSO_3^- \tag{34}$$

$$2.52 = E \longrightarrow E = 2.9$$

$$3.60 = H \longrightarrow H = 7.9$$

$$\Delta G > 0$$
$$\text{unfavorable}$$

The polythio sulfur is much more easily oxidized than thiosulfate.

The sulfite–thiosulfate system (eqs. 27 and 31) is almost *isovoltaic*; the difference in E values is only 0.05 V. Thus, acid can protonate thiosulfate and decompose it to the products shown in equation 31. All the acid–base thio systems, capable of dissolving or reprecipitating elemental sulfur, are nearly isovoltaic. A few examples are SO_3^{-2} and $S_2O_3^{-2}$, HS^- and HS_x^-, $C_2H_5S^-$ and $C_2H_5S_x^-$, etc.

Cyanide and thiocyanate differ by about 1 V (being equivalent to a ΔG of 46 kcal/mole since two electrons are involved). The reverse (eq. 30) requires at least the 46 kcal/mole of ΔG.

The good thiophiles on sulfur–sulfur bonds are ions (or molecules) which are very easily oxidized (E values high, above 2.5 V). The thiophiles are usually quite basic (H large) although a very high E value can accommodate a low H value. An example would be triphenyl phosphine, a good thiophile (25,33) with a very large E and a low H. The usual list includes:

$$\left.\begin{array}{l} HS^- \\ CN^- \\ SO_3^{-2} \\ \phi_3P, \text{ etc.} \end{array}\right\} \xrightarrow{RSSR} \text{Product} + \underset{\substack{\text{legate} \\ \text{anion}}}{{}^-SR} \tag{35}$$

All of these can displace the legate ion, RS^-, which generally has a high E value and a high H value.

Application of the Oxibase Scale to the Cystine System

The reaction of sulfite with cystine is a reversible reaction. The cysteine thiolate anion has a very high E value and a high H value and it can displace sulfite ion (eq. 36). Thus this is nearly an isovoltaic, isobasic system.

$$SO_3^{-2} + RSSR \rightleftharpoons RSSO_3^- + RS^- \tag{36}$$
$$\begin{array}{ll} E = 2.57 & E = 2.7 \\ H = 9.00 & H = 12.4 \end{array}$$

Since both E and H increase a bit from left to right in equation 36, it is not too surprising that the equilibrium constant (34) of equation 36 is $K = 2 \times 10^{-2}$. Thus, the equilibrium lies on the side of the legate nucleophile of the lower E and H. A calculation with these values allows an estimation of K using the oxibase scale.

However, for a small isotope effect to be measurable, the reaction must be driven to over 90%. But equation 36 goes only 14% of the way and an isotope effect on the equilibrium constant (35) is not exactly what a mechanistic chemist wants.

However, the application of the oxibase scale saves the problem from extinction. Observe that RS$^-$ in equation 36 (cysteine thiolate dianion) is a better E and H nucleophile than sulfite ion. Therefore the addition of a good substrate that likes nucleophiles of high E and high H values will destroy RS$^-$ and drive reaction 36 to the right. Then that complex reaction mixture can be disturbed and the last 10% of RSSR isolated. The idea is simple; the execution is not.

Iodoacetate anion was chosen. Since iodide ion (the legate anion) is such a good nucleophile (high E of 2.0 V), the substrate it is in likes nucleophiles with high E values to displace it. The oxibase plot is given in Figure 2 using the available kinetic rate constants. The rate constant of sulfite ion with iodoacetate is a known value. Using the E and H values of cysteine anion, the rate constant can be calculated.

$$^-OOC-CHCH_2S^- + ICH_2COO^- \xrightarrow{k_4} {}^-OOCCHCH_2SCH_2COO^- + I^- \tag{37}$$
$$\begin{array}{ll} \quad \text{NH}_2 & \qquad\qquad \text{NH}_2 \end{array}$$

The iodoacetate is a very water-soluble iodo compound and its sulfide (eq. 37) is water soluble.

The kinetic system (eq. 36) is a bimolecular reversible system. Adding iodoacetate gives a system of two reversible and two irreversible paths.

$$\begin{array}{ccc} A + B & \underset{k_2}{\overset{k_1}{\rightleftharpoons}} & C + D \\ + & & + \\ E & & E \\ k_3 \downarrow & & \downarrow k_4 \\ F & & G \end{array} \tag{38}$$

The values of k_1 is known; k_2 is obtained from K and k_1; k_3 has been measured; and k_4 is determined using the oxibase scale.

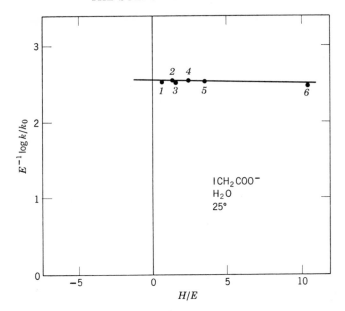

Fig. 2. Plot of $E^{-1} \log k/k_0$ versus H/E for nucleophiles with iodoacetate in water at 25°C. A value of k_{H_2O} of 1.4×10^{-8} M^{-1} sec^{-1} has been obtained in this laboratory. The rate constants with sulfite and thiosulfate were obtained by H. J. Backer and W. H. von Mels (36). The rate constants for reaction with thiocyanate and hydroxide are from C. Wagner (37) and the other thioanions are from H. Nakshbendi and R. E. Davis (38). Points: (1) SCN^-, (2) $C_2H_5OCS_2^-$, (3) $S_2O_3^{-2}$, (4) $(C_2H_5)_2NCS_2^-$, (5) SO_3^{-2}, and (6) OH^-.

The system (eq. 38) is then given to an analog computer and after several runs, many concentration–time curves are obtained. From these, one can guess when to stop the reactions (eq. 38) and remove the unreacted disulfide. This is then degraded to N_2 (14–14 and 14–15) and the isotopic ratio of m/e 28 to 29 determined.

The $^{14}N/^{15}N$ kinetic isotope effect has been determined to 1.0000 ± 0.0005 for reaction 16. Thus it is concluded that this reaction is a simple S_N2 reaction on the sulfur–sulfur bond with involvement of the amino group.

Acknowledgments

The senior author wishes to thank M. Bender for stimulating discussion in 1964 that led to our isotope effect measurements; Dr. A. I. Virtanen for encouragement during the Sulfur Symposium, and his companions in research (ΣX) at the University of Colorado who provided succor during the summer of 1966.

The authors wish to thank the Walter Reed Army Institute of Research for a grant (WRAMC-MD-2107); the National Science Foundation (NSF-G-15750); and the National Institutes of Health (NIH-RH-00279) for support of these studies.

EXPERIMENTAL APPENDIX

Procedure

Sodium sulfite (AR) (0.6–2.0 mmoles) and sodium iodoacetate (recrystallized several times from water) (0.8–2.0 mmoles) were dissolved in 50 ml of $0.1M$ sodium carbonate (AR). A solution of cystine (1–2 mmoles) in 4 ml of $1M$ sodium hydroxide was added and the solution allowed to stand for 15–48 hr. Glacial acetic acid was then added dropwise to lower the pH from 10–11.2 (depending upon the concentrations) to a pH of 5. The unreacted cystine was collected on the filter and washed with a cold solution of dilute acetic acid. The dried cystine was then weighed.

Labeled cystine-^{15}N was prepared in a procedure discussed in great detail in an earlier paper (20). The material had an infrared spectrum identical with a sample of cystine recrystallized three times from water (starting with reagent cystine from Nutritional Biochemicals Corp.). The material contained 1.3% [15]N. *Analysis:* Calcd. for $C_6H_{12}O_4N_2S$: C, 29.99; H, 5.03; N, 11.66; S, 26.69. Found: C, 30.11; H, 5.19; N, 11.49; S, 26.80.

In a typical experiment 528 mg of sodium carbonate, 126 mg of sodium sulfite, and 208 mg of sodium iodoacetate were dissolved and diluted to 100 ml. Cystine (480 mg, 2 mmoles) was dissolved in 4.00 ml of $1M$ sodium hydroxide. Then the two solutions were mixed at 25.00°C (NBS). After 15 hr, the unreacted cystine (256 mg) was recovered. The cystine was recovered by crystallization from the solution by adjusting the pH to 5 with a small amount of glacial acetic acid (Baker AR) (see ref. 20 for the exact details). The solubility of cystine in the solution was determined to be 5.6 mg/100 ml in control experiments.

The recovered cystine was then purified by solution in dilute hydrochloric acid followed by crystallization upon the addition of dilute sodium hydroxide to a pH of 5. *Analysis:* Calcd. for $C_6H_{12}N_2O_4S_2$: C, 29.99; H, 5.03; N, 11.66; S, 26.69. Found: C, 30.03, 30.01; H, 5.05, 5.13; N, 11.38, 11.41; S, 26.72, 26.84.

All cystine samples were subjected to electrophoresis and paper chromatography. The electrophoresis was performed on Whatman No. 3 chromatography paper at 2500 V for 20 min in a pyridine and acetic acid buffer of pH 6.4. The papers were then air dried and eluted for 18 hr in a descending solvent chromatography tank. The solvent was the upper layer of the standard butanol–acetic acid–water mixture (200:50:250). The developed chromatograms were air dried and then treated with the ninhydrin-collidine reagent. The color spot was developed by gentle heating of the paper with an electric hair dryer. All samples of cystine including the cystine-^{15}N were completely homogeneous.

Cystine was converted to ammonium ion using the Kjeldahl method.

Oxidation of the ammonium ion with basic hypobromite was carried out on a high vacuum line (39,40). The exact procedure is discussed in an earlier paper (20).

The resulting gas was handled and manipulated by means of a high vacuum line. Since the gas evolved from the oxidation of ammonia is nitrogen, analysis by means of a mass spectrometer is the most accurate method of determining its isotopic composition.

In the use of the mass spectrometer it is assumed that the peak height intensity is proportional to the concentration of the component and that the use of isotopes does not change the percentage of molecules ionized. A Consolidated-Nier 21-201 mass spectrometer equipped with a Varian Vac-Ion pump and a Cary Vibrating Reed MS 31 electrometer was used to obtain the isotopic ratios.

A PACE-TR-48 analog computer (Electronic Associates, Inc.) was used to obtain graphic solutions of the complex kinetic system.

The Kinetic System

$$A + B \underset{k_2}{\overset{k_1}{\rightleftharpoons}} C + D \tag{i}$$

$$B + E \overset{k_3}{\longrightarrow} F + I \tag{ii}$$

$$D + E \overset{k_4}{\longrightarrow} G + I \tag{iii}$$

The boundary conditions are such that the concentrations of A, B, and E are finite at $t = 0$, and of C, D, F, G, and I are zero. Equations i–iii yield seven differential equations that defy solution in closed form. The electrical analog of equations i–iii and their seven differentials can be drawn using the conventional notation. Amplitude scaling (41,42) was done using the following equations:

$$[10\dot{A}] = -\frac{k_1}{10}[10A][10B] + \frac{k_2}{10,000}[100C][1000D]$$

$$[10\dot{B}] = -\frac{k_1}{10}[10A][10B] + \frac{k_2}{10,000}[100C][1000D] - \frac{k_3}{10}[10B][10E]$$

$$[100\dot{C}] = 10\left(\frac{k_1}{10}[10A][10B] - \frac{k_2}{10,000}[100C][1000D]\right)$$

$$[1000\dot{D}] = 100\left(\frac{k_1}{10}[10A][10B] - \frac{k_2}{10,000}[100C][1000D] - \frac{k_4}{1000}[1000D][10E]\right)$$

$$[10\dot{E}] = -\frac{k_3}{10}[10B][10E] - \frac{k_4}{1000}[1000D][10E]$$

$$[10\dot{F}] = +\frac{k_3}{10}[10B][10E]$$

$$[10\dot{G}] = +\frac{k_4}{1000}[1000D][10E]$$

The wiring diagram is given in Figure 3. The program was run on an Electronic Associates' PACE TR-48 instrument. The graphs of the data are presented in Figure 4 for the initial amount of reaction.

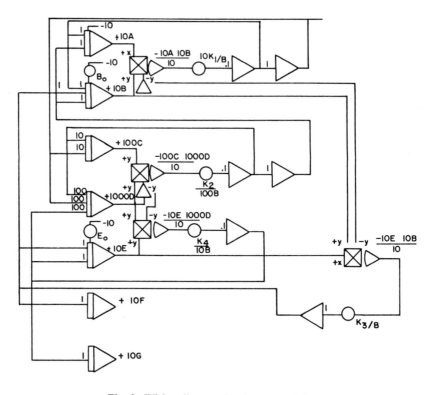

Fig. 3. Wiring diagram for the system i–iii.

In Figure 5 plots of the concentration of F ($\bar{_3}$OSCH$_2$COO$^-$) and G (RSCH$_2$COO$^-$) versus time are presented for various values of k_4. The experimental points are given.

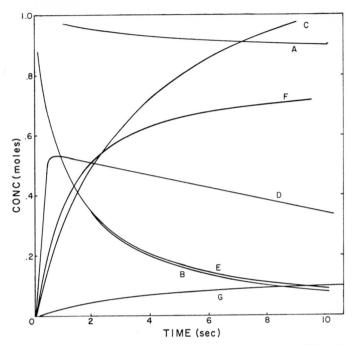

Fig. 4. Time development of the sulfite–cystine–iodoacetate system. Plot of voltage versus computer time (see the Appendix). [A] × 1 mole/liter. [C] × 10^{-1} mole/liter and [D] × 10^{-2} mole/liter.

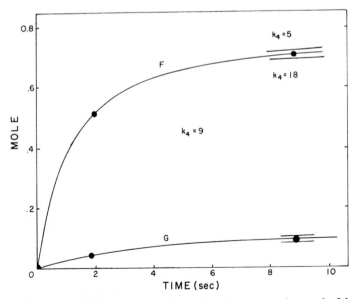

Fig. 5. Concentration of F and G as a function of computer time and of k_4 M^{-1} sec^{-1}. Computed using the analog computer. The four points are experimental values. The errors of determination are reflected in the calculated curves using k_4 values of 5, 9, and 18 M^{-1} sec^{-1}.

References

1. R. E. Davis, Ph.D. Thesis, Harvard University, 1958.
2. R. E. Davis, A. Cohen, and J. B. Louis, *J. Am. Chem. Soc.*, **85**, 3050 (1963).
3. R. E. Davis, J. B. Louis, and A. Cohen, *J.Am. Chem. Soc.*, **88**, 1 (1966).
4. G. Glockler, *J. Chem. Phys.*, **21**, 1242 (1953).
5. O. Foss and A. Hordnik, *Acta. Chem. Scand.*, **11**, 1443 (1957).
6. P. G. Taylor and C. A. Beevers, *Acta. Cryst.*, **5**, 341 (1952).
7. R. E. Davis, *J. Phys. Chem.*, **66**, 956 (1962); P. D. Bartlett and R. E. Davis, *J. Am. Chem. Soc.*, **80**, 2513 (1958).
8. S. C. Abrahams, *Acta Cryst.*, **8**, 611 (1955); A. Caron and J. Donohue, *Acta Cryst.*, **14**, 548 (1961).
9. P. D. Bartlett and R. E. Davis, *J. Am. Chem. Soc.*, **80**, 2513 (1958); E_a estimated in pure water from the data in aqueous methanol.
10. O. Foss and A. Hordnik, *Acta. Chem. Scand.*, **12**, 1700 (1958).
11. R. E. Davis, *J. Phys. Chem.*, **62**, 1599 (1958).
12. W. H. Zachariasen, *J. Chem. Phys.*, **2**, 109 (1934).
13. R. E. Davis, J. B. Louis, and A. Cohen, *J. Chem. Phys.*, **88**, 1 (1966).
14. D. P. Ames and J. E. Willard, *J. Am. Chem. Soc.*, **73**, 164 (1951).
15. A. Fava and G. Pajaro, *Ann. Chim.* (*Rome*), **44**, 551 (1954).
16. R. Cecil and J. R. McPhee, *Biochem. J.*, **60**, 496 (1955); L. K. Steinrauf, J. Peterson, and L. H. Jensen, *J. Am. Chem. Soc.*, **80**, 3855 (1958).
17. H. Foppl, *Angew. Chem.*, **70**, 401 (1958).
18. R. Cecil and J. R. McPhee, *Biochem. J.*, **60**, 496 (1955); **59**, 234 (1955); *Advances in Protein Chemistry*, Vol. XIV, Academic Press, New York, 1959, p. 303.
19. (a) O. Gawron and J. Fernando, *J. Am. Chem. Soc.*, **83**, 2906 (1961); (b) O. Gawron, S. Mahbobb, and J. Fernando, *Ibid.*, **86**, 2283 (1964); (c) Reviewed by O. Gawron, article in press for *Organic Sulphur Compounds*.
20. E. S. Wagner and R. E. Davis, *J. Am. Chem. Soc.*, **88**, 7 (1966).
21. R. E. Davis, *Survey of Progress in Chemistry*, A. Scott, Ed., Academic Press, New York, 1964, pp. 189–238.
22. E. S. Wagner, Ph.D. Thesis, Purdue University, 1964.
23. R. E. Davis, E. S. Wagner, and M. C. Guenthner, unpublished data.
24. C. G. Swain and C. B. Scott, *J. Am. Chem. Soc.*, **75**, 141 (1953).
25. P. D. Bartlett and R. E. Davis, *J. Am. Chem. Soc.*, **80**, 2513 (1958).
26. R. E. Davis and A. Cohen, *J. Am. Chem. Soc.*, **86**, 440 (1964).
27. R. E. Davis, *Survey of Progress in Chemistry*, Vol. 2, A. Scott, Ed., Academic Press, New York, 1964, pp. 189–238.
28. R. E. Davis, *J. Am. Chem. Soc.*, **87**, 3010 (1965).
29. O. Foss, *Acta. Chem. Scand.*, **1**, 307 (1947); **3**, 1385 (1949); **4**, 404, 866 (1950).
30. J. O. Edwards, *J. Am. Chem. Soc.*, **76**, 1540 (1954).
31. J. O. Edwards, *J. Am. Chem. Soc.*, **78**, 1819 (1956).
32. J. O. Edwards and R. G. Pearson, *J. Am. Chem. Soc.*, **84**, 16 (1962).
33. P. D. Bartlett, E. Cox, and R. E. Davis, *J. Am. Chem. Soc.*, **83**, 103 (1961).
34. R. E. Benesch and R. Benesch, *J. Am. Chem. Soc.*, **80**, 1666 (1958).
35. M. Dole, *Introduction to Statistical Thermodynamics*, Prentice-Hall, Englewood Cliffs, N.J., 1954, pp. 163–170.
36. H. J. Backer and W. H. von Mels, *Rec. Trav. Chem.*, **49**, 457 (1930).
37. C. Wagner, *Z. Physik. Chem.*, **A115**, 121 (1925).
38. R. E. Davis, H. Nakshbendi, and A. Ohno, *J. Org. Chem.*, **31**, 2702 (1966).
39. R. Schoenheimer, S. Ratner, and D. Rittenberg, *J. Biol. Chem.*, **130**, 703 (1939).

40. D. Rittenberg, D. W. Wilson, A. O. Nier, and S. P. Reimann, *Preparation and Measurement of Isotopic Tracers*, J. W. Edwards, Ann Arbor, Mich., 1947.
41. D. R. Coughanower and L. B. Koppel, *Process Systems Analysis and Control*, McGraw-Hill, New York, 1965.
42. J. R. Ashley, *Introduction to Analog Computation*, Wiley, New York, 1963.

Cleavage and Disproportionation Reactions in Organic Polysulfides

T. L. PICKERING, K. J. SAUNDERS, and A. V. TOBOLSKY

Princeton University, Princeton, New Jersey

The nature of the sulfur–sulfur bond, particularly in polymeric systems, has been investigated in the authors' laboratory over a period of years. These studies have led to a much greater understanding of the factors governing the physical properties of polymeric systems containing sulfur linkages (1). It has also become apparent that our understanding of the behavior of sulfur–sulfur bonds is still incomplete. In fact, so basic a parameter as the dissociation energy of the sulfur–sulfur bond in polysulfides is still in doubt. We have recently sought to clarify this uncertainty and the results of some of our studies will form the basis for this discussion.

Chemists commonly use two kinds of strength when they talk about bonds, the bond dissociation energy and the thermochemical bond energy. The bond dissociation energy is used when we wish to talk about a specific bond in a specific molecule. It is defined as the heat of the reaction

$$A\text{—}B \longrightarrow A\cdot + B\cdot$$

in the ideal gas state at $0°K$. The product radicals or atoms should be in their ground states. If other than spectroscopic methods are used, the bond dissociation energy so obtained refers to the temperature of measurement. In general the values obtained are sufficiently inaccurate that correction to $0°K$ is unwarranted.

The thermochemical bond energy is used when we wish to generalize about a certain type of bond, for example, a carbon–carbon single bond. For a molecule of the type AB_n the thermochemical bond energy is given by the expression

$$E(A\text{—}B) = -\frac{\Delta H_f^a}{n}(AB_n, g)$$

where ΔH_f^a is the heat of formation of the compound from the gaseous atoms. Thermochemical bond energies are almost always determined by calorimetry.

61

The thermochemical bond energy for the sulfur–sulfur bond is known to be about 63 kcal/mole (2–4). This value can be regarded as well established. Earlier values which are about 10 kcal lower than the value quoted above were based on an incorrect value for the heat of atomization of sulfur.*

In contrast to this value, the bond dissociation energy in polymeric sulfur is thought to be about 33 kcal/mole (1). Recently it was established that the dissociation energy of the tetrasulfide linkage in dimethyl tetrasulfide is about 37 kcal/mole (6). These values are in marked contrast to the values of 65–70 kcal/mole for the dissociation energy of dialkyl disulfides (7). No values have been reported for the dissociation energy of a trisulfide.

It was thought that, as a consequence of its much weaker bond, a tetrasulfide should have enhanced reactivity compared to a disulfide. Accordingly, several reactions have been investigated.

Thermal decomposition of tetrasulfides has been noted by several workers. For example, Twiss (8) recorded that diethyl tetrasulfide gives diethyl trisulfide and free sulfur on distillation *in vacuo*; Jones and Reid (9) reported that the same tetrasulfide decomposes to diethyl disulfide and sulfur at 140–150°. Bloomfield (10) found that dicyclohexyl tetrasulfide gives a material of reduced sulfur content and dicyclohexyl hexasulfide when heated at 140°; and Birch et al. (11) were unable to purify di-*n*-butyl tetrasulfide and presumed the tetrasulfide equilibrated at room temperature into a mixture of disulfides and higher sulfides.

Because the thermal decomposition of tetrasulfides results in products which are both complex and labile, quantitative data based on classical methods of separation are not only difficult to obtain but are also suspect. Recently, an analytical method which obviates these limitations has been applied to mixtures of polysulfides.

The method, due to Van Wazer and Grant (12), involves analysis of the proton NMR spectrum of the material. The chemical shift of appropriate alkyl end groups of polysulfides varies with the length of the sulfur chain. It is possible to resolve the resonances corresponding to various chain lengths (up to a maximum of about six sulfur atoms) and measurement of the NMR peak areas therefore enables the composition of a polysulfide mixture to be estimated. As will be discussed below, this technique has been used by the authors in their studies on the thermal decomposition of tetrasulfides.

An early objective of these studies was to establish precisely the nature of the products resulting from thermal decomposition of a tetrasulfide. Dimethyl tetrasulfide was selected as particularly suitable for investigation

* Readers interested in this area should consult the valuable series of papers by H. Mackle and co-workers beginning with reference 5.

by NMR. The tetrasulfide was heated in the dark at 80° in a sealed tube in the absence of oxygen and the NMR spectrum was obtained at various time intervals. From NMR spectra of known dimethyl polysulfides and mixtures thereof, peaks were assigned and the peak areas were found (Table 1). It appears that the initial decomposition results in the formation

Table 1
Decomposition of Dimethyl Tetrasulfide at 80°

Time (hr)	Percentage molar composition of product				
	Me_2S_2	Me_2S_3	Me_2S_4	Me_2S_5	Me_2S_6
0	0	3	97	0	0
0.5	0	8	80	10	2
1.0	0	13	72	11	4
1.4	0	14	67	14	5
2.5	0	20	60	16	4
5.2	0	31	49	13	7
10.1	0	41	39	15	5
20.1	0	47	30	15	8
43.7	0	49	27	15	9
66.6	0	47	26	15	12
138.0	Trace	48	26	14	12
393.5	1	49	25	14	11
894.8	2	49	25	16	8
1828.8	6	46	24	13	11

of tri-, penta-, and hexasulfides and that this part of the reaction is essentially complete after about 40 hr. Thereafter, disulfide is slowly formed. This almost certainly arises from subsequent decomposition of the trisulfide (see below). At no time was there evidence of monosulfide, and hydrocarbons were not formed since the sum of the peak areas remained constant relative to a tetramethylsilane standard. Further, the CH_3/S mole ratio in the polysulfide mixtures remained approximately constant, eliminating sulfur as a final product of the decomposition.

Strong evidence that dimethyl tetrasulfide undergoes homolytic cleavage at 80° was provided by the fact that the tetrasulfide decolorized the stable free-radical β-(phenylnitrogen oxide)-β-methylpentane-δ-one oxime (Banfield's free radical) (6)

$$CH_3-\overset{\overset{\displaystyle CH_3}{|}}{\underset{\underset{\displaystyle C_6H_5-N-O\cdot}{|}}{C}}-CH_2-\overset{\overset{\displaystyle }{\underset{\underset{\displaystyle O-\overset{+}{\underset{-}{N}}-C_6H_5}{\|}}{C}}}{C}-CH_3$$

It was also found that Banfield's free radical acted as an inhibitor for the formation of trisulfides and higher sulfides when the tetrasulfide was heated (Table 2). The observed inhibition period corresponded very closely

Table 2
Decomposition of Dimethyl Tetrasulfide at 80° in Presence of Banfield's Free Radical

Time (hr)	Percentage molar distribution of dimethyl poly-sulfides in product			
	Me_2S_3	Me_2S_4	Me_2S_5	Me_2S_6
0[a]	3	97	0	0
0.75	3	97	0	0
1.0	3	97	0	0
1.4	4	96	Trace	0
2.75	10	82	8	0
5.5	20	62	15	3
18.75	44	36	15	2

[a] The NMR spectrum was taken before the addition of the Banfield's free radical since it was not possible to obtain the spectrum in the presence of the initial concentration of free radical.

to the calculated period. Thus it is suggested that the products obtained from the tetrasulfide result from free-radical processes.

The following scheme is postulated for the decomposition of dimethyl tetrasulfide at 80°:

Initiation:

$$MeS_4Me \rightleftharpoons 2MeS_2 \cdot \qquad (1)$$

Propagation:

$$MeS_4Me + MeS_2 \cdot \rightleftharpoons MeS_3Me + MeS_3 \cdot \qquad (2)$$
$$MeS_4Me + MeS_3 \cdot \rightleftharpoons MeS_5Me + MeS_2 \cdot \qquad (3)$$
$$MeS_5Me + MeS_3 \cdot \rightleftharpoons MeS_6Me + MeS_2 \cdot \qquad (4)$$
$$\text{etc.}$$

Termination:

$$MeS_2 \cdot + MeS_3 \cdot \rightleftharpoons MeS_5Me \qquad (5)$$
$$\text{etc.}$$

In this scheme, reactions which involve the methyl thiyl radical (MeS·) have been omitted since the presence of this radical would be expected to give rise to dimethyl disulfide (which was not observed until after long heating periods). There is a possibility that dimethyl disulfide is formed when the tetrasulfide is heated but is subsequently rapidly removed by further reaction with the tetrasulfide. This was shown not to be the case since the quantity of disulfide remained unaltered when mixtures of dimethyl disulfide and tetrasulfide were heated at 80°.

Also, Abrahams (13) has found that the central bond in a tetrasulfide is longer than the other two sulfur–sulfur bonds and is presumably weaker. Thus, equation 1 seems to be more likely than the following

$$MeS_4Me \rightleftharpoons MeS_3\cdot + MeS\cdot \qquad (6)$$

The chain length of the sequence of equations 2 and 3 is given by the ratio of the moles of trisulfide formed to the moles of methyl thiothiyl radical ($MeS_2\cdot$) formed. The rate of formation of $MeS_2\cdot$ radicals by cleavage of dimethyl tetrasulfide at 80° was computed from the rate constant obtained by following the decoloration of Banfield's free radical by the tetrasulfide (6). The rate of formation of dimethyl trisulfide from the tetrasulfide was determined by NMR as previously described. The chain length at various intervals of time was thus calculated (Table 3). It is seen

Table 3
Chain Length for $MeS_2\cdot$
(moles Me_2S_3 formed / mole $MeS_2\cdot$ formed)

Time (hr)	Chain length
1	0.65
2.5	0.75
5	0.75
10	0.45
20	0.35

that even at the beginning of the reaction the chain length is very low and recombination processes must be very significant.

The results thus indicate that dimethyl tetrasulfide has greatly reduced thermal stability compared to alkyl disulfides. Further, the importance of recombination processes suggests that $MeS_2\cdot$ radicals are rather inert. Further experiments showed that the $MeS_2\cdot$ radical is, in fact, remarkably unreactive.

First, dimethyl tetrasulfide was heated with triphenylmethane in carbon tetrachloride at both 80 and 130°. In both cases the ratio of phenyl hydrogen to methine hydrogen, as determined by NMR, was unchanged over 130 hr. Thus the $MeS_2\cdot$ radical had not abstracted hydrogen from triphenylmethane. Second, dimethyl tetrasulfide was heated with cyclohexene at 80°. There was no change in the ratio of methylenic to olefinic hydrogen, as determined by NMR, over 110 hr, showing that no addition to the double bond had occurred. It is interesting to note that Kice and

Pawlowski (14) have found that aromatic sulfinyl radicals (ArSO·) in which the functional group is isoelectronic with that of the $MeS_2·$ radical, are unreactive toward the olefin diphenylethylene.

This pattern is consistent with the reactivity of the fragments obtained by homolytic cleavage of polysulfides. The RS· fragments are reactive and add to double bonds and abstract hydrogen. On the other hand, $RS_2·$ fragments are unreactive below 100° and do not react in these ways.

With the pattern of reduced thermal stability and reduced reactivity with increasing sulfur content becoming apparent, it was of interest to investigate the behavior of dimethyl trisulfide.

Thermal decomposition of trisulfides has been reported by several workers. For example, Twiss (8) recorded that diethyl trisulfide gives diethyl disulfide and sulfur on distillation at atmospheric pressure; Fuson et al. (15) found that bis(2-chloroethyl) trisulfide gives a mixture of bis(2-chloroethyl) disulfide, higher sulfides, and sulfur on heating at 145–160°; and Guryanova et al. (16) showed that when ditolyl trisulfide (in which the central sulfur atom is radioactive) is heated with diethyl trisulfide, the latter becomes radioactive through exchange of the central sulfur atoms.

As was the case with tetrasulfides, the authors have used NMR in their investigations into the thermal decomposition of trisulfides. Again, an early objective was to establish the nature of the decomposition products. Dimethyl trisulfide was heated in the dark at 80° in a sealed tube in the absence of oxygen, and the NMR spectrum was obtained at various time intervals and used to estimate the reaction products (Table 4). Dimethyl polysulfides were the only products indicated at each time. It is seen that decomposition occurs much more slowly than is the case with the tetrasulfide and an apparent equilibrium is attained after about 500 hr. Initially, decomposition results in the formation of only dimethyl disulfide and tetrasulfide (in approximately equimolar quantities).

It is not possible at present to be certain of the mechanism of this decomposition. Various experiments which bear on the subject have been performed by the authors and will be described in turn.

1. An attempt was made to react dimethyl trisulfide with Banfield's free radical at 80° in a manner analogous to that used with the tetrasulfide. The rate of decoloration was slow and of the same order of magnitude as that obtained when the free radical was heated in the absence of trisulfide. Thus, if free radicals are involved in the decomposition of the trisulfide, their rate of formation must be much slower than that from the tetrasulfide.

2. When the trisulfide was heated in a solvent with hydroquinone there was no decrease in the hydroxyl hydrogen content of the system and no

Table 4

Decomposition of Dimethyl Trisulfide at 80°

Time (hr)	Percentage molar composition of product				
	Me_2S_2	Me_2S_3	Me_2S_4	Me_2S_5	Me_2S_6
0	0	100	0	0	0
2.5	Trace	100	Trace	0	0
5.2	1	98	1	0	0
10.1	2	96	2	0	0
20.2	3	94	3	0	0
43.8	4	91	5	0	0
64.6	5	89	6	0	0
109.9	8	85	7	0	0
237.2	13	73	12	2	0
362.1	21	61	16	2	0
552.3	21	62	14	3	Trace
767.2	21	61	16	2	Trace
1368.6	23	60	14	3	Trace

change in the products obtained. This might be considered evidence that the decomposition of dimethyl trisulfide does not proceed via the homolytic cleavage

$$MeS_3Me \longrightarrow MeS_2\cdot + MeS\cdot \qquad (7)$$

However, the $MeS_2\cdot$ radical is not sufficiently active to react with hydroquinone. This was demonstrated by the failure of hydroquinone to influence the decomposition of dimethyl tetrasulfide. As has been discussed, the $MeS_2\cdot$ radical also failed to react with other reagents which commonly react with free radicals. In contrast, the $MeS\cdot$ radical is an active species and would be expected to react with hydroquinone. It may be, however, that the trisulfide is simply a very efficient trap for $MeS\cdot$ radicals.

3. When the trisulfide was heated at 80° in benzene with a relatively large amount (8 mole %) of the phenol, 1,3,5-trimethyl-2,4,6-tris(3,5-di-*t*-butyl-4-hydroxybenzyl)benzene, decomposition of the trisulfide was inhibited. After 1000 hr only traces of dimethyl disulfide and dimethyl tetrasulfide could be found in the reaction mixture and there was no evidence of any other reaction product. Under the same conditions in the absence of the phenol, disulfide and tetrasulfide were both formed to the extent of approximately 5 mole %. In contrast, under the same conditions, 1,3,5-trimethyl-2,4,6-tris(3,5-di-*t*-butyl-4-hydroxybenzyl)benzene did not significantly affect the decomposition of dimethyl tetrasulfide in benzene.

At present, the mechanism of this inhibition of decomposition of dimethyl trisulfide is not clear.

4. The trisulfide was heated at 80° with a small quantity (2 mole %) of azobisisobutyronitrile. The rate of trisulfide decomposition was not measurably increased. The quantity of azobisisobutyronitrile was then increased to 8 mole %. After heating for 4 hr, the molar ratio of dimethyl disulfide : dimethyl trisulfide : dimethyl tetrasulfide was Trace : 97 : 3. Thus, the initial formation of tetrasulfide was accelerated. It is almost certain that the role of the azobisisobutyronitrile is to generate isobutyronitrile radicals which subsequently attack the trisulfide. The following possibilities may be envisaged:

$$MeS_3Me + Me_2\dot{C}CN \longrightarrow Me_2(MeS_2)CCN + MeS\cdot \tag{8}$$

$$MeS_3Me + Me_2\dot{C}CN \longrightarrow Me_2(MeS)CCN + MeS_2\cdot \tag{9}$$

Equation 8 may be excluded since the formation of MeS· radicals would almost certainly result in the production of dimethyl disulfide (which was not observed).

From the rate constant for the decomposition of azobisisobutyronitrile and the efficiency of radical production, it is possible to compute a chain length for the formation of dimethyl tetrasulfide. The rate constant and efficiency vary with the solvent used and have not been determined for dimethyl trisulfide. However, taking the lowest values given by Walling (17) (viz. $1.4 \times 10^{-4} \sec^{-1}$ and 0.4, respectively), a chain length (moles tetrasulfide formed/mole isobutyronitrile radical formed) of 0.50 is obtained. This result means that the formation of tetrasulfide does not arise by a free-radical chain reaction. The absence of products other than the tetrasulfide suggests that termination is due only to recombination of $MeS_2\cdot$ radicals.

5. The previous experiment shows that the formation of dimethyl tetrasulfide by thermal decomposition of the trisulfide does not proceed via a free-radical chain reaction involving $MeS_2\cdot$ radicals. This conclusion was verified by heating the trisulfide with a small quantity (2 mole %) of dimethyl tetrasulfide (which has been shown to decompose into $MeS_2\cdot$ radicals). The initial rate of decomposition of the trisulfide was not accelerated.

6. The rates of decomposition of dimethyl trisulfide at 80° in benzene and nitrobenzene were determined. It was found that the two rates were not significantly different. This lack of influence of solvent polarity is more in accordance with a free-radical reaction.

7. The trisulfide was heated at 80° with benzoyl peroxide (2 mole %). The ensuing reaction was much more rapid than that undergone by the pure trisulfide but the same products were formed (Table 5). For the

Table 5

Decomposition of Dimethyl Trisulfide at 80° in the Presence of Benzoyl Peroxide

Time (hr)	Percentage molar composition of product			
	Me_2S_2	Me_2S_3	Me_2S_4	Me_2S_5
0	0	100	0	0
1.0	21	59	17	3
2.0	25	52	20	3
4.0	26	52	19	3
22.0	26	52	19	3

following reasons it is concluded that this reaction is ionic and not free radical:

(i) The reaction is quite different, both in rate and product distribution, from that involving azobisisobutyronitrile which almost certainly is a free-radical reaction.

(ii) A chain reaction is indicated, and as has been discussed previously, a free-radical chain reaction appears improbable.

(iii) When the trisulfide was heated with benzoyl peroxide and Banfield's free radical, the formation of disulfides and tetrasulfides was not inhibited.

(iv) Benzoyl peroxide was found to react with the trisulfide at room temperature. An equimolar solution of benzoyl peroxide and the trisulfide in chloroform was allowed to stand, and the peroxide content was measured iodometrically at intervals according to the procedure of Horner and Scherf (18). The peroxide content decreased with time. Under the same conditions, in the absence of trisulfide, there was no detectable decomposition of peroxide. The extrapolated half-life of the peroxide in the presence of trisulfide was found to be approximately 350 hr. This reaction is slow when compared to that observed by Horner and Scherf for various other sulfur-containing compounds, but it is definite. Presumably, ionic species are involved and these could act as catalysts in the decomposition of the trisulfide at 80°.

It is to be noted that these findings cast some doubt on the free-radical mechanism generally postulated for the vulcanization of sulfur-containing polymers by peroxides.

8. The trisulfide was heated at 80° with triethylamine (5 mole %). After an induction period, the ensuing reaction was much more rapid than that undergone by the pure trisulfide and the stoichiometry of the reaction mixture suggests that some free sulfur is formed (Table 6). It may be noted

Table 6

Decomposition of Dimethyl Trisulfide at 80° in the Presence of Triethylamine

	Percentage molar composition of product			
Time (hr)	Me_2S_2	Me_2S_3	Me_2S_4	Me_2S_5
0	0	100	0	0
2.0	0	100	0	0
20.0	37	40	15	8
43.0	38	38	24	0
137.7	37	37	26	0
358.0	38	40	22	0

here that Hodgson et al. (19) have found that free radicals are formed whenever elemental sulfur dissolves in an amine to give a colored solution. They found that triethylamine formed a colorless solution which gave no ESR signal whereas piperidine and ethylenediamine produced colored solutions which gave strong ESR signals. When piperidine and ethylene-diamine were added to dimethyl trisulfide a brown coloration was observed but addition of triethylamine produced no color change. Davis and Nakshbendi (20) have found that solutions of sulfur in aliphatic primary and secondary amines contain substantial amounts of ions and solutions in tertiary amines contain few ions. Thus it seems likely that the decomposition of dimethyl trisulfide in the presence of triethylamine involves ionic rather than free-radical processes.

Even under the presumably very weakly ionic conditions which prevail in the presence of benzoyl peroxide and triethylamine, the decomposition of dimethyl trisulfide proceeds at a much greater rate than that observed with the pure trisulfide. This observation suggests that the thermal decomposition of pure dimethyl trisulfide is unlikely to proceed through an ionic mechanism. It is certainly true that under highly ionic conditions the trisulfide decomposes at a very fast rate. Milligan et al. (21) have found that substantial amounts of disulfides and tetrasulfides are obtained when the trisulfide is shaken at room temperature with methanethiol or sodium sulfide at pH 8 for only 2 hr.

From these studies a rather clear picture of the overall trends in the reactivity of dimethyl polysulfides has arisen. The thermal stability of the polysulfide decreases as the length of the polysulfide linkage increases. The reactivity of the materials follows the same overall trend. The pertinent results on the dissociation energies are summarized in Table 7.

Gee (22) has suggested that fragments containing more than one sulfur

Table 7
Dissociation Energies

Compound	Dissociation energy (kcal/mole)
Me—S—S—Me	69[a]
Me—S—S—S—Me	(46)[b]
Me—S—S—S—S—Me	37[c]
S_8(ring) $\rightleftharpoons$ ·S—S_6—S·	33[d]
·S·$_{x+y}$ $\rightleftharpoons$ ·S·$_x$ + ·S·$_y$	33[e]

[a] Determined from mass spectroscopic studies (23).

[b] Estimated from data given by Hobrick and Kiser (24) on the appearance potentials of various ions observed in the mass spectroscopic study of dimethyl trisulfide. (For details see T. L. Pickering, Ph.D. thesis, Princeton, 1966.)

[c] Determined by a free-radical scavenger technique (25).

[d] Determined from an equilibrium treatment of the polymerization of sulfur (26).

[e] Determined from ESR studies on polymeric sulfur using the assumptions of the equilibrium treatment of the polymerization (27).

atom may be stabilized by some sort of resonance interaction of the free electron with the sulfur chain. Using this concept, we may consider the following reactions

$$Me—S—S—Me \longrightarrow 2\ Me—S·$$

$$Me—S—S—S—Me \longrightarrow Me—S· + Me—S—S·$$

$$Me—S—S—S—S—Me \longrightarrow 2\ Me—S—S·$$

$$Me—S—S· \longleftrightarrow Me—S\text{····}S$$

If Me—S····S fragments are indeed more stable than Me—S· fragments, then we can predict that the ease of cleavage of the polysulfide linkage is in the order disulfide < trisulfide < tetrasulfide $\sim S_8 \sim$ polymeric sulfur. This, of course, assumes that the difference in resonance stabilization between fragments such as Me—S····S and Me—S—S····S is negligible. This appears to be a resonable assumption since the value of the dissociation energy of dimethyl tetrasulfide is quite close to that of polymeric sulfur. This scheme also provides a rationalization for the decrease in reactivity in the same series.

References

1. A. V. Tobolsky and W. J. MacKnight, *Polymeric Sulfur and Related Polymers,* Interscience, New York, 1965.
2. T. L. Allen, *J. Chem. Phys.,* **31**, 1039 (1959).
3. H. Mackle and R. G. Mayrich, *Trans. Faraday Soc.,* **58**, 238 (1962).
4. F. Feher and G. Winkhaus, *Z. Anorg. Allgem. Chem.,* **292**, 210 (1957).
5. H. Mackle, *Tetrahedron,* **19**, 961 (1963).
6. I. Kende, T. L. Pickering, and A. V. Tobolsky, *J. Am. Chem. Soc.,* **87**, 5582 (1965).
7. H. Mackle, *Tetrahedron,* **19**, 1159 (1963).
8. D. Twiss, *J. Am. Chem. Soc.,* **49**, 493 (1927).
9. S. O. Jones and E. E. Reid, *J. Am. Chem. Soc.,* **60**, 2452 (1938).
10. G. F. Bloomfield, *J. Chem. Soc.,* **1947**, 1547.
11. S. F. Birch, T. V. Cullum, and R. A. Dean, *J. Inst. Petrol.,* **39**, 206 (1963).
12. J. R. Van Wazer and D. Grant, *J. Am. Chem. Soc.,* **86**, 1450 (1964); *ibid.,* **86**, 3012 (1964).
13. S. C. Abrahams, *Acta Cryst.,* **7**, 413 (1954).
14. J. L. Kice and N. E. Pawlowski, *J. Am. Chem. Soc.,* **86**, 4898 (1964).
15. R. C. Fuson, C. C. Price, D. M. Burness, R. E. Foster, W. R. Hatchard, and R. D. Lipscomb, *J. Org. Chem.,* **11**, 487 (1946).
16. E. N. Guryanova, V. N. Vasilyeva, and L. S. Kuzina, *Rubber Chem. Technol.,* **29**, 534 (1956).
17. C. Walling, *Free Radicals in Solution,* Wiley, New York, 1957.
18. L. Horner and K. Scherf, *Ann. Chem.,* **573**, 35 (1951).
19. W. G. Hodgson, S. A. Buckler, and G. Peters, *J. Am. Chem. Soc.,* **85**, 543 (1963).
20. R. E. Davis and H. Nakshbendi, *J. Am. Chem. Soc.,* **84**, 2085 (1962).
21. B. Milligan, B. Saville, and J. M. Swan, *J. Chem. Soc.,* **1963**, 2608.
22. F. Fairbrother, G. Gee, and G. T. Merall, *J. Polymer Sci.,* **16**, 459 (1955).
23. J. L. Franklin and H. E. Lumpkin, *J. Am. Chem. Soc.,* **74**, 1023 (1952).
24. B. G. Hobrick and R. W. Kiser, *J. Phys. Chem.,* **67**, 1283 (1963).
25. I. Kende, T. L. Pickering, and A. V. Tobolsky, *J. Am. Chem. Soc.,* **87**, 5582 (1965).
26. A. V. Tobolsky and A. Eisenberg, *J. Am. Chem. Soc.,* **81**, 780 (1959).
27. D. M. Gardner and G. K. Fraenkel, *J. Am. Chem. Soc.,* **78**, 3279 (1956).

The Synthesis of Novel Bicyclic Sulfides from Sulfur Dichloride and Cyclic Diolefins

F. LAUTENSCHLAEGER

Dunlop Research Centre, Sheridan Park, Ontario, Canada

The reactions of sulfur chlorides in organic chemistry have been studied extensively. Of considerable synthetic importance are their reactions with olefins (eqs. 1 and 2). The ease of substitution on the resulting dichloro-

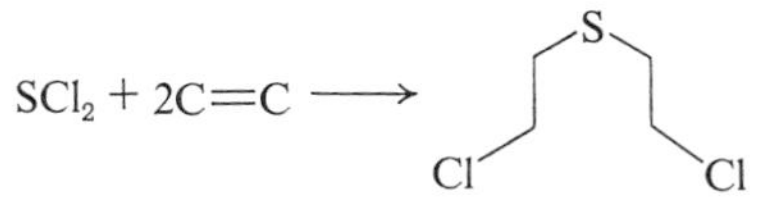

$$SCl_2 + 2C{=}C \longrightarrow \qquad\qquad\qquad (1)$$

$$S_2Cl_2 + \qquad\qquad \longrightarrow \qquad\qquad\qquad (2)$$

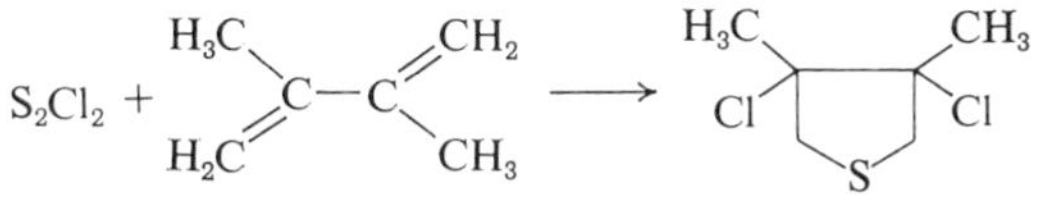

(1)

sulfides provides a convenient synthesis to a large number of bifunctional derivatives. Whereas sulfur monochloride has long been recognized as a relatively stable compound, sulfur dichloride shows a tendency for rapid dissociation. The recent discovery that sulfur dichloride may be stabilized by adding traces of phosphorous trichloride or phosphorous sulfide (1) means that sulfur dichloride is now available in a purity of more than 97%.

In the past, little attention has been given to the possibility that cyclic derivatives may result from reactions with diolefins, presumably because the reaction with dimethylbutadiene was reported to give dichloro-dimethyl dihydrothiophene **(1)** in a yield of only 1% (2). The synthetic significance of this reaction was realized only recently. In June of 1966, Weil reported the addition of sulfur dichloride to cyclooctadiene-1,5 and cyclooctadiene-1,3 (3), Corey reported the reaction with cyclohexadiene-1,4 (4), and we reported the reaction with bicycloheptadiene (5).

We have investigated the scope of that addition reaction and found the reaction to be not only quite general but also that unusual cyclic structures can be obtained (Table 1). The corresponding addition products were also obtained from the commercially available 1,5,9-cyclododecatrienes, from

73

Table 1

1 : 1 Additions of Sulfur Dichloride to Cyclic Olefins

Olefin		Yield	m.p., °C		
Bicyclo(2.2.1)-2,5-heptadiene[a]		81	46		(2)
cis,cis-Cyclooctadiene-1,5[b]		83	102		(3)
Cyclooctadiene-1,3[c]		23	186.5		(4)
2-Methylene-5-norbornene		22	47		(5)
Cycloheptatriene		45	47		(6)
Cyclooctatraene		37	102		(7)

[a] Reference 5.
[b] References 3, 4, and 6.
[c] Reference 3.

bicyclo[3.4]nonadiene and linear diolefins such as diallyl ether, diallyl sulfide, pentadiene-1,4, hexadiene-1,5, and 2,5-dimethyl hexadiene-1,5 in yields up to 60%. Structural features of several products and derivatives are reported inasmuch as they are representative of these novel β,β'-dichlorosulfides.

A simple approach was considered for the structure analysis of the resulting novel ring systems, involving the formation of the sulfoxides and sulfones from these sulfides. Addition to a cyclic diolefin can lead either to a dichlorosulfide with both chlorine atoms on one side of the sulfur atom or to a structure with these atoms on both sides of the sulfur atom. Two sulfoxides should be obtained in the former case but only one in the latter, provided that the structure is symmetric. The sulfoxides should be interconvertible with triethyloxonium fluoroborate (7) in the first case, but no isomer should be obtained with a symmetric sulfide. In the nuclear magnetic resonance spectrum, shielding by the sulfoxide oxygen affects either both CHCl groups or neither in the former case, but only one CHCl group should be affected in the latter. This is demonstrated on the reaction products obtained from bicycloheptadiene and *cis,cis*-cyclooctadiene-1,5.

An example of an addition of a sulfenyl chloride to bicycloheptadiene is the addition of *p*-toluene sulfenyl chloride (8) which leads exclusively to the *endo*-3-chloro-*exo*-5-norbornen-2-yl-*p*-tolyl-thioether. Surprisingly, *endo* addition was observed in the reaction with sulfur dichloride (2). The assigned configuration is supported by the observed dipole moment of 0.8 D, its nuclear magnetic resonance spectrum (Fig. 1), and the isolation of two sulfoxides but only one sulfone.

The structure of the product was evident from its nuclear magnetic resonance spectrum (Fig. 1). The proton adjacent to chlorine is represented by a singlet, in agreement with the general absence of coupling between *endo* and bridgehead protons. Both bridgehead protons are not identical, ruling out the symmetric structure **2a**. The configurations of the sulfoxides were assigned on the basis of their nuclear magnetic resonance spectra (Figs. 2 and 3). In hexachlorobutadiene, the *endo*-sulfoxide shows a diamagnetic shift of 0.5 ppm for the proton H_c from the position of that proton

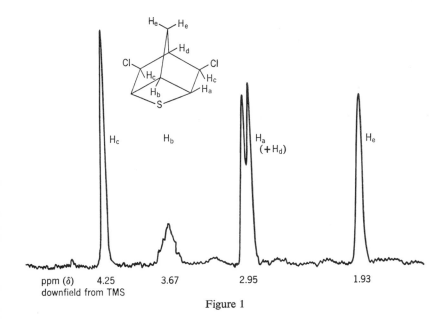

ppm (δ)   4.25   3.67   2.95   1.93
downfield from TMS

Figure 1

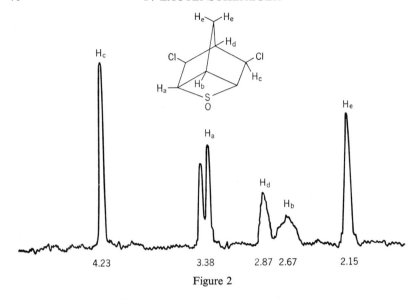

Figure 2

in the sulfide, whereas the chemical shift of that proton in the *exo* sulfoxide is identical with that of the sulfide. This deshielding arises from both the anisotropy and the field effect of the S—O group (9), and only the *endo* isomer provides a favorable steric arrangement for that effect. The position

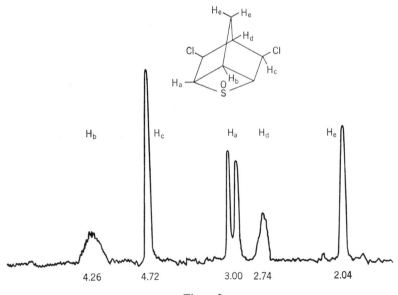

Figure 3

of the resonance of H_c in the sulfone is between that of the sulfide and the *endo*-sulfoxide (Fig. 4).

The effect on the proton adjacent to sulfur is remarkable. The chemical shift of that proton in the *endo*-sulfoxide is very similar to that in the sulfide. But its chemical shift is 0.4 ppm downfield in the *exo*-sulfoxide and 0.6 ppm downfield in the sulfone.

The resonance position of the bridgehead hydrogen H_b is strongly influenced. Its chemical shift is 0.6 ppm downfield from the sulfide in the *endo*-sulfoxide and 1.0 ppm and 0.8 ppm upfield in the *exo*-sulfoxide and the sulfone, respectively.

The identical shielding of both protons H_c in both the *endo*-sulfoxide and the sulfone supports the conclusions from the observed dipole moment in that it excludes a structure with a *trans* arrangement of the chlorine groups.

The thermal stability of both sulfoxides is of interest. Complete decomposition occurs if the *endo*-sulfoxide is heated to 200°C at a rate of 10°/min. Under the same conditions its isomer can be recovered unchanged. The thermal decomposition of the *endo* isomer under conditions which do not affect the *exo* isomer suggests the closer proximity and increased availability of the *cis-β*-hydrogen atoms in the thermally unstable isomer. Only the bridgehead *cis-β*-hydrogen is available in the *exo* isomer and its orientation with respect to the sulfoxide oxygen does not allow the formation of a five-membered cyclic transition state necessary for that elimination.

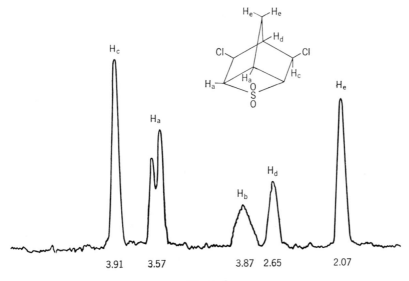

Figure 4

Compound **2** undergoes rearrangement to the episulfide **2b** with potassium cyanide in ethanol. Addition of chlorine to **2b** leads back to the chlorosulfide (**2**) in a yield of 80% (eq. 3).

(2b)   (2)   (2a)

The addition product from methylene–norbornene (**4**) is obtained in low yield. The structure was tentatively assigned on the basis of an NMR signal for the chloromethyl group and the unsymmetric shielding of the sulfoxide group on the hydrogen alpha to sulfur (**4**, **4a–4d**). This can be rationalized on the basis of structure **4** in which that proton and the chloromethyl group represent *cis* substituents on a thietane ring and the oxygen in the sulfoxide (**4a**) is *cis* in respect with these substituents but *trans* in the *endo*-sulfoxide (**4c**). Consequently, the NMR signal for both the proton H_a and the chloromethyl group are shifted downfield in the *exo* isomer. The *endo*-sulfoxide shows a very small effect on these groups, 0.14 and 0.07 ppm, respectively. By contrast, in the hypothetical ring system **4d**, bonds H_a—C—S—C—CH_2Cl are in one plane and the orientation of the S=O bond is not expected to affect these protons.

The opposite sign of that effect in this ring system and the ring system obtained from norbornadiene is remarkable. In the latter system, H_c is shifted upfield from 4.3 ppm to 3.7 ppm, whereas the shift is downfield from 3.6 to 4.4 ppm in the ring system obtained from methylene norbornene. However, the effect on the proton alpha to sulfur is in the same direction in both ring systems.

Of the two possible transannular reaction products from cyclooctadiene, only one is obtained. We believe that in this case the question of the alternative ring structure, the configuration, and possibly the conformation of the product can be assigned on the basis of the shielding of the sulfoxides. In oxidation with hydrogen peroxide, only one sulfoxide was obtained (**3a**). The NMR spectrum of the sulfide shows a closely spaced multiplet for the proton adjacent to chlorine. By contrast, the spectrum of the sulfoxide shows two sets of resonances for these protons, one of which remains in the position in which it is observed in the sulfide whereas the other is shifted 0.6 ppm upfield. The magnitude of that shielding effect is identical with that effect observed on the product obtained from norbornadiene. This suggests a similar proximity of the sulfoxide oxygen to

(4)   (4d)   (4e)   (4f)

(4a)   (4b)   (4c)

$X = -CH_2Cl$

(4g)

the hydrogen on the β-carbon atom in both ring systems and therefore identical configuration and possibly identical conformation. The shielding of only one CHCl group therefore cannot be explained on the basis of the isomeric [4.2.1] ring system (3d).

As expected, attempted inversion of the sulfoxide to an isomer via reaction with triethyloxonium fluoroborate failed.

Sulfoxide shielding values suggest the existence of the bicyclic system in a twin-chair conformation, and the dipole moment confirms this assignment. It is identical with the moment of the product obtained from norbornadiene. The thiane ring in the latter compound has necessarily a rigid chair conformation with both chlorine atoms equatorial. In both ring systems, the resultant moment of both chlorine groups forms an angle of 180° with the moment of the C—S—C bond in the twin-chair conformation. The observed moment therefore supports the twin-chair conformation.

The chlorosulfide (3; see Table 1) shows the characteristic reactivity of β,β'-dichlorosulfides (eq. 4). The diol (3b) is obtained in near quantitative yield. Treatment of 3b with concentrated hydrochloric acid (eqs. 5 and 6) leads to only one dichloride.

The participation of the free electrons on sulfur in the stabilization of the carbonium ion can be demonstrated qualitatively by a comparison of the reactivity in nucleophilic reactions of sulfide versus sulfoxide and sulfone. In contrast to the dihydroxy sulfide, the dihydroxy sulfone (3c) is recovered unchanged from its solution in concentrated hydrochloric acid. Also, the dichloro sulfoxide is not hydrolyzed under conditions under which rapid hydrolysis of the dichlorosulfide proceeds.

The absence of the isomeric [4.2.1] ring system is surprising if an episulfonium intermediate is involved. Both carbon atoms of the episulfonium ring appear equally accessible and, therefore, both ring systems would be

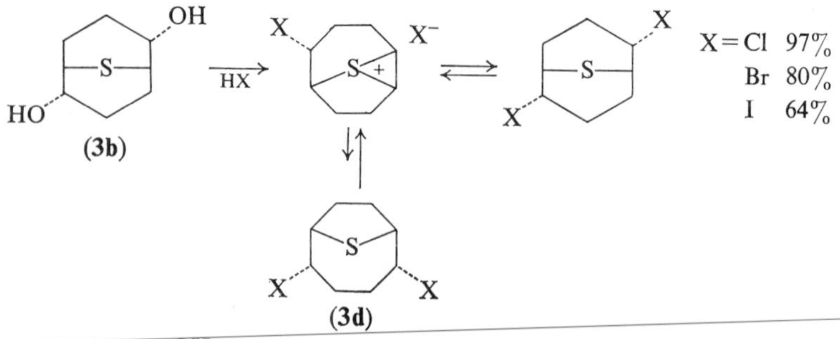

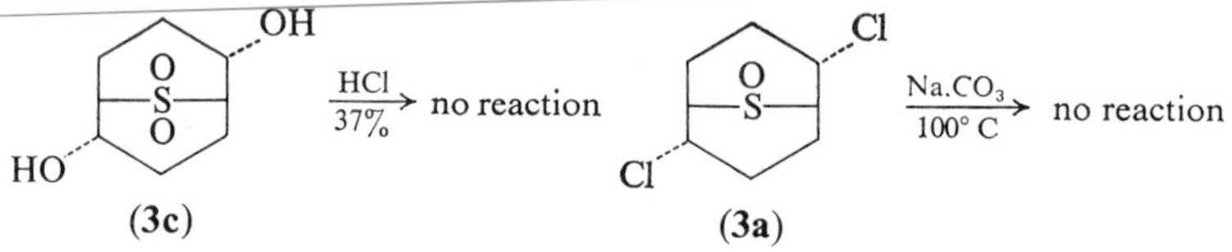

$$X = Cl \quad 97\%$$
$$Br \quad 80\%$$
$$I \quad 64\%$$

expected. To explain the predominance of one ring system, rapid equilibration via the episulfonium structure is assumed, whereby the more
favorable staggering of the carbon–hydrogen bonds in the [3.3.1] ring
system could be the deciding factor for the product distribution.

Cyclooctatetraene leads to the symmetric product 7 (see Table 1). A
single sulfoxide is obtained which is recovered after attempted conversion
with triethyloxonium fluoroborate. Whereas the proton adjacent to
chlorine forms one doublet in the sulfide, two doublets 0.2 ppm apart
represent these protons in the sulfoxide and the signal at higher field
corresponds to the chemical shift of that proton in the sulfide. In the
sulfone, the protons of the CHCl groups are also identical.

Cycloheptatriene leads to product 6 in a yield of 45% (eq. 7), whereby

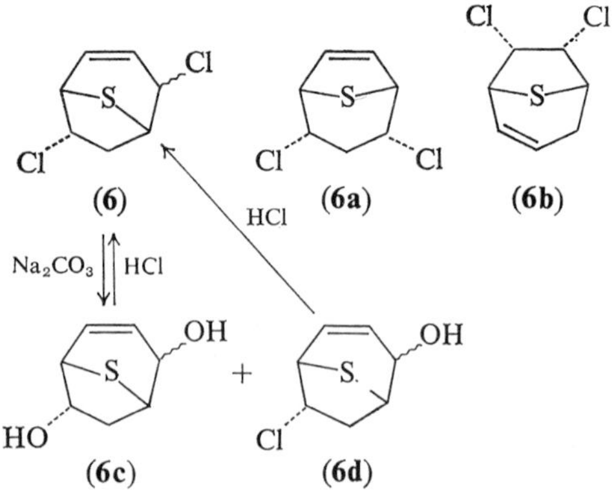

the presence of isomers 6b and 6c cannot yet be ruled out. Treatment of
the crude reaction product with sodium carbonate leads either to the diol

(6c) or the chloro-alcohol (6d), which can be converted to 6 with concentrated hydrochloric acid.

The *endo* approach of sulfur dichloride in the reaction with bicycloheptadiene and methylene norbornene suggests that a similar approach to the tub-shaped cyclooctadiene-1,5 and cycloheptatriene may occur. Since these olefins are known to form complexes with inorganic ions, a π-complex of the chlorosulfenium ion is suggested as a possible first step in the reaction of sulfur dichloride with at least some of the cyclic olefins.

References

1. J. H. Schmadebeck, U.S. Pats. 3,071,441 and 3,071,442 (1963); *Chem. Abstr.*, **58**, 7640h, 7641a (1963).
2. H. J. Backer and J. Strating, *Rec. Trav. Chim.*, **54**, 52 (1935).
3. E. D. Weil, K. J. Smith, and R. J. Gruber, *J. Org. Chem.*, **31**, 1669 (1966).
4. E. J. Corey and E. Block, *J. Org. Chem.*, **31**, 1663 (1966).
5. F. Lautenschlaeger, *J. Org. Chem.*, **31**, 1679 (1966).
6. F. Lautenschlaeger, *Can. J. Chem.*, **44**, 2813 (1966).
7. C. R. Johnson and D. McCants, *J. Am. Chem. Soc.*, **87**, 5404 (1965).
8. G. Brindell and S. J. Cristol, in *Organic Sulfur Compounds*, Vol. I, N. Kharasch, Ed., Pergamon Press, New York, p. 121.
9. J. G. Pritchard and P. C. Lauterbur, *J. Am. Chem. Soc.*, **83**, 2105 (1961).

Transmission of Electronic Effects in Certain Sulfides

J. B. HYNE and J. W. GREIDANUS

Fundamental Sulphur Research Group, Alberta Sulphur Research Ltd.,
University of Calgary, Alberta, Canada

INTRODUCTION AND REVIEW

Fundamental to the whole question of the transmission of electronic effects across bridging atoms or groups located between potential donor and acceptor functions in any molecule is the state of hybridization of the bridging atom or atoms and the electronic configuration within this hybridized state. As the energy differences between the various possible electronic energy levels of more complex hybridization states become smaller, it becomes increasingly difficult to establish whether there exists sufficient "incentive" for the molecule to promote electrons from apparently lower lying orbital energy levels to slightly higher ones in order to benefit from molecular orbital interactions that will increase the overall stability of the molecular assembly.

The comparison between —O— and —S— as bridging atoms represents a case in point. The six valence electrons of ground-state oxygen are generally accepted to be in the $2s^2 2p^4$ configuration and little if any evidence has been obtained to suggest that the considerably higher energy level $3s,p$, or d orbitals of oxygen are ever involved to any significant extent in the ground state of covalently bonded oxygen. The ground-state configuration of the valence electrons of sulfur, however, can be correspondingly considered as being $3s^2 3p^4$. The proximity of the $3d$ energy level immediately raises the question of possible $3d$ orbital involvement in the hybridization states of covalently bonded sulfur.

It would be presumptuous in this paper to attempt to review all the arguments that have been presented, pro and con, regarding the question of d-orbital involvement in covalent sulfur bonding. Arguments related to the possibility of expansion of the sulfur valence shell from an octet to a decet configuration have been common ever since the advent of the Lewis octet theory. In recent years, however, the application of more sophisticated physicochemical investigation methods has permitted a more direct examination of the problem and, with the increasing sensitivity of such

83

measurements, effects that were previously obscured by lack of sensitivity of the experimental probe have been brought to light.

The reviews of Cilento (3) and Price and Oae (19,20) represent very adequate coverage of the published material until recent date and no attempt will be made to repeat this coverage. It is perhaps appropriate, however, to quote briefly from the conclusions of these two reviewers. Cilento (3) offers the opinion that: "There is little, if any, doubt that in certain sulfur compounds d-orbitals are utilized or can be utilized. Normally this is only possible if, by the very nature of the molecular system, contraction of the $3d$-orbitals occurs. Then these orbitals can take part in σ-bonds, localized π-bonds, and delocalized π-bonds of the aromatic type." The crucial aspects of this statement are that d-orbital involvement should not be *generally* expected in covalently bonded sulfur and that the particular nature of the molecular system will determine whether or not the "incentive" exists for such participation to be operative. This might well mean that under a particular set of circumstances, say reaction conditions, a given sulfur-containing compound might evidence d-orbital participation, while the same compound under a different set of environmental conditions might fail to demonstrate any such involvement of higher energy level orbitals. Accordingly, great care must be exercised in the interpretation of the results of different experiments designed to elucidate this question since the differing experimental conditions may suffice to bring into operation or exclude the very participation being examined.

Price's comment (20) is perhaps more guarded. "Perhaps at best, the large role ascribed to d-orbital π-bonding is controversial. Much useful data for better understanding may come from further careful studies of reactivity, spectra, bond energies, and dipole moments of inorganic as well as organic compounds involving these elements." Clearly there can be no question that further experimental data are essential for the resolution of the controversy, but again the question of the differing factors that may be influential in different types of experiments must be considered. More *direct* studies of the phenomenon in question are certainly called for; while reactivity studies would be expected to reflect specific variations in orbital involvement, such experiments are often complicated by other factors not directly related to the specific question being examined. The advent of new physical techniques and the refinement of established ones for direct, nondestructive examination of such molecular phenomena as electron density, bond vibrations, and bond angles may well provide the additional data needed for the resolution of the controversy.

Why is the question of the state of hybridization and the electronic configuration of the bridging atom so crucial to the question of electronic effect transmission across the bridge? Clearly the answer must be that until we understand the *mechanism* of the transmission we cannot hope to predict or explain transmission phenomena; and, in turn, an understanding of the mechanism of transmission depends upon a knowledge of the means by which the transmission may be effected, i.e., a knowledge of the configuration of the electrons in the bridge. Consider the general case of a bridging atom (or group) Z lying between two functions, one of which is a potential donor (A) and the other a potential acceptor (B) of electron density. If Z is a monoatomic bridge, as in the case of —S—, then the relationship of the nearest atom of function A to that of function B is a 1–3 relationship.

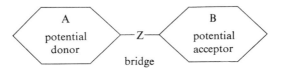

While direct transmission of electronic effects between atoms other than those directly connected (i.e., 1–2 relationship) is not unknown, particularly where geometry is favorable (e.g., olefinic double bond stabilization of the 7-norbornenonium cation through space), intramolecular transmission along the bonding network is a preferable mechanism if for no other reason than the fact that such transmission is less crucially dependent on geometrical considerations of configuration and conformation. Accordingly, if evidence exists for transmission of electronic effects from A to B, the question immediately arises as to the capability of the bridging function Z to act as a direct "conductor" rather than as an "insulator" requiring some type of "bypass" mechanism of transmission. Furthermore, if Z is seen as a "conductor" a distinction must presumably be made between σ-conduction through the σ-bond skeleton of the bridge and localized or delocalized π-conduction through a superimposed π-bonding orbital system extending from A to B through Z. There can be little doubt that in any bridged system there will exist σ-conduction and effects so transmitted are normally referred to as inductive effects. Such effects, however, have been shown to diminish rapidly with distance and, while they must be taken into account in any analysis of overall transmission of effects, the contribution from this mechanism is frequently minor. Transmission of effects through a delocalized π-bonding system, however, can be long range and of major importance. It is in such a mechanism that the hybridization state of the bridging Z atom becomes crucial since, in order to maintain a continuous orbital overlap across the bridge, a suitable atomic orbital (or orbitals) of the bridging Z function must be available.

In the case of sulfur as the bridging atom there are several possibilities as far as suitable, available orbitals are concerned. In compounds of the R—S—R type it is normally assumed that two of the $3p$ orbitals of sulfur are employed in establishing the two covalent σ-bonds to the flanking R functions, the remaining four valence shell electrons being accommodated in the $3s$ and third $3p$ orbitals. This configuration would lead to a predicted R—S—R bond angle of close to 90° since the $3p$ orbitals are orthogonal. Such is the experimental finding in H—S—H (4). However, the R—S—R bond angle for diphenyl sulfide is near 120° (6), far from that expected if the σ-bonding to each flanking phenyl utilized two $3p$ orbitals. Gibbs (5) has commented that such bond-angle widening is probably due to more than steric repulsion and that fundamental changes in hybridization state may be involved. Accordingly, even in R—S—R type compounds it cannot be generally assumed that the hybridization state of the bridging sulfur atom is necessarily $3s^2 3p^4$. The rehybridization of the bridging sulfur atom involving the $3d$ orbitals becomes a possibility and this in turn will be reflected in the hybrid orbital location of the remaining four valence electrons which can be involved in the π-bonding overlap with the adjacent R groups, leading to more effective transmission.

Having examined the nature of the problem from the standpoint of the mechanism by which the bridging atom *could* transmit electronic effects when called upon to do so, it is appropriate to examine briefly the results of various types of experiments that have been carried out for the purpose of demonstrating the presence or absence of transmission through sulfur and related bridges. Only the general nature of the experiment, the particular system studied, and the conclusions drawn from the results will be discussed.

In the following paragraphs an attempt has been made to review the whole spectrum of experimental techniques that have been applied to the study of transmission through a bridging function. The range of techniques is wide; the answers inconclusive.

Ultraviolet Spectroscopy

Mangini and co-workers have reported the results of UV spectral studies of a large variety of sulfur-containing aromatic compounds (13–15). These experiments were intended to show the presence or absence of extended conjugation effects resulting from the participation of sulfur in an extended π-type conjugated system, i.e., sulfur acting as a "transmitter." We will consider here only two of the many examples cited by these workers. A comparison of the UV spectral absorptions of CH_3—S—C_6H_4 (**1**) and C_6H_5—S—C_6H_4—$N(CH_3)_2$ (**2**) shows a UV absorption shift in the appropriate direction for the presence of extended conjugation in (**2**).

Mangini and co-workers, however, consider that these shifts have little significance as far as evidence for "transmission" is concerned since: The shift is very modest compared with those normally observed in extended conjugation cases; the shift is of the same order of magnitude as the zero-point vibration correction and solvent effects; and the shifts observed in the case of the symmetrically disubstituted $(CH_3)_2N$—C_6H_4—S—C_6H_4—$N(CH_3)_2$, where extended conjugation cannot be operative but only donor group perturbation of the adjacent aromatic π-system, are of a magnitude comparable to the shift between **1** and **2**.

In addition, there appears to be no evidence of increased extended conjugation in NO_2—C_6H_4—S—C_6H_4—$N(CH_3)_2$ (**3**) when the UV spectrum is compared with that of NO_2—C_6H_4—S—CH_2—C_6H_4—$N(CH_3)_2$ (**4**). This evidence suggests that the S atom in **3** is not responding to the incentive to transmit the effect of the donating $N(CH_3)_2$ group into the electron-accepting NO_2-substituted ring to any extent greater than that in the much less favorable "insulated" case of **4**. These workers conclude that "as far as the first few excited states of aromatic molecules are concerned, the UV spectral modifications observed are not self-contained evidence for the particpation of $3d$-orbitals."

These conclusions are contrary to those of Szmant and McIntosh (21), who concluded from similar UV studies that while there appeared to be no evidence of transmission via extended conjugated structures of type **5** and **6** in monosubstituted diphenyl sulfides, when both electron-donating and

(**5**) (**6**)

electron-withdrawing ring substituents were introduced, there was evidence for "transmission" over an extended conjugated system of the type shown in **7**. This conclusion implies that the expansion of the sulfur octet

(**7**)

to a decet takes place only when there is sufficient "driving force"—in this case *both* a powerful electron-donating *and* an electron-accepting potential within the molecule. Nonetheless, the conclusion drawn by Szmant and McIntosh is in direct conflict with that of Mangini and co-workers.

While not directly related to the question of transmission of electronic effects through a single sulfur-atom bridge, Campaigne, Tsurugi, and

Meyer (2) have reported that they found no UV evidence for transmission through the disulfide link in diaryl disulfides. In particular, compound **8**, in which the "incentive" might be considered greatest, showed no evidence of transmission.

$$NO_2-\langle\!\!\langle\rangle\!\!\rangle-S-S-\langle\!\!\langle\rangle\!\!\rangle-OCH_3$$

(**8**)

One can only conclude from these and other UV results that the postulated transmission effects through sulfur bridges between π-electron systems have such a minor influence on the UV spectral shifts that it is difficult to reach agreement as to whether the minor shifts that are observed are due to transmission effects or other factors which are known to be influential.

Infrared Spectroscopy

Zahradnik and co-workers (1,22) have reported infrared studies of the influence of variation of substituent Y on the stretching vibrations of the NO_2 group in compounds of the type **9**. They demonstrated that the stretching vibrations are not very sensitive to the influence of the sub-

$$Y-\langle\!\!\langle\rangle\!\!\rangle-S-\langle\!\!\langle\rangle\!\!\rangle-NO_2$$

(**9**)

stituent Y (in each case a powerful electron donor) and conclude that there is very limited transmission through the sulfur bridge. Since the infrared experiment is essentially a study of the properties of the ground-state molecule, the finding that there appears to be very limited interaction can be coupled with the UV findings noted previously, which did not favor transmission, and the general conclusion can be drawn that in neither the ground state nor the lower electronically excited states of diaryl sulfides does there appear to be conclusive evidence for transmission. A word of caution is, however, appropriate again in this instance, namely that consideration must be given to the question of how sensitive the vibrational modes might be expected to be toward substituent changes. It is interesting to note that in both papers cited above the terms "limited interaction" were used and not "no interaction"!

Polarography

The influence of substituent variation (Y) on the halfwave potential for reduction of the NO_2 function in compounds of type **9** have been reported by Jaffé and Otsuji (8) and Boček, Mangini, and Zahradník (1).

Again, this experimental technique does not demonstrate any significant variation of $E_{1/2}$ with Y (all donors), and both sets of authors conclude that the results support the hypothesis that interaction through the bridge atom is not appreciable. It is, however, interesting to note that the $E_{1/2}$ values for the two compounds **10** and **11** do not differ within the experimental error. If a change from sulfur to oxygen *directly attached* to the ring carrying the reducible NO_2 function has no measurable effect on $E_{1/2}$, despite the electronegativity change involved, then it is hardly surprising that relatively minor and more distant substituent changes would have relatively little effect on $E_{1/2}$ values. Again, therefore, the question as to how sensitive the $E_{1/2}$ value might be expected to be is raised.

	(10)	(11)
$E_{1/2}$: (pH = 2.15)	−0.28(± 0.01)	−0.30(± 0.01)

Acid Strengths

Three relatively recent papers on the effect of substituent variation on the strengths of carboxylic acids where the substituent effects must be transmitted through a sulfur bridge are directly related to the problem under consideration.

Hogeveen (7) has studied the effect of variation of *meta* and *para* substituents Y on the pK_a of the acids **12**, **13**, and **14** in both *cis* and *trans* configurations.

$$Y—C_6H_4—S—CH{=}CH—COOH \qquad (12)$$

$$Y—C_6H_4—SO—CH{=}CH—COOH \qquad (13)$$

$$Y—C_6H_4—SO_2—CH{=}CH—COOH \qquad (14)$$

Since little or no difference was found between the behavior of the *cis* and *trans* series, only the *trans* results will be considered here. In Figure 1a Hogeveen's pK_a values are plotted against the appropriate Hammett σ-constant for the substituent Y. There can be little doubt that the effect of substituent Y variation is being transmitted to the —COOH-ionizing center and that this effect is more efficiently transmitted in the case of the —S— bridge than in the cases of —SO— or —SO_2—. Hogeveen estimates that the —S— bridge transmits some 1.7 times better than do the higher sulfur valence states.

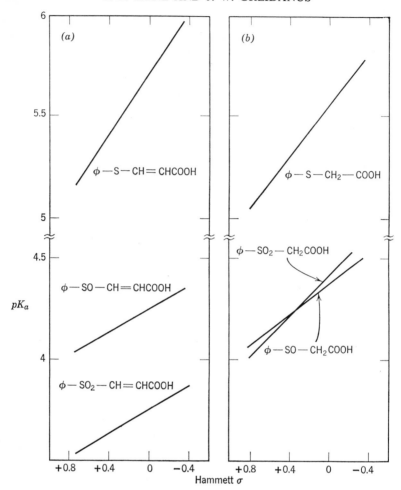

Fig. 1. Acid strength variation with ring substitution involving transmission through sulfur atom. (a) Hogeveen data (7); (b) Pasto et al. data (18).

Pasto, McMillan, and Murphy (18) have carried out a similar study on the three substituted acetic acids, **15–17**. Their results are plotted in Figure 1b.

$$\text{Y—C}_6\text{H}_4\text{—S—CH}_2\text{COOH} \qquad \textbf{(15)}$$

$$\text{Y—C}_6\text{H}_4\text{—SO—CH}_2\text{COOH} \qquad \textbf{(16)}$$

$$\text{Y—C}_6\text{H}_4\text{—SO}_2\text{—CH}_2\text{COOH} \qquad \textbf{(17)}$$

The results are wholly compatible with those of Hogeveen even to the point of establishing the —S— bridge as a more effective transmitter than either

—SO— or —SO$_2$—. Pasto, McMillan, and Murphy also cite the recent work of Meyers (17) on the ionization of hydroxydiphenyl sulfides, sulfoxides, and sulfones. Meyers concluded that since *p*-phenylmercapto-phenol is a stronger acid than the *meta* isomer, the thio group is capable of electron withdrawal by *d*-orbital interaction with the π-electron system of the aromatic ring, thus stabilizing the phenoxide anion in the acid–base equilibrium. Pasto et al. *suggested* that a further factor in this case might be the possible transmission of resonance effects through the sulfur atom bridge as shown in **18**.

etc.

(18)

The evidence available from these acid-strength studies, therefore, must be interpreted as being *in favor* of significant electronic effect transmission through —S— bridges. Whether "significant" can be equated with "limited" as was suggested by UV and other results is not a matter that the present authors wish to debate. Suffice it to say that whatever the extent of transmission may be, it is sufficiently great to bring about measurable and significant changes in the strengths of the acids studied even though it may not be of a magnitude sufficient to manifest itself clearly in other forms of experimental investigation.

Reactivity Studies

Litvinenko and co-workers (9–12) have published a series of papers in which they report the effects of substituent variation (Y) on the acylation of the primary amino group in compounds of type **19**, where

$$Y—C_6H_4—X—C_6H_4—NH_2 \quad (19)$$

X has also been varied among O, S, Se, and NH; simple biphenyl systems were also studied. Some of the results reported are surprising but none-theless interesting. The authors suggest that the order of transmittability through these one-atom bridges is —NH— > —S— > —Se— > —O—. In addition, with picrylchloride as the reagent, acylation of 4′-nitro, 4-amino diphenyl ether, sulfide, and selenide showed a greater *para*-substituent effect on the reactivity of the 4-amino group than was the case in the simple, directly linked 4′-nitro, 4-amino biphenyl! This effect the authors described as a "positive bridge atom effect." It would appear to be unwarranted at this stage to ascribe this "positive" effect to enhanced π-electron transmission in the bridged cases compared with the directly linked biphenyl case but the results illustrate that the overall observed effects in such reactivity studies may be complicated by other factors which, though important in determining reactivity may have no *direct* bearing on the question of the mechanism of electronic effect transmission through such bridging atoms.

Summary

It would appear that in the experimental examination of systems with a view to elucidating the question of electronic effect transmission through sulfur-atom bridges, two basic factors must be borne in mind. First the question as to whether excited states are involved in the experimental technique employed must be clearly answerable. Transmission effects that are operative in excited states may not be operative in ground states. Such a distinction clearly separates evidence obtained from UV spectra and reactivity studies involving high energy intermediates such as radicals, carbonium, or carbanion species from evidence obtained from what might be termed ground-state studies such as dipole moment, infrared spectroscopy, and nuclear magnetic resonance. It is true that Mangini found no evidence for transmission effects in either UV or IR studies of compounds of the Y—C_6H_4—S—C_6H_4—Z type (15), suggesting that the differentiation between ground and excited states might not be meaningful. It would be surprising, however, if this lack of difference were so; in any event it can hardly be assumed on the basis of the limited evidence presently available. The second point concerns the expectation of finding an effect observable with the experimental tool being applied. It is more than likely that the effects of any possible transmission across a sulfide bridge will be subtle and energetically of minor magnitude compared, for example, with bond energies. Accordingly, if experimental techniques are applied to the problem that involve large energy changes of an order comparable with bond energies (e.g., electronic excitation, chemical reaction), the influence of any transmission effect may be lost in the much higher energies involved in the primary process taking place.

If the nature of the transmission process is indeed subtle and energetically of minor magnitude, then it would seem appropriate to apply subtle tools to the elucidation of the problem. Accordingly, we have chosen to apply nuclear magnetic resonance techniques to the study of a number of di-*para* substituted diphenyl compounds of the sulfide, sulfoxide, sulfone, ether, and methylene types. A review of the results of these studies is presented in the following section.

NMR STUDIES

The application of nuclear magnetic resonance spectroscopy to the study of electronic transmission effects is a relatively recent development. Mangini (15) has reported the results of an NMR study of certain of the compounds previously investigated by his group using infrared and ultraviolet spectroscopic techniques, and concluded that the NMR results substantiated the previous findings, supporting the lack of any significant transmission effects through sulfide bridges. Recently Marcus, Reynolds, and Miller (16) reported the results of an NMR study of transmission effects in toluenes, acetophenones, and thioanisoles and concluded that in these cases oxygen "appears to be a far better conductor of electronic effects for the PMR property than any other group examined thus far." It must be noted in these cases, however, that the bridging function, O, S, or CH_2, is not flanked by two π-electron systems but by an alkyl function on one side and an aromatic ring on the other. Accordingly, the necessary driving force to invoke d-orbital or other higher hybridization involvement of the bridging function may not be present.

The specific aim of the NMR study was to investigate changes in electron density in the two aromatic rings of the disubstituted diphenyl systems by using the fact that the chemical shift associated with the protons of each aromatic ring is related to the electron density in the aromatic ring. Since in all of the compounds studied each aromatic ring is unsymmetrically 1,4-disubstituted, the splitting pattern associated with the NMR response of each set of four-ring protons is strictly A_2B_2. However, to a good approximation the pattern may be considered as being two superimposed identical AB patterns yielding the characteristic AB quartet as shown in Figure 2.

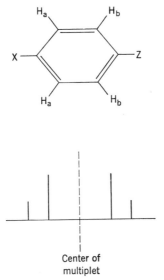

Fig. 2. Ring proton NMR spectrum.

This quartet pattern rendered the assignment of NMR peaks relatively simple particularly in more complex spectra. The average NMR shift associated with the four ring protons can then be obtained by measuring the position of the center of the multiplet. This shift value can then be taken to be a measure of the *relative* electron density in each aromatic ring in the various diphenyl compounds studied.

The basic question to be answered is whether the bridging Z function in molecules of the type **20** acts as an insulator or a transmitter of electronic effects. While the approach used may appear to be naive it has the merits of being internally consistent and synthetically feasible as far as the required compounds are concerned, and certain of the possible complicating factors can be cancelled out by virtue of the technique of using differences between otherwise very similar molecular structures. The technique will be illustrated by reference to a specific set of compounds chosen from the large number of compounds studied. The ring-electron densities, as measured

$$CH_3 - \langle ~ \rangle - Z - \langle ~ \rangle - NO_2$$

$$(20)$$

$$CH_3 - \langle ~ \rangle - Z - CH_3$$

$$CH_3 - Z - \langle ~ \rangle - NO_2$$

$$Z = -S-, \ -SO-, \ -SO_2-$$

by the average chemical shift of the protons of each ring, of the "whole molecule" of interest 4-methyl, 4-nitro diphenyl sulfide, sulfoxide, or sulfone, are compared with the ring-electron densities of the two corresponding "half molecules." If the sum of the NMR ring spectra of the half molecules shows no significant difference from that of the whole molecule, then it must be concluded that the —Z— function bridge is an insulator corresponding to the "no bond" between the two halves. Even if there is no transmission across the —Z— function it would not be expected that the additivity would be strictly observed since replacing the terminal methyl function in the half molecule by a substituted phenyl ring in the whole molecule must lead to minor changes in electron density due to inductive effects (σ-conduction).

The appropriate NMR spectra for the three systems considered here are shown diagrammatically in Figures 3*a*, *b*, and *c*. The additivity observed in the sulfone (3*a*) and sulfoxide (3*b*) cases is almost within the experimental error (± 0.5 cps). In striking contrast is the complete nonadditivity

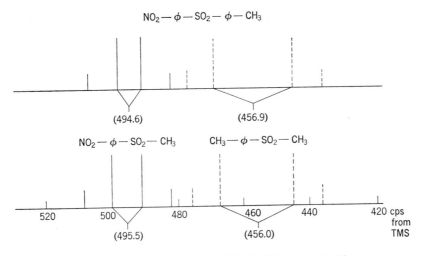

Fig. 3a. Diagrammatic spectrum for 4-NO₂,4′-CH₃-diphenyl sulfone.

in the case of the sulfide bridge (3c). In this molecule the electron density (chemical shift) of the ring carrying the methyl function is *decreased* (downfield shift) on combining the two half molecules, while that in the ring carrying the nitro function is *increased* (upfield shift) on combination. These shifts are presented in tabular form in Table 1 where the difference

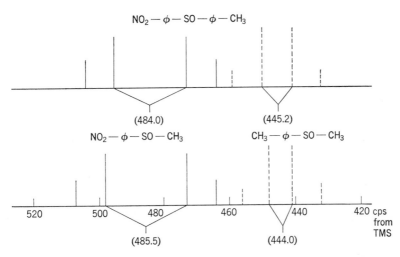

Fig. 3b. Diagrammatic spectrum for 4-NO₂,4′-CH₃-diphenyl sulfoxide.

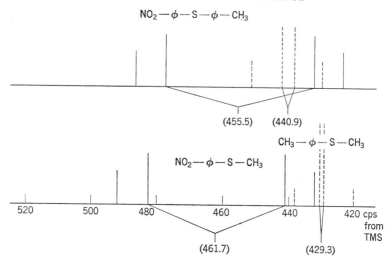

Fig. 3c. Diagrammatic spectrum for 4-NO₂,4′-CH₃-diphenyl sulfide.

Table 1[a]

Shift Analysis

CH₃—⟨benzene ring⟩—Z—⟨benzene ring⟩—NO₂

Z	Species	Tolyl ring protons	Nitro-phenyl ring protons
S	Half molecule	429.3	461.7
	Whole molecule	440.9	455.5
	Shift	−11.6	+6.2
SO	Half molecule	444.0	485.5
	Whole molecule	445.2	484.0
	Shift	−1.2	+1.5
SO₂	Half molecule	456.0	495.5
	Whole molecule	456.9	494.6
	Shift	−0.9	+0.9

[a] −ve Shifts = downfield shift = less shielded protons; all figures in cps from TMS internal standard.

in the chemical shift associated with the center of each quartet is shown for each ring in the half and whole molecule. The sign convention used for the differences is indicated in the table.

The shifts observed in the sulfide bridge case are in agreement with transmission through the sulfur bridge (Scheme I). The decrease in electron density in the ring carrying the methyl and increase in density in the ring carrying the nitro function could only arise if the molecule were polarized

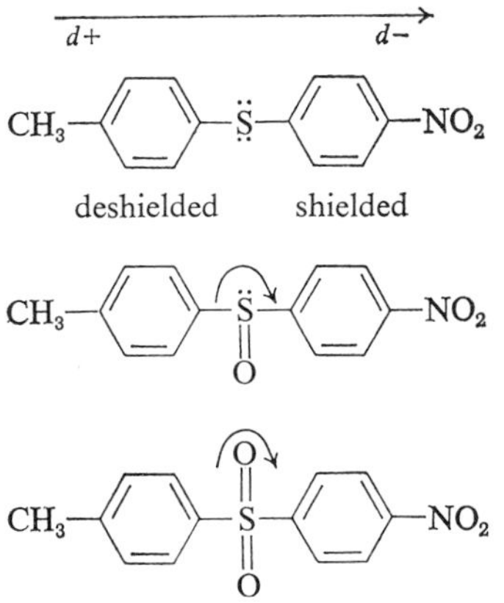

(Scheme I)

along its entire length permitting a "leakage" of electron density from the donor ring to the acceptor ring. The very minor shifts observed in the sulfoxide and sulfone cases are probably due to inductive effects mentioned above but, more importantly, establish the fact that a transmission mechanism operative in the sulfide case is not operative in the sulfone or sulfoxide cases.

Having established this interesting behavior in the specific set of three compounds noted above the program was extended to cover a much wider range of X and Y para-substituents and oxygen and methylene were added as additional Z-bridging functions. The shift data, obtained in a manner similar to that illustrated above and, using the same sign convention, are shown in Table 2.

The trend observed in the sample cases discussed in detail above is, in general, maintained throughout the data in Table 2 but with some notable exceptions. While the shifts, indicating positive transmission, are by far the largest in the sulfide column, those for the 4-CH$_3$O,4'-CH$_3$ sulfide are much smaller and comparable to those for the sulfoxides and sulfones. This may be a reflection of the fact that both substituents are electron donors and are therefore working against each other. The necessary "incentive" for the bridging sulfur to transmit in this case may therefore

Table 2
NMR Shift Data

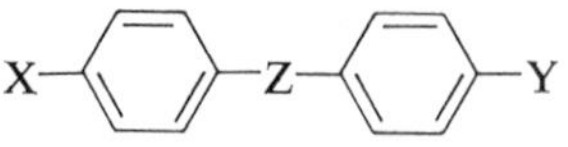

$$X-\!\!\left\langle\bigcirc\right\rangle\!\!-Z-\!\!\left\langle\bigcirc\right\rangle\!\!-Y$$

		\-S\-		\-SO\-		\-SO$_2$\-		\-O\-		\-CH$_2$\-	
X	Y	X—φ	Y—φ	X—φ	Y—φ	X—φ	Y—φ	X—φ	Y—φ	X—φ	Y—φ
CH$_3$	NO$_2$	−11.6	+6.2	−1.2	+1.5	−0.5	+1.0	−9.1	−2.0		
CH$_3$O	NO$_2$	−9.9	+7.7	+0.8	+3.3	−1.1	+2.4	−9.3	−0.8	+0.8	+1.4
NH$_2$	NO$_2$	−8.0	+7.5	+2.4	+3.7	−0.6	+4.8	−7.3	+1.2	+1.2	+2.4
CH$_3$O	CH$_3$	−3.7	+2.3	+2.0	+2.4	+1.5	+3.6	−3.3	−2.3	+0.5	+1.4

be missing as was suggested by Szmant and McIntosh (21) in their IR studies.

The behavior of the methylene-bridged compounds serves as a reference point since it would not be expected that the methylene bridge would transmit by other than an inductive mechanism. The "all-positive" shifts in *both* rings observed in the whole molecule strongly suggests that these shifts arise from a diamagnetic anisotropy effect resulting from the replacement of the terminal methyl group of the half molecule by the aromatic ring in the whole molecule. It is generally accepted that the rings in such diphenyl compounds are not coplanar and hence each set of ring protons will lie above the basal plane of the other aromatic ring and in a generally diamagnetic region as illustrated in Figure 4. Since this shift effect is extraneous to the transmission effect, the methylene bridge data serve to establish that shifts of the order of 2 cps cannot be considered meaningful as far as the transmission study is concerned either for reasons of unknown magnitude of diamagnetic effects or inductive effects.

While this last comment conveniently takes care of many of the minor shift variations shown in Table 2, it does not account for the very sizable negative (less electron density) shifts observed in the X-ring of the oxygen-bridged cases. It should further be noted that there is no corresponding positive shift observed in the Y-ring as was the case in the sulfide-bridged

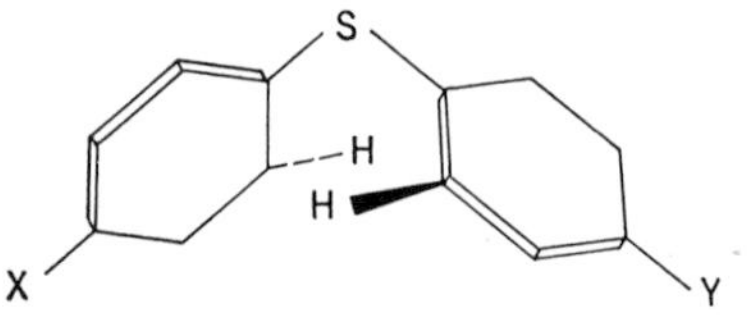

Fig. 4. Nonplanarity of diphenyl sulfide.

cases. At this stage we can offer no plausible explanation for this observation since it is hardly conceivable that the decrease in electron density in the donor ring of the oxygen-bridged cases would find its way to the bridging oxygen (which is generally considered a donor rather than an acceptor) without being subsequently transmitted to the acceptor ring by some mechanism. In this regard it is of interest to note the findings of Marcus et al. (16), who concluded from their NMR study of transmission effects in toluenes, acetophenones, and thioanisoles that in conjugative roles sulfur is a better transmitter than oxygen when functioning as an acceptor or an acceptor–donor (i.e., transmitter) of negative charge, but the situation is reversed when only conjugative donation by the bridging atom is called for. Accordingly, the relative order of the sulfur and oxygen bridge effects may depend to a considerable extent on the role they are called upon to play by the specific relative nature of the two para substituents on the aromatic rings.

In certain of the cases reported in Table 2 it is possible to observe the proton shift associated with the X or Y substituents. These shifts are surprisingly insensitive to the effect of combining the half molecules to yield the diphenyl compound (less than ± 2 cps) and no useful information appears to be available from this source.

There are undoubtedly many interesting facts relevant to the problem hidden within the many minor shifts tabulated in Table 2. As pointed out above, however, there are an equally large number of minor perturbing factors at work which are not directly related to the transmission problem. At this stage, therefore, we are obliged to restrict our attention to the more salient features of the data and accordingly limit our conclusion to the fact that there is evidence for the existence of a transmission mechanism across a sulfide bridge that is absent in the cases of sulfoxide, sulfone, and methylene bridges. There does not appear to be a similar transmission mechanism operative in the oxygen-bridge case, but some type of deshielding of the donor-ring protons does take place when the oxygen bridge is flanked by two π-electron systems.

Although the data reported in Table 2 represent an extension of our study covering a variety of bridging functions, the substituent variation is still rather limited. Accordingly, in the sulfide case, where transmission appears to be operative, we have extended the study to cover a much wider range of 4,4'-substituents. These additional results together with the four systems already reported in the sulfide column of Table 2 are presented in Table 3. In this considerably expanded list of shifts the deshielding of the donor ring and increased shielding of the acceptor ring is further substantiated. Only in the case of 4-methyl,4'-chloro, where there is some uncertainty in spectral assignment, is the deshielding–shielding transmission effect not clearly observed. Again there are some interesting secondary features in the data of Table 3. In the 4-methyl,4'-hydrogen case the shifts are very small as might be expected with two "substituents" that have relatively weak conjugative interaction properties. The unexpected large deshielding of the donor ring in the 4-hydrogen, 4'-nitro case is surprising in view of the relatively small increase in shielding in the

Table 3

Ring Shifts Compared with Half-Molecules

Substituent —⟨ ⟩— S —⟨ ⟩— Substituent

Substituent			Substituent
CH$_3$	−11.6	+6.2	NO$_2$
CH$_3$	−2.4	+0.8	H
H	−14.5	+4.7	NO$_2$
CH$_3$O	−3.7	+2.3	CH$_3$
CH$_3$O	−9.9	+7.7	NO$_2$
NH$_2$	−8.0	+7.5	NO$_2$
(CH$_3$)$_2$N	−4.6	+8.5	NO$_2$
NH$_2$	−4.6	+5.1	CH$_3$
Cl	−13.3	+3.6	NO$_2$
CH$_3$	−4.1	+1.0	Br
CH$_3$	−2.5[a]	−0.8[a]	Cl

[a] Uncertainty in peak positions; negative shift = downfield (less shielded).

acceptor nitro-substituted ring. This does suggest, however, that the conclusion of Szmant and McIntosh from UV studies that there is no evidence for involvement of structure **5** may be in error. The similar behavior of the 4-chloro, 4'-nitro compound indicates that in the presence of the powerful electron-withdrawing nitro group the chloro substituent is forced to function as a "positive halogen" in the manner shown in **21**.

$$\overset{+}{Cl}=\!\!\left\langle\right\rangle\!\!=S=\!\!\left\langle\right\rangle\!\!=NO_2^{-}$$

(21)

Up to this point we have restricted our discussion to a *qualitative* examination of the NMR results. As suggested above, this is perhaps wise in view of the number of unknown minor factors that may be operative in determining the precise values of the observed shifts. However, with the rather extensive data shown in Table 3 there is the irresistible temptation to attempt to relate the data in some *quantitative* manner. By using an analytical method based essentially on *differences* between compounds many of the unknown perturbing factors might be expected to cancel out; just such a method has been applied to the data of Table 3.

The compounds shown in Table 3 were taken in pairs with each pair having a common X substituent but a different Y substituent. The *difference* in the shifts associated with the common X-ring in each pair was then associated with the difference between the electronic effects of the two different Y substituents. The method is illustrated in Table 4. In this

Table 4

$$X-\!\!\left\langle \bigcirc \right\rangle\!\!-S-\!\!\left\langle \bigcirc \right\rangle\!\!-Y$$

X	X-ϕ proton shift	Shift difference		
CH₃—	− 11.6	—NO₂		
CH₃—	− 2.4	—H $\Big]$ 9.2	$\Big]$ 16.7	
CH₃—	+ 5.1	—NH₂		
NO₂—	+ 3.6	—Cl		
NO₂—	+ 7.5	—NH₂ $\Big]$ 3.9		
H—	− 14.5	—NO₂		
H—	+ 0.8	—CH₃ $\Big]$ 15.3	$\Big]$ − 1.3	
NO₂—	+ 6.2	—CH₃		

manner it is possible to construct a scale of shift differences corresponding to the whole series of substituents Y. In order to provide a reference point on the scale all other substituent shift differences were referred to NO_2 which was assigned a zero value. Since there are a number of ways of combining the pairs of compounds, there is frequently more than one way of obtaining the shift difference between the NO_2 value and a given substituent. This is illustrated in Table 4 where the NO_2/CH_3 difference can be obtained directly (15.3) but also indirectly from

$$NO_2/NH_2(16.7) - NH_2/CH_3(1.3) = NO_2/CH_3(15.4)$$

The agreement between the two methods in this case is fortuitous but the examples serve to illustrate that a range of values for the shift differences will be obtained for each substituent. Having thus established a scale of shift differences for each substituent relative to $NO_2 = 0$, these differences can be plotted against the Hammett σ_p value for each substituent. Such a plot is shown in Figure 5. Despite the considerable uncertainty in the shift

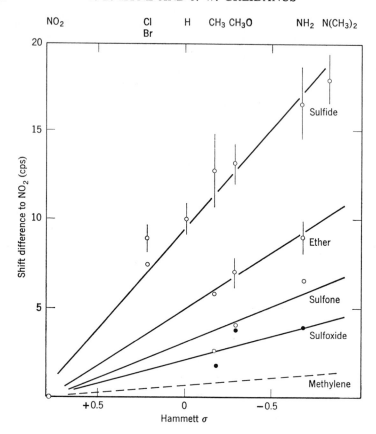

Fig. 5. Hammett-type plot illustrating variation in transmission through various bridging functions.

difference values for the various substituents, it is clear that there is a relationship between the Hammett σ values and the differences. More important, however, is the comparison with similar plots for sulfoxide, sulfones, and ethers generated in the same manner from the much more limited data of Table 2. It is clear from Figure 5 that the dependence of the shift differences, and hence ring-electron densities, on substituent effects is considerably greater in the sulfide-bridge case than for any of the other bridging functions. Because data are lacking it is not possible to present a similar plot for the methylene-bridged compounds. It can, however, be estimated that the slope of the plot *will not be* greater than the dotted line shown in Figure 5. Accordingly, it can be concluded that the order of effectiveness of transmission of electronic effects across the bridging function between two aromatic π-electron systems is $S > O > SO_2 \geqslant$ $SO > CH_2$. In view of the uncertainties associated with the points in Figure 5 we feel it would be unjustified at this stage to express this order in quantitative terms although this could clearly be done in terms of the slopes of the plots, i.e., in ρ values using Hammett terminology.

The NMR findings clearly substantiate those of Hogeveen and Pasto and co-workers (see Figs. 1 and 2), using acid strength dependence as the criterion for establishing transmission effects. The relative order of S and O as effective transmitters also agrees with the Russian workers' conclusions based on amine reactivity. If the results of all of these investigations are combined, we obtain the sequence $NH > S > Se > O >$ $SO_2 \geqslant SO > CH_2$.

In conclusion, we would suggest that as far as the sulfide bridges are concerned transmission of electronic effects by an extended π-electron system mechanism is of sufficient magnitude that it could well be influential in determining the physical and chemical properties of such molecules but that transmission through sulfoxide and sulfone bridges is of relatively minor importance and can probably be accounted for almost entirely on the basis of an inductive effect mechanism.

References

The recent review of Cilento (3) and the book by Price and Oae (19) provide an adequate review of references on the subject of transmission up to 1960. The references cited in this paper cover work reported since 1960. In addition, however, we have included several more recent references (24–29) which contain pertinent information on the subjects of expansion of the valence shell, transmission of electronic effects, etc., but were not specifically cited in the main text of the paper.

1. K. Boček, A. Mangini, and R. Zahradník, *J. Chem. Soc.*, **1963**, 225.
2. E. Campaigne, J. Tsurugi, and W. W. Meyer, *J. Org. Chem.*, **26**, 2486 (1961).
3. G. Cilento, *Chem. Rev.*, **60**, 147 (1960).
4. L. N. Ferguson, *The Modern Structural Theory of Organic Chemistry*, Prentice-Hall, Englewood Cliffs, N.J., 1963, p. 20.
5. J. H. Gibbs, *J. Phys. Chem.*, **59**, 644 (1955).
6. G. C. Hampson, R. H. Farmer, and L. E. Sutton, *Proc. Roy. Soc.* (*London*), *Ser. A*, **143**, 147 (1933).
7. H. Hogeveen, *Rec. Trav. Chim.*, **83**, 813 (1964).
8. H. Jaffé and K. Otsuji, *Report Petroleum Research Fund 301A*, 60 (1960) (through ref. 1).
9. L. M. Litvinenko, S. V. Tsukerman, R. S. Cheshko, and B. M. Kolesnikova, *Zh. Obshch. Khim.*, **27**, 1663 (1957).
10. L. M. Litvinenko, R. S. Cheshko, and S. V. Tsukerman, *Dokl. Akad. Nauk SSSR*, **118**, 946 (1958).
11. L. M. Litvinenko and R. S. Cheshko, *Zh. Obshch. Khim.*, **30**, 3682 (1960).
12. L. M. Litvinenko, *Izv. Akad. Nauk SSSR, Otd. Khim. Nauk*, **1962**, 1737.
13. A. Mangini and R. Passerini, *J. Chem. Soc.*, **1952**, 1168.
14. A. Mangini and R. Passerini, *J. Chem. Soc.*, **1956**, 4954.

15. A. Mangini, *Pure Appl. Chem.*, **1963**, 103.
16. S. H. Marcus, W. F. Reynolds, and S. I. Miller, *Org. Div. Abstr.* No. 116, 151st Meeting of the American Chemical Society, Pittsburgh, 1966.
17. C. A. Meyers, *Gazz. Chim. Ital.*, **93**, 1206 (1963).
18. D. J. Pasto, D. McMillan, and T. Murphy, *J. Org. Chem.*, **30**, 2688 (1965).
19. C. C. Price and S. Oae, *Sulfur Bonding*, Ronald Press, New York, 1962.
20. C. C. Price, *Chem. Eng. News*, **42** (48), 58 (1964).
21. H. H. Szmant and J. J. McIntosh, *J. Am. Chem. Soc.*, **73**, 4356 (1951).
22. R. Zahradnik and K. Boček, *Collection Czech. Chem. Commun.*, **26**, 1733 (1961).
23. R. E. Benson, D. R. Eaton, A. D. Josey, and W. D. Phillips, *J. Am. Chem. Soc.*, **83**, 3714 (1961).
24. C. A. Coulson and C. Zauli, *Mol. Phys.*, **6**, 525 (1963).
25. S. Ghersetti, *Boll. Sci. Fac. Chim. Ind. Bologna*, **21**, 228 (1963).
26. L. Goodman and R. W. Taft, *J. Am. Chem. Soc.*, **87**, 4385 (1965).
27. A. Mangini, "Contributi teorici e sperimentali di polarografia," Vol. 5 in *Ric. Sci. Suppl.*, **30** (1960).
28. A. Mangini, *Boll. Sci. Fac. Chim. Ind. Bologna*, **18**, 191 (1960).
29. A. Mangini, *Rev. Chim., Acad. Rep. Populaire Roumaine*, **7**, No. 1, 313 (1962).

Photolysis of Organic Sulfides and of Related Substances

NORMAN KHARASCH and AHMED I. KHODAIR

University of Southern California, Los Angeles, California

For the purposes of this discussion, organic sulfides may be broadly defined as substances of general structure X—S—Y, where X and Y represent any desired covalently bound organic radicals. While the photochemical behavior of these substances is obviously of great theoretical and practical interest, surprisingly little work has as yet been done to establish what this behavior is. The purpose of the present paper is therefore to note some current and recent studies, to emphasize the scope of the field, and to suggest particular objectives. The oxidation products, X—S(O)Y and X—SO₂—Y, are considered as related substances.

Initial studies of Kharasch and co-workers on photolysis of organic sulfur compounds have involved substances of the types noted above, using irradiation procedures similar to those employed by these investigators (1) in photolyses of organic halogen compounds (especially iodoaromatic compounds). The photolysis of the iodoaromatic and related substances has therefore been outlined, and the irradiation source generally used (a 2537 Å low pressure cold-cathode mercury arc) has been described (1). This type of lamp delivers mainly quanta of sufficient energy (112 kcal), even when moderated by a solvent of high absorptivity—such as benzene, which is involved in the energy transfer step to the substrate— to photolyze all types of carbon–sulfur bonds (bond energy ca. 70 kcal/mole). To avoid undesired decomposition of substrates, i.e., to make the photolyses selective, radiations of energies higher than those of 2400 Å wavelength should be filtered out. This can be done effectively by using a lamp housing of a selected Vycor glass.

Sulfenyl halides, RSX and ArSX, where X is generally chlorine but may also be bromine or thiocyanate, represent a group of sulfides (defined as above) which have long been of special interest to the authors; and substances like ClSCl also belong to this group. To illustrate the current interest in photolyses of these types of substances, studies of their photochemically induced reactions with alkanes and alkenes have been described. Pertinent studies are those of Kloosterziel (2,3) on Cl₃CSCl (trichloromethanesulfenyl chloride), and of Harris on additions of CF_3SCl to fluoroolefins (4). Also to be mentioned are the studies of Müller and Schmidt (5,7) on the reactions of sulfur dichloride and of sulfur monochloride with alkanes and cycloalkanes, leading, e.g., to cycloalkanesulfenyl chlorides, RSCl (R = cyclopentyl, etc.) and to RSSCl. The initial step in all these reactions, as well as in the related reactions of thiocyanogen chloride, Cl—SCN, is the homolytic scission of the S—Cl bond, followed by free-radical chain reactions (see below).

Kloosterziel (3,4) has extended the earlier studies of Prey and Gutschik (9) on the photochemically initiated reactions of trichloromethanesulfenyl chloride. In particular, he further demonstrated the high selectivity of the sulfenyl chloride as a chlorinating agent (preferred chlorination of 3°, vs. 2°, vs. 1° hydrogen atoms) and suggested that this is because it is the trichloro-methanesulfenyl radicals, $Cl_3CS\cdot$, rather than $Cl\cdot$, which abstract the hydrogen. Polar effects of substituents on the course of the chlorination have also been described. The reaction chain is shown in equations la–lc. The formation of the disulfide occurs in a separate, rapid reaction of Cl_3CSH with Cl_3CSCl (eq. 2).

$$Cl_3CSCl \longrightarrow Cl_3CS\cdot + Cl\cdot \tag{1a}$$

$$RH + Cl_3CS\cdot \longrightarrow R\cdot + Cl_3CSH \tag{1b}$$

$$R\cdot + Cl_3CSCl \longrightarrow RCl + Cl_3CS\cdot \text{ etc.} \tag{1c}$$

$$Cl_3CSH + Cl_3CSCl \longrightarrow Cl_3CS\text{—}SCCl_3 + HCl \tag{2}$$

The overall reaction with cyclohexane is essentially quantitative and provides a good route for synthesis of bis(trichloromethyl) disulfide (eq. 3).

$$C_6H_{12} + 2Cl_3CSCl \longrightarrow C_6H_{11}Cl + HCl + Cl_3CS\text{—}SCCl_3 \tag{3}$$

The value of Cl_3CSCl as a selective chlorination agent is also suggested by this conversion and by related reactions with alkanes.

Kharasch and Ariyan (10) have examined some photochemically initiated reactions of pentachlorobenzenesulfenyl chloride. Of special interest was the finding that, with cyclohexane, *both* sulfenylation and chlorination occur competitively, leading to cyclohexyl pentachlorophenyl sulfide as the major product, and lesser amounts of cyclohexyl chloride and bis(penta-chlorophenyl) disulfide. With toluene, however, only the sulfide was found, together with some bis(pentachlorophenyl) disulfide, and no benzyl chloride was observed (Ar = pentachlorophenyl)*:

$$ArSCl + C_6H_{12} \longrightarrow \underset{(69\%)}{ArSC_6H_{11}} + \underset{(87\%)}{HCl} + \underset{(12\%)}{C_6H_{11}Cl} + \underset{(12\%)}{ArSSAr} \tag{4}$$

$$ArSCl + C_6H_5CH_3 \longrightarrow \underset{(94\%)}{ArSCH_2C_6H_5} + \underset{(98\%)}{HCl} + \underset{(none)}{C_6H_5CH_2Cl} + \underset{(6\%)}{ArSSAr} \tag{5}$$

* The exclusive formation of the benzyl sulfide, and nonformation of benzyl chloride, was not reported in reference 10, but has been established to be the case.

The distinct preference for sulfenylation in the case of toluene may possibly involve formation of a charge-transfer complex (I) between the electronegatively substituted sulfenyl chloride and toluene. In such a complex, formation of the sulfide could be facilitated.

$$[I] \longrightarrow Cl_5C_6-S-CH_2C_6H_5 + HCl$$

In the presence of benzoquinone, photolysis of pentachlorobenzene-sulfenyl chloride leads to mono- and disulfenylation of the quinone (11) (eq. 7), whereas irradiation in carbon tetrachloride (12) leads to the unique conversion to octachlorobenzothiophene (eq. 8). The mechanism of this latter conversion has not yet been elucidated. Octachlorothian-threne (which was isolated as one product) may also be the intermediate to the octachlorodibenzothiophene; but another possibility involves a tetrachlorobenzyne intermediate. The elimination of SCl_2 to form the benzyne, by irradiation, would parallel the formation of benzynes by photolysis of 1,2-diiodobenzenes. The latter reaction has been demonstrated

$$ArSCl \xrightarrow{\text{benzoquinone}}$$

to occur in studies of Kampmeier and Hofmeister (12) and of Kharasch and Sharma (12a).

The conversion of the bis(pentachlorophenyl) sulfide to the octachlorobenzothiophene (42% yield) was shown to take place. The steps leading to the sulfide are, however, only projected at this time.

Trichloromethanesulfenyl chloride does not add to olefins readily under conditions where benzenesulfenyl chloride, methanesulfenyl chloride, etc. do so easily (13). Additions can, however, be effected by photochemical irradiation or by thermal, free-radical initiation, e.g., with peroxides. The assignments of structures to the adducts, as those expected in accord with Markownikoff's rules, may, however, be in error in some cases (14). These additions, no doubt, involve free-radical chain reactions, but details of the precise mechanisms in some cases must yet be elucidated.

Studies of Harris on additions of CF_3SCl to fluorinated olefins (4) again illustrate that photochemically initiated reactions of CF_3SCl lead to olefin adducts by free-radical chain sequences. In these cases, the adducts include those with Cl added terminally, as well as with CF_3S at the terminal position. It is suggested that the intermediate radical $R—CH—CH_2Cl$, can attack CF_3SCl to abstract chlorine (the 1,2-dichloride was found as product), or it can attack on sulfur, giving the β-chloro sulfide. In some instances the product resulting from addition of two CF_3S groups was also found, and the product of alternate additions of Cl and SCF_3 to the unsymmetrical olefin was also detected. A consistent interpretation, based on free-radical reactions, was achieved.

In the studies described above, sulfide products have been obtained, and they remained intact under the photochemical conditions used to initiate the reactions of the sulfur–halogen compounds. More recently, Kharasch and Khodair (15) explored the photolysis of diphenyl sulfide, diphenyl sulfoxide, and diphenyl sulfone, as well as benzenesulfonyl halides (X=Cl, F, and I). This study has shown that diphenyl sulfone can be photolyzed smoothly in benzene solution, acting as a source of phenyl radicals. Bisphenyl sulfide and bisphenyl sulfoxide also undergo photolysis to give phenyl radicals in substantial yields. With diphenyl sulfoxide in benzene, there was found 53% biphenyl and 77% bisphenyl sulfide besides a trace of bisphenyl disulfide. The photolysis was 66–71% complete in 17–18 hr. Photolysis of diphenyl sulfide, in benzene, led to 39% biphenyl, 19% bisphenyl disulfide, and a trace of thiophenol. The latter may be an intermediate, however, since it was shown (16) that thiophenol readily undergoes photolysis in benzene solution when irradiated at 2537 Å, giving a considerable variety of products. Phenyl disulfide, however, which is also among the products, appears to be resistant to photochemical decomposition under these conditions. It is probable that the dissociation in this case is highly reversible. Dibenzothiophene and dibenzothiophene dioxide are also stable to the irradiation conditions used (15), in contrast to diphenyl sulfide and diphenyl sulfone.

In photolysis of $C_6H_5SO_2X$, the extent of phenyl radical formation from $C_6H_5SO_2X$ varies as a function of X. As anticipated, it is highest with the sulfonyl fluoride, in which preferential cleavage of the sulfur–halogen bond does not compete as effectively.

By studying the photolysis of bis-p-tolyl sulfone in benzene, and of bisphenyl sulfone in fluorobenzene, it was shown that the photochemical decomposition of the sulfone is *intermolecular*. Only 4-methylbiphenyl or the isomeric fluorobiphenyls were found, and no 4,4'-dimethylbiphenyl was observed.

The photolysis of bisphenyl sulfide in benzene, yielding biphenyl cleanly, contrasts with the experiments of Horner (17), who found only polymers. Carruthers (18), using light petroleum as solvent, found benzene and bis-phenyl disulfide as products, but only traces of biphenyl. Cyclization to 9-thiafluorene was not found by Carruthers, nor by Kharasch and Khodair. The possible ring closure (eq. 9) was also studied more recently, by Stege-meyer (19), who also found no evidence for cyclization—in contrast to the

$$\tag{9}$$

case with diphenylamine (20) or with stilbene (21). The mechanisms of these cyclization reactions are of particular interest.

Some further pertinent studies of the photolysis of selected sulfur compounds have been reviewed. Selected references are given (22–27), together with annotations to indicate the nature of each study.

The studies of the authors, and of the other workers cited, on the photolysis of sulfur compounds, are mainly exploratory. There is, however, a good basis now for more intensive efforts in specific areas, and such may now be expected to be made in greater number. Much additional exploratory work, however, is also needed. Among current investigations in the authors' laboratories, the following may be mentioned: (*1*) Studies of the photolysis of aryl thiocyanates; (*2*) studies of the photolysis of unsymmetrical sulfones; and (*3*) studies of the photolysis of *o*-phenylene sulfides, as a possible route to benzynes. In the photolyses of diaryl sulfones, there are wide variations in rates of photochemical decompositions. Thus, di-p-xenyl sulfone undergoes very slow and incomplete photolysis under conditions where diphenyl sulfone photolyzes rapidly. The study of photolysis of the mixed sulfone, i.e., phenyl, p-xenyl sulfone, will be of special interest.

References

1. W. Wolf and N. Kharasch, *J. Org. Chem.*, **30**, 2493 (1965). See also R. K. Sharma and N. Kharasch, *Angew. Chem.*, in press, for a review on photolysis of iodo-aromatic compounds.
2. H. Kloosterziel, *Rec. Trav. Chim.*, **82**, 497 (1963).
3. H. Kloosterziel, *Rec. Trav. Chim.*, **82**, 508 (1963).
4. J. F. Harris, Jr., *J. Am. Chem. Soc.*, **84**, 3148 (1962).
5. E. Müller and E. W. Schmidt, *Chem. Ber.*, **96**, 3050 (1963).
6. E. Müller and E. W. Schmidt, *Chem. Ber.*, **97**, 2614 (1964).
7. E. Müller and E. W. Schmidt, *Chem. Ber.*, **97**, 2622 (1964).
8. R. G. R. Bacon, R. G. Guy, and R. S. Irwin, *J. Chem. Soc.*, **1961**, 2436.
9. V. Prey, E. Gutschik, and H. Berbalk, *Monatsh.*, **91**, 356 (1960); E. Gutschik and V. Prey, *ibid.*, **92**, 827 (1962).
10. N. Kharasch and Z. S. Ariyan, *Chem. Ind. (London)*, **1964**, 929.
11. N. Kharasch and Z. S. Ariyan, *Chem. Ind. (London)*, **1964**, 302.
12. J. A. Kampmeier and E. Hofmeister, *J. Am. Chem. Soc.*, **84**, 3787 (1962).
12a. N. Kharasch and R. K. Sharma, *Chem. Commun.*, **1967**, 493.
13. A. Senning, *Chem. Rev.*, **65**, 385 (1965). See, however, F. Boberg, *Ann.*, **679**, 109 1964) for some recent examples of addition.
14. See the comments in *Quart. Repts. Sulfur Chem.*, **1**, 134 (1966).
15. N. Kharasch and A. I. Khodair, *Chem. Commun.*, **1967**, 87.
16. R. B. Langford, private communication, August, 1966.
17. L. Horner and J. Dörges, *Tetrahedron Letters*, **1963**, 757. Photochemical (light) reactions. XV. photolyses of thioethers.
18. W. Carruthers, *Nature*, **209**, 908 (1966).
19. H. Stegemeyer, *Naturwiss.*, **53**, 582 (1966).
20. K.-H. Grellman, G. M. Sherman, and H. Linschitz, *J. Am. Chem. Soc.*, **85**, 1881 (1963); H. Linschitz and K.-H. Grellman, *J. Am. Chem. Soc.*, **86**, 303 (1964); E. J. Brown and J. H. D. Eland, *Proc. Chem. Soc.*, **1963**, 202.
21. F. B. Mallory, C. S. Wood, J. T. Gordon, L. C. Lindquist, and M. L. Savitz, *J. Am. Chem. Soc.*, **84**, 4361 (1962). Cf. also, N. Kharasch, T. G. Alston, and H. B. Lewis, *Chem. Commun.*, **1967**, 435.
22. V. Ramakrishnan, S. D. Thompson, and S. P. McGlynn, *Photochem. Photobiol.*, **4**, 907 (1965). Photolysis of some cyclic disulfides.
23. W. E. Haines, *J. Am. Chem. Soc.*, **78**, 5213 (1956). Decomposition products of thiols and disulfides exposed to light.
24. R. J. Gritter, *J. Org. Chem.*, **28**, 3437 (1963). Ultraviolet photolysis of cyclic ethers and sulfides.
25. C. L. McIntosh, P. de Mayo, and R. W. Yip, *Tetrahedron Letters*, **1967**, 37.
26. A. J. Beckwith and L. B. See, *J. Chem. Soc.*, **1964**, 2571. Thiyl radicals. Part 4. (Includes reactions of photochemically generated benzoylthio radicals.)
27. E. T. Kaiser and T. F. Wulfers, *J. Am. Chem. Soc.*, **86**, 1897 (1964). Photolysis of thiobenzophenone in the presence of olefins: Novel reaction.

PART II

Sulfide-Containing Polymers

Adduct Rubber—Elastomers Obtained by Reaction of Mercaptans with Diene Polymers and Copolymers

G. E. MEYER

The Goodyear Tire & Rubber Company Research Laboratory, Akron, Ohio

The term "adduct rubber" has been used to describe the elastomers obtained by the chemical addition of mercaptans to the double bonds of diene polymers and copolymers. The work that will be covered in this chapter includes the preparation and chemical properties of some of these adduct rubbers. The compounding of the rubbers and the physical properties of the products have been covered in earlier papers (1) and will not be discussed here except where pertinent to the chemical properties being considered.

When methyl mercaptan is added to the double bond in a segmer of polybutadiene, the product may be represented by the oversimplified structures shown in Figure 1. At 100% saturation of a 1,4-polybutadiene, the polymer would be composed completely of the type of segmers shown on the first line. Much of our experimental work has been directed toward obtaining a less saturated adduct that could be cured in sulfur-vulcanization recipes. Since most of our work was with emulsion polybutadiene, the product would have about 20% pendant thioether groups, of the type shown on the second line, obtained from the addition of the mercaptan to the side vinyl groups of the original 1,2 segmers in the polybutadiene. The reaction mechanism will be discussed later in some detail. Table 1 shows

---

1,4 segmer

$$-CH_2-CH-CH_2-CH_2-$$
$$|$$
$$SCH_3$$

1,2 segmer

$$-CH_2-CH-$$
$$|$$
$$CH_2-CH_2-SCH_3$$

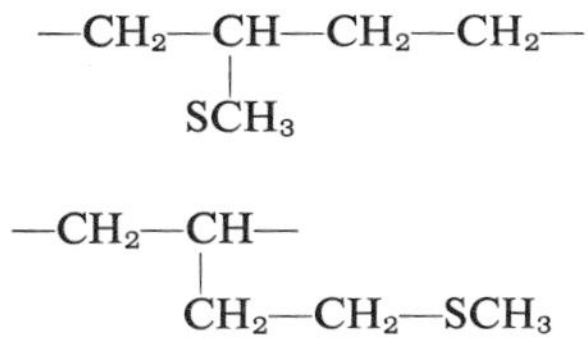

Fig. 1. CH_3SH adduct of polybutadiene.

113

Table 1

Some Adduct Rubbers Investigated

Mercaptans	Base polymers
CH_3SH	Polybutadienes
CH_3SH	BD/styrene
CH_3SH	BD/acrylonitrile
CH_3SH	Polyisoprenes
C_2H_5SH	Polybutadiene
$n\text{-}C_3H_7SH$	Polybutadiene
$i\text{-}C_3H_7SH$	Polybutadiene
$n\text{-}C_4TOC_{12}SH$	Polybutadiene

a partial list of the adduct rubbers that have been investigated. Though the methyl mercaptan adduct of polybutadiene has received the largest share of attention, some investigations of the adducts produced by the higher molecular weight mercaptans up through dodecyl (C_{12}) mercaptan have also been made. The normal mercaptans added quite readily. Isopropyl was the only secondary mercaptan that added significantly; t-butyl appeared not to add at all. The adducts of natural rubber and various synthetic polyisoprenes as well as butadiene copolymers formed with styrene and acrylonitrile were screened. The effect of some of these variables on the properties of the adducts will be mentioned later.

This work was undertaken as part of a program to develop an elastomer possessing a more nearly ideal balance of solvent resistance, low-temperature flexibility, high-temperature aging stability, and low production cost. Since new monomers had already received exhaustive attention, a different approach seemed warranted. Certain resinous rubber derivatives, such as the HCl adduct, had already been commercialized but we were not aware that any elastomeric rubber derivatives had reached the commercial stage largely because there are so few coreactants available that would yield an elastomeric product.

The reaction of a mercaptan with an olefin to form a thioether has been known since Posner's paper (2) was published in 1905. The 1932 paper by Holmberg (3) which reports soaking of a piece of pale crepe in thioglycolic acid for 16 months appears to be the first account of work with polymers. Quite a bit of work on the reaction of alkyl mercaptans with butadiene polymers and copolymers, which eventually appeared in the form of patents and technical publications (4) was first reported to the U.S. government in the "Rubber Reserve Reports" in 1944 and 1945. Serniuk, Banes, and Swaney, in the group at Standard Oil of New Jersey, reacted ethyl mercaptan with butadiene–styrene copolymers in latex. Under certain conditions, in the absence of air, up to about 25% of the double bonds in the butadiene portion of the polymer would react with the mercaptan. Since this corresponded roughly to the vinyl content of the polymer—that is, the portion of the polymer in which most reactive double bonds are located—they suggested this as a procedure for eliminating these bonds thereby increasing the oxidation resistance of the polymer. However, air in their system promoted the ethyl mercaptan adduct reaction to over 80% saturation. There seems to be no report of any further investigation of these products. About this same time, Fryling (5) at Phillips Petroleum found that ethyl and higher molecular weight mercaptans reacted with polybutadiene and SBR latices in the presence of air, causing extensive degradation of the polymer simultaneously with the adduct reaction. He obtained low molecular weight, viscous, liquid polymers which he proposed to use as plasticizers or processing aids in the manufacture of rubber products.

Methyl mercaptan was not mentioned in the reports of this early work. Goodyear's first laboratory samples were the products resulting from the addition of methyl mercaptan to polybutadiene. The reaction proceeds by the well-known free-radical mechanism of which the initiation and propagation steps are illustrated by equations 1 and 2.

$$I\cdot + RSH \longrightarrow RS\cdot + IH \tag{1}$$

$$RS\cdot + R'\overset{H}{C}=\overset{H}{C}R'' \longrightarrow R'\overset{H}{\underset{SR}{C}}-\overset{H}{C}R'' \overset{RSH}{\longrightarrow} R'\overset{H}{\underset{SR}{C}}-\overset{H}{\underset{H}{C}}R'' + RS\cdot \tag{2}$$

Many of the standard emulsion polymerization catalysts can be used as initiators which is why oxygen can be a problem in the reaction. In the absence of other materials to generate free radicals a rather low level of oxygen serves almost exclusively as an initiator; at higher levels, oxygen also promotes a chain-scission reaction. When other initiators are used, oxygen can act independently to influence the nature of the product. We found it quite important to take precautionary measures to exclude oxygen from the reaction system. Gamma radiation and AIBN serve very well as initiators for both solution and latex systems. Water-soluble initiators such as t-butyl hydroperoxide or potassium persulfate are also good initiators in latex systems. There are the normal three steps consisting of initiation, propagation, and termination.

Although the arrows in equations 2 and 3 indicate that the reactions proceed in only one direction, a very noteworthy effect results from the reversibility of the propagation step. Work by Golub (6) as well as work in our own laboratory has shown that mercaptans cause isomerization of double bonds. When the adduct reaction is carried out with stereoregular polymers such as natural rubber or *cis*-1,4-polybutadiene, the unadducted double bonds are soon converted to a mixture of *cis* and *trans* orientations. This isomerization is accomplished by a reversal of the propagation reaction which yields the equilibrium *cis–trans* ratio of the remaining double bonds.

The termination step, not indicated in equations 2 and 3, is important because of the possibility of the formation of undesirable end products. That is, materials, polymeric or otherwise, form that could influence the properties of the adduct. Three possibilities are shown in reactions 3–5.

$$2RS^\cdot \longrightarrow RSSR \qquad\qquad (3)$$
$$(1)$$

$$
\begin{array}{c}
2R'{-}CH{-}\overset{\displaystyle\cdot}{C}HR'' \longrightarrow R'\overset{\displaystyle SR}{\underset{\displaystyle |}{C}}H{-}CHR'' \\
\quad | \qquad\qquad\qquad\quad | \\
\;SR \qquad\qquad\qquad R'CH{-}CHR'' \\
\qquad\qquad\qquad\qquad\qquad | \\
\qquad\qquad\qquad\qquad\; SR \quad (2)
\end{array}
\qquad (4)
$$

$$
\begin{array}{c}
R'CH{-}\overset{\displaystyle\cdot}{C}{-}HR'' \xrightarrow{\;RS^\cdot\;} R'CH{-}CHR'' \\
\;\; | \qquad\qquad\qquad\quad | \quad\;\; | \\
\;SR \qquad\qquad\qquad SR \;\; SR \\
\qquad\qquad\qquad\qquad (3)
\end{array}
\qquad (5)
$$

Since the disulfide is highly soluble in adduct and has a high boiling point, it is difficult to remove. On aging, pure disulfide acquires an unpleasant odor. Small amounts of the disulfide are usually found in the mixture at completion of the adduct reaction. Possible product **2** would be a crosslink, and if enough were formed, the adduct would have a high gel content. The adduct obtained from normal reaction conditions appears not to have changed in solubility. Therefore, little, if any, of this forms. Actually, the formation of this product should be more hindered than the addition of high molecular weight secondary mercaptan since it involves the reaction of two secondary radicals. As mentioned earlier, the addition of high molecular weight secondary mercaptans is extremely difficult compared to the addition of methyl mercaptan, which is normally present in excess. Therefore, this crosslinking reaction seems to be no problem. The formation of vicinal bisthioether (**3**) would be highly undesirable because of its relatively low stability. Under mild aging conditions, it decomposes liberating mercaptan. There is a sensitive chemical test for this type of compound that detects low molecular weight vicinal bisthioethers very well. Neither this test nor any other observations have indicated the presence of this structure in the adduct. Also, since we have never been able to obtain a sulfur content higher than a value equivalent to 98% saturation, there must be little, if any, of this vicinal bisthioether present.

Normal SBR isolation and processing procedures work very well for the adduct rubbers. Gum stocks as well as those containing fillers such as carbon black and silicas have about the same tensile and elongation properties as similar stocks from SBR. The properties of adducts that are significantly different from those of the base polymers are listed in Table 2.

Table 2

Changes in Properties of Adduct Rubbers
with Increased Saturation

Increase
>   Solvent resistance
>   Oxidation resistance
>   Ozone resistance
>   High temperature aging

Decrease
>   Low temperature flexibility
>   Resilience
>   Vulcanizability

In general, the change in these properties is proportional to the saturation level. Although, as mentioned earlier, most of our work has been on the methyl mercaptan adduct of polybutadiene, the trends noted here would be observed in other combinations of mercaptans and base polymers. The greatest change in solvent resistance is observed with methyl mercaptan adduct of polybutadiene because this adduct provides the maximum sulfur content. The higher molecular weight mercaptans would provide a thioether group containing proportionally more hydrocarbon content and, therefore, less hydrocarbon solvent resistance. The same trend is found in adducts of polyisoprene or copolymers of butadiene–styrene since the amount of mercaptan that can be added will be less per unit weight of base polymer. Actually the aliphatic and aromatic hydrocarbon solvent resistance of the 95% saturated methyl mercaptan adduct of polybutadiene is equal to or better than neoprene. For other solvents and chemicals, the resistance varies, depending on the chemical nature of the material being considered. In the usual laboratory oxidation, ozone, and temperature-evaluation tests, adduct rubber outperforms neoprene.

The methyl mercaptan adduct of emulsion polybutadiene has about the same low-temperature flexibility and resilience characteristics as neoprene. Other combinations of mercaptan and base polymers are generally quite different. The methyl mercaptan adducts of polyisoprene and SBR have T_g values near 0°C, compared to approximately $-40°$ for the adduct of polybutadiene. Therefore, of the combinations mentioned, this adduct provides the best compromise of solvent resistance versus low-temperature stiffening. The methyl mercaptan adducts of butadiene–acrylonitrile copolymers obviously offer a natural avenue for attaining higher levels of solvent resistance. As with polybutadiene, saturating the double bonds of the butadiene segmers in these copolymers greatly enhances the oxidation resistance and high-temperature stability over the unadducted elastomers. Solvent resistance increases somewhat but not nearly as much as for the adduct of the homopolymer of butadiene.

The ability of the highly saturated adduct to vulcanize is quite different from that of the base polymer when sulfur vulcanization recipes are being considered because of the lower level of residual double bonds. The completely saturated adducts require other types of curing such as peroxides or a system based on the chemical reactions of the thioethers.

Although it would be very desirable to have an accurate method for determining residual unsaturation, one has not yet been found. The standard halogenation techniques for double bonds are not applicable because the halogens form complexes with the thioether groups. Although total sulfur content is used to calculate the amount of mercaptan that has reacted with the base polymer, the difference between the number of double bonds consumed and the original number available does not always correlate with the properties of the adduct. A possible explanation for this discrepancy will be mentioned later. Sulfur contents equivalent to 97–98% saturation are the largest achieved and these adducts will not cure adequately even in highly accelerated sulfur-vulcanization recipes. The 94–95% saturated adduct, based on sulfur content, can be vulcanized and appears to yield the most desirable balance of properties. The rate of cure in a standardized test recipe decreases rapidly as saturation level increases in the 90–95% range and this can be used as a relative measure of residual unsaturation. However, cure rate studies do not meet process control requirements for monitoring production where a figure that correlates with residual unsaturation is needed within a few minutes after a sample is obtained for analysis. Rather rapid refractive index and infrared absorption measurements are used for control but are not considered entirely satisfactory.

Infrared spectra studies also yielded information on the rates of adduction of the side vinyl and internal double bonds. The peak at 11.0 μ for the side vinyl decreases at a somewhat higher rate than the peak for internal unsaturation at 10.35 μ. For methyl mercaptan adducts of polybutadiene, the side vinyl absorption disappears at about 80% saturation level. For the isopropyl mercaptan adduct, as well as ethyl and higher molecular weight normal mercaptans, this peak disappears closer to the 50% saturation level.

The chemical properties of the adducts are, in general, the chemical properties of corresponding thioethers. However, sometimes these have peculiar results when they occur in polythioethers.

A great deal of our information on the chemistry of the adducts was generated in conjunction with basic research on reactions occurring with various curing systems; we were particularly seeking those reactions that would yield products having the most acceptable odor levels. A rather elaborate evaluation of odor-masking agents for rubber yielded many different and interesting odors, usually of a nature unsatisfactory to most people. Many potential odor-scavenging agents, of course, interfere with vulcanization systems. Epoxy resins appeared to be possible scavengers since they would react with malodorous products having reactive hydrogens. It was rather surprising to find that the addition of a few parts of almost any epoxy resin to a normal sulfur-curing recipe caused the mixture to cure on the mill or within a few hours at room temperature. Investigations soon established that only three ingredients (adduct rubber, organic acid, and epoxy resin) were necessary for the reaction. A simple representation of the reaction is given in reaction 6.

$$\underset{\text{Thioether}}{RSCH_3} + \underset{\text{Epoxide}}{R'\text{—}\overset{H}{\underset{\underset{O}{\diagdown\diagup}}{C}}\text{———}CH_2} + \underset{\text{Acid}}{R''COOH} \longrightarrow \underset{\text{Sulfonium salt}}{R\text{—}\overset{+}{\underset{\underset{CH_3}{|}}{S}}\text{—}\overset{H}{\underset{H}{C}}\text{—}\overset{H}{\underset{OH}{C}}\text{—}R' + R''CO\overline{O}} \qquad (6)$$

There are some reports in the literature (7) describing sulfonium salts of this type but they have always been made following a much more complicated procedure. At first glance, this may look like a new and exciting procedure for curing adduct because it can be carried out rapidly at room temperature. Either a difunctional epoxide or a difunctional acid forms crosslinks and also yields a stock with a relatively low odor. However, like all sulfonium salts, this one is low in stability and begins to decompose at temperatures as low as 100°C and generates malodorous products.

Another type of sulfonium salt that is much better known may be obtained by reacting an organic iodide with a thioether. One example is illustrated in Figure 2.

Under mild conditions and with approximately equivalent quantities of methyl iodide, enough of the sulfonium salt forms so that the adducts become water soluble. In nature, these are surface-active agents and the higher molecular weight polymers act as thickening agents. They are interesting laboratory curiosities but no commercial use has yet been found for them. Since a crosslink will be formed when a diiodide is used, this is another potential curing procedure. To our surprise, it didn't matter whether a monoiodide or a diiodide was used. Upon heating for a short

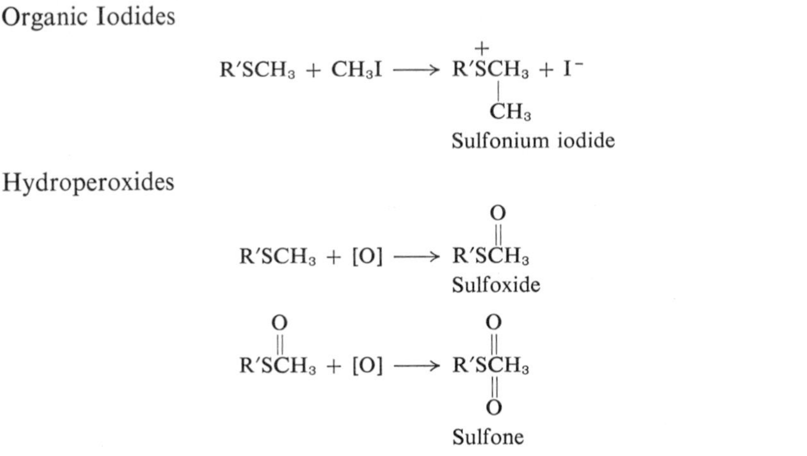

Organic Iodides

$$R'SCH_3 + CH_3I \longrightarrow R'\overset{+}{\underset{\underset{CH_3}{|}}{S}}CH_3 + I^-$$

Sulfonium iodide

Hydroperoxides

$$R'SCH_3 + [O] \longrightarrow R'\overset{O}{\overset{||}{S}}CH_3$$

Sulfoxide

$$R'\overset{O}{\overset{||}{S}}CH_3 + [O] \longrightarrow R'\underset{\underset{O}{||}}{\overset{\overset{O}{||}}{S}}CH_3$$

Sulfone

Fig. 2. Formation of a sulfonium salt by reaction of an organic iodide with a thioether.

period of time the mixture cured. In fact, the longer the mixture was heated the tighter became the cure. Here, again, the instability of the sulfonium salt has its effect; this should actually be considered an equilibrium-type situation. In the reverse reaction, when a dimethyl sulfide is split out, the iodide ion becomes attached to the polymer molecule, forming an organic iodide which, in turn, can react with some other thioether group to form a sulfonium salt. When the appropriate groups come together, a crosslink is formed. Since in this reaction the halide is continuously regenerated, crosslinks can continue to form until a true equilibrium is reached. However, some rather malodorous compounds are generated, so another potential curing system had to be eliminated.

To investigate the properties of sulfoxide and sulfone derivatives the methyl mercaptan adduct of emulsion polybutadiene was subjected to rather strong oxidizing treatment. When the adduct is swollen in appropriate solvents, hydrogen peroxide or organic hydroperoxides react to produce first the polysulfoxide and then the polysulfone. There is no clearcut sequential separation between these two steps: Before all the thioether groups have been converted to sulfoxides, there is significant sulfone formation. Complete conversion to sulfone is not easy because there is a tremendous change in solubility characteristics as the reaction proceeds. The original adduct is soluble in such solvents as benzene and carbon tetrachloride but at a high sulfoxide level the product becomes water soluble. In contrast, the sulfone is insoluble in most solvents except materials like dimethyl sulfoxide and dimethyl formamide. The poly-sulfoxide is elastomeric but, like the sulfonium salts, decomposes at quite low temperatures. The polysulfone is a "tough" plastic with quite high stability but all those we made had softening points around 75°C or less. It is an interesting polysulfone because it has a hydrocarbon backbone. This characteristic is quite different from the polysulfones made by the copolymerization of olefins and sulfur dioxide.

In the course of extensive research on by-products generated during cure which were associated with odor, a great deal of effort was directed toward analyzing the volatile products that could be obtained by heating cured stocks at both moderate and quite high temperatures. The products formed by heating low molecular weight thioether model compounds in simulated vulcanization recipes were also analyzed. This work was reported by Dr. Tewksbury at the Detroit (8) ACS Meeting in April 1965. Usually, if significant amounts of curing-type reactions occurred, malodorous materials formed. Normally some dimethyl polysulfides such as the di- and trisulfides could be detected.

If the preparation of the adduct proceeds by what is recognized as a normal reaction mechanism, it would contain the secondary thioether groups formed by reaction of the internal double bonds and the primary, pendant thioethers formed by reaction of the vinyl groups (Fig. 1) as well as residual internal double bonds. In a 95% saturated adduct there would be about four times as many secondary as primary thioethers, and there should be approximately 20 thioether groups for each double bond. No tertiary thioethers are expected unless there is a shifting of the double bonds or some attack that abstracts the tertiary hydrogen atom. These considerations led to a study of the stabilities, under vulcanization conditions, of primary, secondary, and tertiary methyl thioethers having structures similar to those that would be predicted as segmers in the adduct.

The three thioethers chosen for study are listed in the order of primary, secondary, and tertiary and illustrated here as structures I, II, and III. Under vulcanization conditions, the primary thioether was found to be significantly more stable than the secondary which, in turn, was more stable than the tertiary.

$$CH_3S—CH_2CH_2CH(CH_3)_2 \qquad CH_3S—\underset{\underset{CH_3}{|}}{C}HCH_2CH_2CH_3$$

$$(I) \qquad\qquad\qquad (II)$$

$$CH_3S—\underset{\underset{CH_3}{|}}{\overset{\overset{CH_3}{|}}{C}}—CH_2CH_3$$

$$(III)$$

A mechanism which seems to fit the observations made in this study is indicated in Figure 3. The combination of sulfur, zinc oxide, fatty acid, and accelerators as used in normal curing recipes promotes almost the equivalent of a reversal of the adduct reaction. This is believed to occur via an ionic mechanism instead of a free-radical mechanism, indicating that the mercaptide ion is formed and is probably stabilized as the zinc salt. By subsequent reactions, the methyl di- and trisulfides are formed. The addition of olefins to this mixture significantly decreases the amount of dimethyl polysulfide formation. In fact, the difference in odor can be readily observed. A similar reduction in odor can be obtained by the addition of olefins to the vulcanization recipe for adduct, but unfortunately, the adduct comes out undercured. All attempts to achieve adequate odor reduction in cured adduct by the addition of olefins were unsatisfactory.

Since the primary thioether was significantly more stable than the others, it seemed desirable to prepare an adduct having only primary thioethers by adding methyl mercaptan to 1,2-polybutadiene.

Though the 100% 1,2 polymer could not be found, Professor Morton of the University of Akron provided some polymer that was about 85% saturated. This reaction led to some interesting and unexpected results. A sulfur content equivalent to higher than about 50% saturation was never obtained. Infrared absorption spectra, however, indicated the adduct contained no residual double bonds. Further investigation showed that this was another way of preparing ladder polymers.

This would be quite an imperfect ladder polymer since the original polymer was composed of only 85% of 1,2 structure. Also, since the initiator or mercaptyl radicals would attack the polymer in random positions, even the original sequences of 1,2 structures would seldom have an opportunity to form a ladder their full length. The ratio of adduct to ladder

$$
\begin{array}{c}
CH_3 \\
| \\
CH_3S\!-\!CHCH_2CH_2CH_3 \xrightarrow{\ S_8,\ etc\ } \left\{ \begin{array}{l} CH_3CH\!=\!CHCH_2CH_3* \\ +\ CH_2\!=\!CHCH_2CH_2CH_3* \\ +\ CH_3\bar{S}\!: \end{array}\right.
\end{array}
$$

$$CH_3\bar{S}\!: +\ S_8 \longrightarrow CH_3S\!-\!S_7\!-\!\bar{S}\!:$$

$$CH_3S\!-\!S_7\!-\!\bar{S}\!: \longrightarrow (CH_3S\!-\!S_7\!-\!S\!-\!S_7\!-\!SCH_3) + S^{-2}$$
$$\downarrow$$
$$CH_3SSS\dot{C}H_3* + CH_3SSCH_3*$$

Fig. 3. Degradation of thioether by sulfur vulcanizing combination. Asterisk (*) indicates compounds found in reaction mixtures.

formation varied some with the amount of mercaptan charged but even at ten- to twentyfold excess of methyl mercaptan, ladder formation consumed about half the original double bonds.

This experience with the 1,2-polybutadiene offers a possible clue for the inability to achieve more than 97–98% saturation of emulsion polybutadiene as calculated from sulfur contents. Since the original polybutadiene contained about 20% 1,2 segmers, only a small portion would have to form the ladder structure to prevent achieving an apparent 100% saturation.

On the basis of a very promising balance of such properties as solvent resistance, aging, heat, ozone, and radiation resistance, adduct rubbers would appear to be excellent prospects for commercialization as low-cost rubbers. This has been the purpose of our program, but odorous compounds generated during cure have thwarted our attempts at commercialization.

References

1. R. M. Pierson, W. E. Gibbs, G. E. Meyer, F. J. Naples, W. M. Saltman, R. W. Schrock, L. B. Tewksbury, and G. S. Trick, *Rubber Plastics Age*, **38**, 592–599 and 708–721 (1957); shortened version of this paper appeared in *Rubber World*, **136**, 529–536 and 695–701 (1957) and *Rubber Chem. Technol.*, **31**, 213 (1958); G. E. Meyer, F. J. Naples, and H. M. Rice, *Rubber World*, **140**, 435 (1959).
2. J. Posner, *Ber.*, **38**, 646 (1905).
3. B. Holmberg, *Ber.*, **65**, 1349 (1932); *Rubber Chem. Technol.*, **6**, 71 (1933); **20**, 978 (1947); latter from *Arkiv Mintl. Geol.*, **23B**, 1 (1946).
4. G. E. Serniuk, U.S. Patent 2,589,151 (1952); G. E. Serniuk, F. W. Banes, and M. W. Swaney, *J. Am. Chem. Soc.*, **70**, 1804 (1948); M. W. Swaney and F. W. Banes, U.S. Patent 2,556,856 (1951).
5. C. F. Fryling, U.S. Patent 2,543,844 (1951).
6. M. A. Golub, *J. Polymer Sci.*, **25**, 373 (1957); *Rubber Chem. Technol.*, **30**, 1142 (1957).
7. N. F. Blau, J. W. Johnson, and C. G. Stuckwisch, *J. Am. Chem. Soc.*, **76**, 5106 (1954).
8. *Am. Chem. Soc. Div. Polymer Chem., Preprints*, **6** (No. 1), 132 (April 1965).

Polymerization of Cyclic Sulfides

J. K. STILLE and J. A. EMPEN

University of Iowa, Iowa City, Iowa

INTRODUCTION

The ring-opening polymerizations of cyclic ethers in the oxirane, oxetane, and tetrahydrofuran series have received wide attention. The mechanisms of these polymerizations have been investigated and the properties of the resulting linear aliphatic polyethers have been examined. However, comparatively little is known concerning the polymerization of the heterocyclic sulfur analogs or the properties of the corresponding polysulfides.

The lowest and most strained member of the cyclic sulfides, thiiranes, can polymerize by either cationic or anionic mechanisms. Cationic catalysts such as mineral acids (1), triethylaluminum (2), chlorocadmium mercaptide (3), and boron trifluoride have been employed, and an anionic catalyst, sodium ethoxide (4), is also effective. Thietanes, however, are reported to polymerize only in the presence of cationic catalysts (5–7). Thus, it appears that a cationic polymerization mechanism, which operates for both the thiirane and thietane series, involves an attack by the cyclic sulfide nucleophile on the α carbon of a sulfonium ion complex.

Propagation

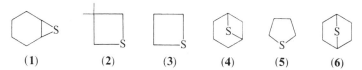

For this study, six cyclic sulfides (**1–6**) representing the thiirane, thietane, and tetrahydrothiophene series were employed. Additional ring strain was imposed in **4** and **6** by a bridge fused to thietane and tetrahydrothiophene.

(**1**)	(**2**)	(**3**)	(**4**)	(**5**)	(**6**)

DISCUSSION

Four different catalysts were employed for the polymerization of the cyclic sulfides. A catalyst formed from triethylaluminum, water, and epichlorohydrin (1:1:1) (8–10), phosphorus pentafluoride (11,12), boron trifluoride etherate (5,6)—both in solution and bulk, and trimethyloxonium fluoroborate (13) were surveyed. Although cyclohexene sulfide (1) (14), 3,3-dimethyl thietane (2) (15), thietane (3), and 6-thiabicyclo[3.1.1]heptane (4) (16) could be polymerized, none of these catalysts would polymerize the five-membered sulfur heterocycles, tetrahydrothiophene (5) and 7-thiabicyclo[2.2.1]heptane (6) (16) (Table 1). Monomers in the thiirane and thietane series could be converted to high molecular weight polymer and in high yield, with the exception of 6-thiabicyclo[3.1.1]heptane (4). This bridged thietane tends to give moderate to poor conversions to polymer—even though it should be more strained than thietane—possibly because attack at the tertiary α carbon in the sulfonium ion complex by a sulfide monomer is sterically hindered.

The primary factor in these polymerizations would appear to be ring strain. Tetrahydrofuran affords high molecular weight polyether in the presence of cationic catalysts, but neither tetrahydrothiophene nor 7-thiabicyclo[2.2.1]heptane would polymerize. The heats of polymerization of oxirane (22.6 kcal/mole) and oxetane (19.3 kcal/mole) are large, while the heat of polymerization of tetrahydrofuran (3.5 kcal/mole) is border-line for polymerization (17).

An insight into the differences in the ability to polymerize can be gained by a comparison of the strain energies of the cyclic monomers (Table 2) (18).

The calculated strain energy is a composite of angle strain, lone-pair interaction, hydrogen–hydrogen crowding, bond length and atom size as well as other factors relating to the geometry of the ring system. It can be seen that the strain energies for cyclic alkanes, cyclic ethers, and cyclic imines are nearly the same for ring systems of similar size. However, the cyclic sulfides all have considerably lower strain energy; this was postulated as being due in part to the large difference in the bond length of the C—S bond as compared with the other heterocycles listed in Table 2. The bond lengths between C—X (where X = C, O, N, or S) are as follows: C—C = 1.54 Å, C—O = 1.43 Å, C—N = 1.47 Å and C—S = 1.81 Å. The longer C—S bond tends to allow more normal carbon bond angles in the ring.

It is interesting to note that tetrahydropyran has not been polymerized. This isomer is known to exist in the stable chair form and has a very low strain energy (1.16). The strain energy of tetrahydrothiophene (1.97) is only slightly greater than that of tetrahydropyran. Although thermodynamic data have not been reported for the bicyclic isomers, it would seem reasonable to assume that 7-thiabicyclo[2.2.1]heptane has considerably less strain energy than 7-oxabicyclo[2.2.1]heptane.

The bulk polymerizations with boron fluoride were very rapid, and in

Table 1

Polymerization of Cyclic Sulfides[a]

Monomer	AlEt$_3$:H$_2$O:ECH[b]		PF$_5$[c]		BF$_3$[d]		BF$_3$ (bulk)		Me$_3$O$^+$BF$_4$$^-$ [e]	
	Conv., %	[η]	Conv., %	[η]	Conv., %	[η]	Conv., %	[η]	Conv., %	[η]
1. ⬡—S[f]	100	0.44	97	0.38	90	0.34	96	0.33	47	0.18
2. ⬜—S	55	0.35	55	0.54	80	0.29	70	0.76	55	0.31
3. ⬜—S[g]	53	0.30	67	0.37	67	0.23	63	0.64	41	0.09
4. ⬡—S	26	0.37	54	0.31	58	0.23	—[h]		20	—[h]

[a] Catalyst concentrations were 5 mole-% based on monomer. Methylene chloride, 5 ml/g of monomer, was employed in solution polymerizations. Inherent viscosities (dl/g) were carried out in chloroform at 25°C at concentrations of 0.2 g/100 ml.

[b] AlEt$_3$:H$_2$O:ECH (epichlorohydrin) 1:1:1, 25°C, 72 hr.

[c] −20°C, 24 hr followed by 25°C for 48 hr.

[d] 5 mole-% ECH cocatalyst, 25°C, 72 hr.

[e] Bulk polymerization, except for 4 which was dissolved in the minimum amount of nitromethane; 25°C, 120 hr.

[f] $K = 2.3 \times 10^{-4}$, $a = 0.85$ (CHCl$_3$);

[g] $K = 3.98 \times 10^{-4}$, $a = 0.75$ (CHCl$_3$).

[h] Not carried out.

Table 2

Strain Energy, kcal/mole

Ring size	Alkane	Ether	Sulfide	Imine
3	27.43	27.21	19.78	26.87
4	26.04	25.51	19.64	
5	6.05	5.63	1.97	5.80
6	−0.02	1.16	−0.27	−0.15

the case of cyclohexene sulfide, almost explosive. Trimethyloxonium tetrafluoroborate was employed as a polymerization catalyst since it is reported (13) to be a good source of methyl carbonium ion. The reaction of diethyl sulfide with triethyloxonium fluoroborate yields a tertiary sulfonium salt (17) and presumably the trimethyl analog would also provide a sulfonium ion with the cyclic sulfide monomers to initiate the polymerization. Initiation could also take place by hydride abstraction from the cyclic sulfide to form a sulfur-stabilized carbonium ion. A reaction of this stable carbonium ion with more cyclic sulfide would then give the necessary sulfonium ion (Scheme I).

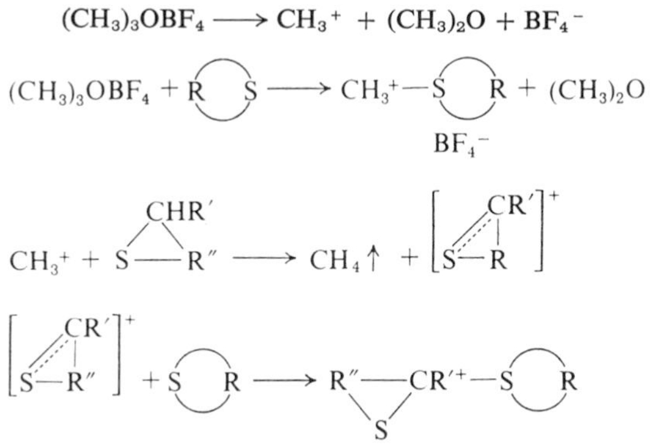
(CH3)3OBF4 ⟶ CH3+ + (CH3)2O + BF4−
(CH3)3OBF4 + R S ⟶ CH3+—S R + (CH3)2O
BF4−
CHR′
CH3+ + S—R″ ⟶ CH4↑ + [CR′ S—R]+
[CR′ S—R″]+ + S R ⟶ R″—CR′+—S R
S

Scheme 1

The glass transition (second-order transition) temperature of a number of polymers was obtained (Table 3). The −40 to −60° transition for linear polyethers has been attributed to movement of the —C—O—C— segments of the polymer chain (19). It seems likely, therefore, that the low-temperature transitions that were observed for sulfur polymers were also due to this motion.

It was observed from x-ray powder patterns that the sulfide polymers possessed some degree of crystallinity. A difference in the crystalline

Table 3

Transition Temperatures of Polysulfides

Polymer	T_g, °C			T_m, °C		
	AlEt$_3$:H$_2$O:ECH	PF$_5$	Me$_3$OBF$_4$	AlEt$_3$:H$_2$O:ECH	PF$_5$	Me$_3$OBF$_4$
	−43	−45	−47	130	86	85
	−53	−40	−55	117	140	102
$+(CH_2)_3S+$	−56	−51	−59	53	55	49
	−52	−58	−53	134	139	135

transition temperature, T_M, was noted for the polymers obtained from cyclohexene sulfide. An explanation of this observed difference is not readily available; however, it should be noted that this monomer could polymerize by both a *cis* and a *trans* addition to the cyclohexene ring. An increase in the ordered polymer segments would tend to lead to an increase in the melting point of the resulting polymer and the molecular weight of the polymer is another factor that could affect the melting transition. This difference was noted in the polymers obtained from 3,3-dimethyl thietane; the polymer with the highest molecular weight ($[\eta] = 0.54$) recorded in Table 1 had a somewhat higher melting transition than the analogs with lower molecular weights.

For a comparison of these transition temperatures with those of the corresponding polysulfones, samples of the polysulfides were converted to polysulfones by a peracid oxidation. Reaction of the polysulfides in formic acid with 30% hydrogen peroxide gave polysulfones which contained $>90\%$ sulfone units.

$$+R-S+ \xrightarrow[\text{HCOOH}]{\text{H}_2\text{O}_2} \begin{bmatrix} & \overset{\text{O}}{\underset{\text{O}}{\overset{\uparrow}{\underset{\downarrow}{S}}}} \\ R- & \end{bmatrix}$$

Both the glass and crystalline transition temperatures (Table 4) are high.

Table 4

Transition Temperatures of Polysulfones

Polymer	T_g, °C	T_m, °C (with decomposition)
[cyclohexane ring with SO₂]	128	284
$+CH_2-\underset{\underset{CH_3}{\mid}}{\overset{\overset{CH_3}{\mid}}{C}}-CH_2-SO_2+$	113	303
$+(CH_2)_3-SO_2+$	—	290
[cyclohexane ring with SO₂]	108	309

References

1. J. Lal, *The Chemistry of Cationic Polymerization*, P. H. Plesch, Ed., Macmillan, New York, 1963, p. 487.
2. R. Bacskai, *J. Polymer Sci. A*, **1**, 2777 (1963).
3. A. Noshay and C. C. Price, *J. Polymer Sci.*, **54**, 533 (1961).
4. C. S. Marvel and E. D. Weil, *J. Am. Chem. Soc.*, **76**, 61 (1959).
5. V. S. Foldi and W. Sweeney, *Makromol. Chem.*, **72**, 208 (1964).
6. G. L. Brode, *Am. Chem. Soc. Div. Polymer Chem., Preprints*, **6** (No. 2), 626 (1965).
7. J. K. Stille and J. A. Empen, *Am. Chem. Soc. Div. Polymer Chem., Preprints*, **6** (No. 2), 619 (1965).
8. T. Saegusa, H. Imai, and J. Furukawa, *Makromol. Chem.*, **65**, 60 (1963).
9. T. Saegusa, T. Uishima, H. Imai, and J. Furukawa, *Makromol. Chem.*, **79**, 201 (1965).
10. H. Imai, T. Saegusa, S. Ohsugi, and J. Furukawa, *Makromol. Chem.*, **81**, 119 (1965).
11. D. Sims, *J. Chem. Soc.*, **1964**, 864.
12. E. L. Wittbecker, H. K. Hall, and T. W. Campbell, *J. Am. Chem. Soc.*, **82**, 1218 (1960).
13. H. Meerwein, G. Hinz, P. Hoffman, E. Kroning, and E. Pfeil, *J. Prakt. Chem.*, **147**, 257 (1937).
14. E. E. van Tamelen, *Organic Syntheses*, Vol. IV, N. Rabjohn, Ed., Wiley, New York, 1963, p. 232.
15. S. Searles, H. R. Hayes, and E. F. Lutz, *J. Org. Chem.*, **27**, 2828 (1962).
16. S. F. Birch, R. A. Dean, and N. J. Hunter, *J. Org. Chem.*, **23**, 1026 (1958).
17. F. S. Dainton, K. J. Ivin, and D. A. G. Walmsley, *Trans. Faraday Soc.*, **56**, 1784 (1960).
18. A. S. Pell and G. Pilcher, *Trans. Faraday Soc.*, **61** (1), 71 (1965).
19. J. J. Stratta, E. P. Reding, and J. A. Faucher, *J. Polymer Sci. A*, **2**, 5017 (1964).

The Relationship of Thermal Stability and Molecular Structure in Sulfone Compounds and Polymers

G. L. BRODE

Union Carbide Corporation, Bound Brook, New Jersey

Homolytic bond cleavage appears to be one clearly established mechanism of decomposition in sulfone pyrolysis ($RSO_2R \rightarrow R\cdot + \cdot SO_2R$) (1,2). Other modes of sulfone decomposition, generally occurring at much lower temperatures, include: (*1*) base catalyzed (3) or unimolecular (4) heterolytic cleavage to sulfinate anion ($RSO_2^{\ominus}$) and (*2*) radical-induced decomposition, probably via hydrogen atom abstraction, from carbon alpha or beta to the sulfone group (5). A number of experimental observations on the stability, decomposition rate, and degradation products of various sulfone-containing compounds and polymers suggest that another mechanism by which sulfones may degrade is a cyclic, beta-elimination reaction.

$$
\underset{\underset{O}{\overset{\shortparallel}{|}}}{\overset{\overset{\textstyle H\cdots\cdots O}{\overset{|}{}\quad\overset{|}{}}}{RCHCH_2SR}} \xrightarrow{\Delta} RCH{=}CH_2 + HO\overset{\overset{\textstyle O}{\shortparallel}}{S}R \qquad (1)
$$

Beta-elimination is the major decomposition route of aliphatic mercaptans, with homolytic cleavage of the carbon–sulfur bond occurring at higher temperatures as a minor secondary reaction (6). Sulfoxides also exhibit a duality in decomposition mechanism, although homolytic bond cleavage apparently occurs to a larger extent than with mercaptans (7). Direct evidence for a beta-elimination mechanism in sulfone decomposition is lacking. Indirect evidence, stemming from unexpected low orders of thermal stability of certain sulfones (far below those calculated from bond dissociation energies), suggests that degradation may be proceeding by beta-elimination.

The classic example of thermal instability in sulfone materials is that exhibited by most olefin–SO_2 copolymers (8). Dainton and Ivin determined the ceiling temperatures of a large number of olefin–SO_2 copolymers (9), above which the polymers are thermodynamically unstable. It was also

133

demonstrated that at the ceiling temperature, reversal of the propagation reaction occurs (10–12).

$$\sim\!\!\sim\!\!\sim RSO_2\cdot + \text{olefin} \longrightarrow \sim\!\!\sim\!\!\sim RSO_2R'\cdot \qquad \text{(propagation)} \qquad (2)$$

$$\sim\!\!\sim\!\!\sim RSO_2R'\cdot + SO_2 \longrightarrow \sim\!\!\sim\!\!\sim RSO_2\cdot \qquad \text{(propagation)} \qquad (3)$$

In the absence of propagating radicals, or agents capable of producing propagating species, the thermal instability observed with olefin–SO_2 copolymers, and aliphatic sulfone materials in general, would appear to be related to something other than the ceiling temperature and a depropagation reaction.

Naylor and Anderson (13) were the first to suggest that olefin–SO_2 copolymers might also degrade by a beta-elimination reaction. The kinetics of decomposition of olefin–SO_2 copolymers studied by these workers (except for the case of butadiene) closely followed those of a first-order reaction for over 80% conversion, in a temperature range of 179–259°C. The first-order rate constants paralleled the number of beta-hydrogen atoms in the copolymer, although the decomposition rate, corrected for the number of beta-hydrogens, is not a constant as shown with the polymers from SO_2 and, respectively, ethylene, propylene, butene-2, and isobutene (Table 1). Furthermore, a "precipitous" drop in intrinsic viscosity

Table 1

Rates of Decomposition of Olefin–SO_2 Copolymers (13)

Copolymer structure[a]	k (first order)	β-Hydrogens
$-CH_2CH_2SO_2CH_2CH_2SO_2-$	2.7×10^{-4}	4
$\begin{matrix} CH_3 & CH_3 \\ \mid & \mid \\ -CH_2CHSO_2CH_2CHSO_2- \end{matrix}$	3.0×10^{-3}	6
$\begin{matrix} CH_3\ CH_3 & CH_3\ CH_3 \\ \mid\ \ \mid & \mid\ \ \mid \\ -CH-CHSO_2CH- & CH-SO_2- \end{matrix}$	2.6×10^{-2}	8
$\begin{matrix} CH_3 & CH_3 \\ \mid & \mid \\ -C-CH_2SO_2C-CH_2SO_2- \\ \mid & \mid \\ CH_3 & CH_3 \end{matrix}$	1.8×10^{-2}	8

[a] C. S. Marvel and E. D. Weil, *J. Am. Chem. Soc.*, **76**, 61 (1954), published evidence for a head-to-tail structure in propylene-SO_2 copolymers, reversing the previously held position of a head-to-head structure in this and other unsymmetrical olefin–SO_2 copolymers.

was observed at very low weight loss, indicating random cleavage. The presence of weak links (e.g., sulfinic ester) in the polymer chains can be excluded with a fair amount of certainty since preparation of copolymers under widely different conditions failed to show any differences in activation energy of the degradation (13). Dainton and Ivin (14) also observed a significant drop in specific viscosity, without any appreciable loss in weight, when the copolymer from butene-1 and SO_2 was heated alone or in solution at temperatures as low as 70°C. At 130°C, a temperature at which butylsulfinic acid also decomposes, low molecular weight sulfur compounds were reported with odors resembling those of sulfinic acids. Certainly at 70°C, and probably much higher temperatures as well, homolytic cleavage cannot be the explanation for the random degradation observed, and depolymerization by reversal of the propagation step seems doubtful.

Recently Gipstein, Wellisch, and Sweeting (15) studied the relationship of the number of beta-hydrogens to thermal stability in model sulfone compounds (Table 2) and concluded that the absence of beta-hydrogens and their substitution by stabilizing groups, long methylene chains or alicyclic rings, enhances the thermal stability of sulfones. The thermal stability of several sulfone compounds, with roughly the same carbon–sulfur bond dissociation energy, did appear to be a function of the number of beta-hydrogen atoms in the molecule. Two important exceptions were noted, however; dibutyl and didodecyl sulfone were considerably more stable than compounds with fewer beta-hydrogens. Unfortunately, the thermal

Table 2
Thermal Stability of Sulfone Compounds (15)

Sulfone compound	β-Hydrogens	Mole % de-comp. at 275°C after 1 hr
1. $CH_3SO_2CH_3$	0	0.03
2. $CH_3\overset{\underset{\textstyle CH_3}{\mid}}{C}HCH_2SO_2\phi$	1	1.2
3. $CH_3\overset{\underset{\textstyle CH_3}{\mid}}{C}HCH_2SO_2CH_2\overset{\underset{\textstyle CH_3}{\mid}}{C}HCH_3$	2	3.1
4. $CH_3CH_2CH_2CH_2SO_2CH_2CH_2CH_2CH_3$	4	0.7
5. $CH_3\overset{\underset{\textstyle CH_3}{\mid}}{C}HSO_2\phi$	6	2.8
6. $CH_3\overset{\underset{\textstyle CH_3}{\mid}}{C}HSO_2\overset{\underset{\textstyle CH_3}{\mid}}{C}HCH_3$	12	4.5

stability of bis-*n*-propylsulfone or bis-neopentyl sulfone was not studied. The apparent discrepancy in thermal stability between compounds 3 and 5 may be due to the electron-withdrawing effects of the benzene ring in compound 5. Therefore, a more realistic comparison would be that of compound 2 with compound 5, and compounds 3 and 6. Wellisch et al. (15) ascribed the greater stability of dibutyl and didodecyl sulfone to the shielding effect of a long methylene chain. Whether the analogy with the increased stability of long-chain alkyl sulfones in base-catalyzed beta-elimination reactions (16) is valid, is questionable.

A cyclic decomposition mechanism was also proposed by Drews, Fields, and Meyerson (17) to explain the products, and relatively facile rearrangement, that occurred on pyrolysis of *ortho*-methyl-substituted aromatic sulfones. Both dimesityl sulfone and *o*-tolyl phenyl sulfone rearranged to diaryl methanes on heating at ~400°C; di-*p*-tolyl sulfone, after a considerably longer heating period, gave only about one percent coupled product, the major products being heavier sulfones and hydrocarbons resulting, apparently, from free-radical intermediates. The presence of an *ortho*-methyl group facilitates decomposition, possibly by providing a path for a cyclic elimination reaction (eq. 6).

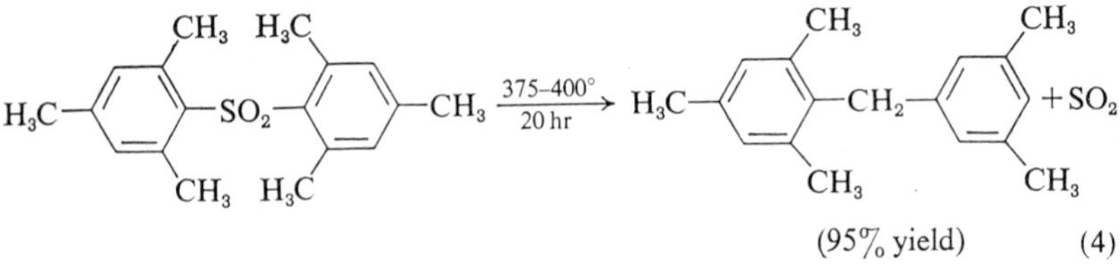

(95% yield)   (4)

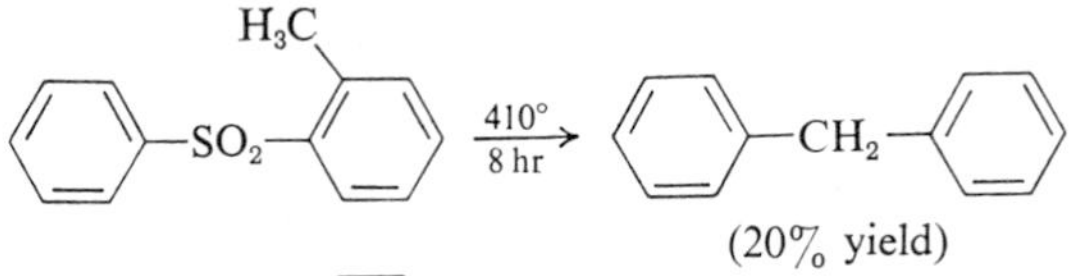

(20% yield)

(5)

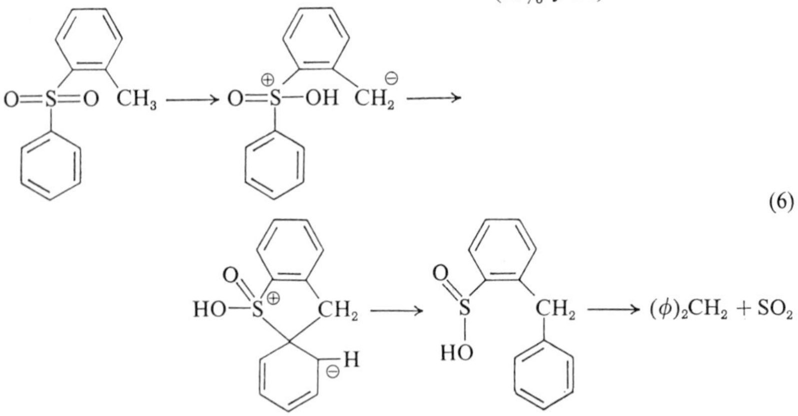

(6)

$(\phi)_2CH_2 + SO_2$

Recent studies by Johnson et al. and Hale et al. (18,19) (Table 3) on aromatic sulfone polymers and model compounds point up the high order of thermal stability in systems devoid of *ortho*-substituted methyl groups, and are in accord with the reported high thermal stability of diphenyl and di-*p*-tolyl sulfone (20,21).

Table 3

Thermal Stability of Some Aromatic Sulfones (18,19)

Compound (ref. 19)	Wt. loss, %	Hours at 400°C
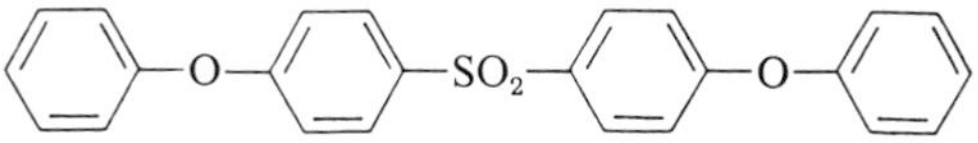 phenyl–O–phenyl–SO$_2$–phenyl–O–phenyl	0.19 (N$_2$) / 4.04 (air)	5 / 5
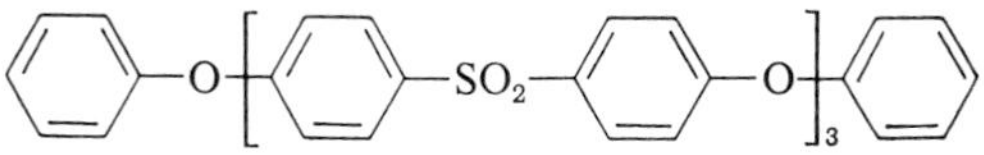 phenyl–O–[phenyl–SO$_2$–phenyl–O]$_3$–phenyl	0.2 (N$_2$)	5
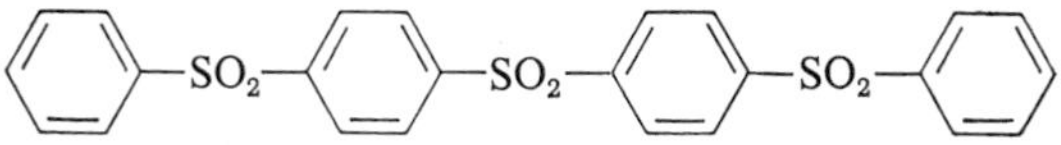 phenyl–SO$_2$–phenyl–SO$_2$–phenyl–SO$_2$–phenyl	5.1 (N$_2$)	5

The possibility of a beta-elimination reaction in sulfide or sulfone degradation prompted the author to prepare sulfur systems with high carbon–sulfur bond dissociation energies and no beta-hydrogen atoms. The bond dissociation energy is in part determined by the stability of radicals generated on homolytic cleavage in both sulfones (1,22–24) and sulfides (25,26). Dimethyl sulfone, for example, exhibits much greater stability than benzyl or allyl sulfone, and recently Truce and Norell (27) reported that while 2-phenyl-3,3-diethoxythietane-1,1-dioxide (1) decomposed on attempted distillation, 3,3-diethoxythietane-1,1-dioxide (2) passed unchanged through a gas chromatograph at 200°C, and pyrolysis at 300°C resulted in total recovery of the sulfone.

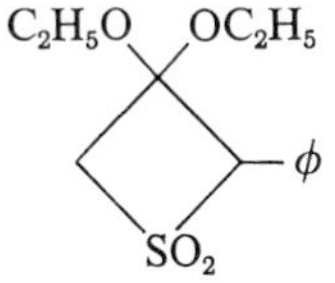

$$C_2H_5O \quad OC_2H_5$$

(1)
(thermally unstable)

$$C_2H_5O \quad OCH_2H_5$$

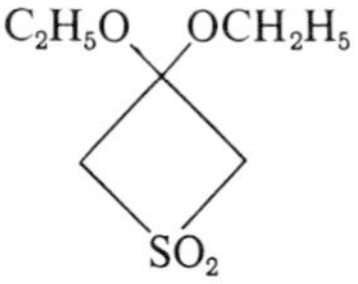

(2)
(thermally stable)

The thermal stability of neopentyl sulfide or sulfone systems had apparently not been studied, but the carbon–sulfur bond energy would be expected to be high. Furthermore, the neopentyl system is devoid of beta-hydrogens and shows no tendency for rearrangement under nonacidic conditions (28,30). Therefore, sulfide and sulfone compounds and polymers based on the neopentyl and related structures were synthesized and evaluated in this laboratory (31,32). The work can most conveniently be divided into two parts, condensation polymers and addition polymers.

CONDENSATION POLYMERS

Condensation polymers were synthesized from bis(hydroxyneopentyl) sulfide (3) and sulfone (4) (31) and their derivatives. The sulfide and sulfone diols were prepared as shown in equation 7 and rigorously purified; hydroxyneopentyl mercaptan and bis(hydroxyneopentyl) disulfide, characterized impurities in the sulfide diol (3), were thus removed. Both the sulfide diol (3) and the sulfone diol (4), as well as the acetoxy derivative of bis(hydroxyneopentyl) disulfide, could be distilled without apparent decomposition, the sulfone diol having a boiling point of 210°C/0.05 mm. Furthermore, bis(acetoxyneopentyl) sulfone was recovered, essentially in quantitative yield, from attempted transesterification reactions which

$$BrCH_2CCH_2OH \xrightarrow{NaHS} \left[HOCH_2CCH_2 \right]_2 S \xrightarrow[\substack{2.\ H_2O_2 \\ 3.\ CH_3OH\text{—}HCl}]{1.\ \left(CH_3C\right)_2 O} \left[HOCH_2CCH_2 \right]_2 SO_2 \qquad (7)$$

$$\text{(3)} \qquad\qquad\qquad \text{(4)}$$

involved a 16 hr heating period at 200°C, followed by 1 hr each at 250°C and 275°C. By comparison, Searles reported $(HOCH_2CH_2CH_2)_2$—S to be a nondistillable oil (33).

The enhanced thermal stability of the neopentyl-based sulfide and sulfone monomers (3, 4, and derivatives) was also observed in their respective polymer systems. Table 4 summarizes the heating cycles, yields, etc., of several polycondensation reactions; there was no noticeable degradation. In Table 5, thermogravimetric–molecular weight analyses of terephthalate polymers from bis(hydroxyneopentyl) sulfone are recorded. As can be seen from this data, both polymers exhibit excellent thermal stability at 250–260°C. No olefin or sulfur dioxide by-product could be detected in either experiment and in neither case was a reduction in molecular weight observed. The slight increase in molecular weight suggests the small weight loss was due either to entrapped solvent from polymer recovery, or from removal of by-product from further polymerization. Both polymers had been dissolved and precipitated by coagulation prior to thermogravimetric analysis.

Table 4

Condensation Polymers Based on the Neopentyl Sulfide and Sulfone System

No.	Polymer structure $R = CH_2C(CH_3)_2CH_2$	Reactants $R = CH_2C(CH_3)_2CH_2$	Heating cycle °C	Time, hr	Yield and reduced viscosity[a]
I	$+[ORSO_2ROCN\text{–}\underset{}{\bigcirc}\text{–}NC=O]+$	$(\phi OCOR)_2SO_2 + HN\text{–}\underset{}{\bigcirc}\text{–}NH$	→ 250° 270° 280°/0.08 mm	0.5 2.0 0.5	Quant. 0.32(m-cresol)
II	$+[ORSO_2ROCN\text{–}\underset{CH_3}{\overset{H_3C}{\bigcirc}}\text{–}NC=O]+$	$(\phi OCOR)_2SO_2 + HN\text{–}\underset{CH_3}{\overset{CH_3}{\bigcirc}}\text{–}NH$	→ 245° 255°/0.08 mm	1.0 1.25	Quant. 0.34(CHCl$_3$)
III	$[(+[ORSO_2ROC\phi C]_{0.67}\text{–}[OCH_2CH_2OC\phi C]_{0.33})]$	$(HOR)_2SO_2 + D.M.T. + HOCH_2CH_2OH$	190° 250° 275°/0.08 mm	7 1 2.5	— 1.08(ϕOH-TCE)
IV	$+[ORSROCN\text{–}\underset{CH_3}{\overset{CH_3}{\bigcirc}}\text{–}NC=O]+$	$(\phi OCOR)_2S + HN\text{–}\underset{CH_3}{\overset{CH_3}{\bigcirc}}\text{–}NH$	Identical to I		Quant. 0.24(CHCl$_3$)

[a] Reduced viscosity equals $(t - t_0)/t_0C$, where t is the efflux time required for a specified volume of polymer solution to flow through a capillary tube and t_0 is the efflux time of the solvent through the same capillary. The concentration employed was 0.2 g/100 ml.

Table 5

Thermal Stability of Terephthalate Polymers from
Bis(hydroxyneopentyl) Sulfone

(Conditions: 155–255°C/45 min; 255–260°C/3 hr; N$_2$ atmos.)

Structure (R = CH$_2$C(CH$_3$)$_2$CH$_2$)	Reduced viscosity		Wt. loss, %
	Initial	Final	
$\left(ORSO_2ROC\phi C\right)_{0.8}\left(OCH_2CH_2OC\phi C\right)_{0.2}$	0.46	0.49	2.6
$\left(ORSO_2ROC\phi C\right)$	0.22	0.27	3.5

The thermal stability apparently conveyed by the neopentyl structure to the sulfide and sulfone condensation polymers prompted efforts to prepare poly(neopentylene sulfide) and sulfone, neopentyl systems with the highest possible sulfur content. The classical reaction of a dimercaptan with a dibromide (34) produced only low molecular weight polymer when neopentylene dimercaptan and neopentylene dibromide were reacted under a host of different conditions. Therefore, the cationic polymerization of thietanes, with subsequent oxidation to polysulfones, was studied as an alternative route to these two classes of polymers.

ADDITION POLYMERS

A number of 3,3-substituted thietanes were prepared by reacting the corresponding cyclic carbonate with potassium thiocyanate, as described by Searles (35). These four-membered cyclic thioethers (**5**) could be easily polymerized at ambient temperature with any of several Lewis acid catalysts, including PF$_5$, BF$_3$·(C$_2$H$_5$)$_2$O, NbF$_5$ or TaF$_5$ (31); polymerization was not effected by dibutylzinc or potassium *tert*-butoxide. The polymers (**6**) from 3,3-dimethyl thiacyclobutane (R=R′=CH$_3$), or 3-ethyl-3-methyl thiacyclobutane (R=CH$_3$, R′=C$_2$H$_5$) were water-white elastomers with glass transition temperatures around −50°C. Depending on reaction

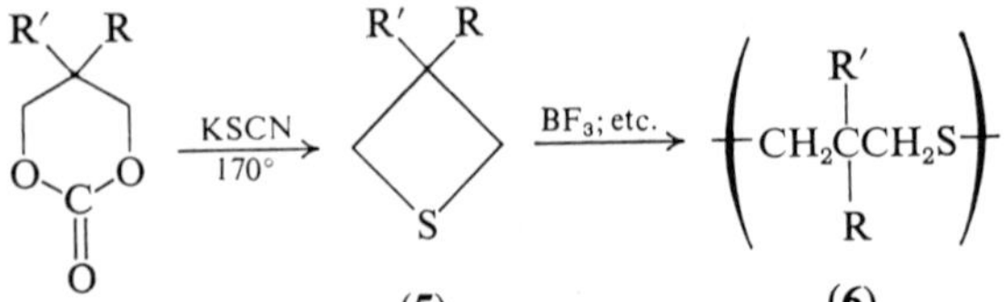

(**5**)　(**6**)

conditions, viscous syrups through tough, elastomeric products, were obtained. The fact that low molecular weight oligomers were not found, plus the apparent independence of molecular weight on yield, indicates the polymerization is analogous to an addition, rather than stepwise, polymerization. At the time this work was carried out, no report on the cationic polymerization of thietanes had appeared in the literature, except for an obscure statement that trimethylene sulfide yielded a viscous liquid when treated with strong acid (36); recently, Foldi and Sweeny also described thietane polymerizations and oxidation of the resulting polysulfides (37). Prior to oxidation and thermal stability studies in this laboratory, the polysulfides were carefully characterized. Nuclear magnetic resonance analysis of poly(neopentylene sulfide), poly(2-ethyl-2-methyl propylene sulfide), and the corresponding sulfone oxidation products (see Table 6) showed no evidence of molecular rearrangement, and it was concluded that the polymers were, conservatively, at least 98% unrearranged; end groups could not be determined.

The polysulfones in Table 6 were prepared from the corresponding polysulfides by oxidation with 30% hydrogen peroxide in formic acid, according to the method of Noether (38). Both polymers precipitated as formed, and at least in the case of poly(2-ethyl-2-methyl propylene sulfone), some degradation accompanied the oxidation. By differential thermal analysis, poly(neopentylene sulfone) was found to have an apparent glass transition temperature of $\sim 104°C$ and a crystalline melting point of 290°C (Foldi and Sweeny report 266°C (37)). Poly(2-ethyl-2-methyl propylene sulfone) melted at 280°C. Both polysulfones were found to be extremely insoluble, and purification as in the case of the condensation polymers was prevented. Elemental analyses were, however, in excellent agreement with theory. The thermal stability of poly(neopentylene sulfone) and poly(2-ethyl-2-methyl propylene sulfone), as prepared above, was not sufficiently good at 280–290°C to allow fabrication. Foldi and Sweeny report (37) that all of the 2,2-dialkyltrimethylene sulfones investigated by them showed poor stability above 250°C. Poly(neopentylene sulfone), studied in greatest detail by these workers, reportedly evolved sulfur dioxide and 2-methyl butadiene at 266°C, while at 240°C a weight loss of 1.4% per hour was observed. This low order of thermal stability is surprising though not nearly as puzzling as the by-products of decomposition reported.

Considering the rather good thermal stability of condensation polymers based on bis(hydroxyneopentyl sulfone), etc., and the difficulties encountered in rigorously purifying the poly(2,2-dialkyl propylene sulfones), bisneopentyl 2,2-dimethylpropyl-1,3-disulfone (8) was prepared to further probe the inherent stability of this class of polysulfones.

Table 6

Chemical Shift Values of Poly(neopentylene sulfide),
Sulfone and Related Materials[a]

Structure	Chemical shift, cps			
	a	b	c	d
$\left(\!\!\begin{array}{c} \text{CH}_3 \\ {}^{(b)}| \\ \text{CH}_2\text{CCH}_2\text{S} \\ | \\ \text{CH}_3 \\ {}_{(a)} \end{array}\!\!\right)$	62	155		
$\left(\!\!\begin{array}{c} {}^{(b)} \\ \text{CH}_3 \\ | \\ \text{CH}_2\text{CCH}_2\text{S} \\ {}_{(d)}| \\ \text{CH}_2\text{CH}_3 \\ {}_{(c)}\;{}_{(a)} \end{array}\!\!\right)$	50	59	86	154
$\left(\!\!\begin{array}{c} \text{CH}_3 \\ {}^{(b)}| \\ \text{CH}_2\text{CCH}_2\text{SO}_2 \\ | \\ \text{CH}_3 \\ {}_{(a)} \end{array}\!\!\right)$	93	224		
$\left(\!\!\begin{array}{c} {}^{(b)} \\ \text{CH}_3 \\ {}^{(d)}| \\ \text{CH}_2\text{CCH}_2\text{SO}_2 \\ | \\ \text{CH}_2\text{CH}_3 \\ {}_{(c)}\;{}_{(a)} \end{array}\!\!\right)$	63	90	114	226
$\left(\!\!\begin{array}{c} \text{CH}_3 \\ {}^{(c)}|\;{}^{(b)} \\ \text{HOCH}_2\text{CCH}_2 \\ | \\ \text{CH}_3 \\ {}_{(a)} \end{array}\!\!\right)_{\!2}\!\!\text{S}$	57	154	204	
$\left[\begin{array}{c} \text{O} \quad\;\; \text{CH}_3 \\ \| \quad\;\; | \\ \text{CH}_3\text{COCH}_2\text{CCH}_2\text{S} \\ {}_{(b)}\quad{}_{(d)}|\;{}_{(c)} \\ \text{CH}_3 \\ {}_{(a)} \end{array}\right]_{\!2}$	61	123	172	233

[a] The spectra were obtained at 60 Mc using a Varian A-60 spectrometer. The chemical shifts reported are in cycles per second, downfield from tetramethyl silane. The sulfide spectra were taken in deuterochloroform; the sulfone spectra in trifluoroacetic acid.

$$\text{KSCH}_2\overset{\overset{\text{CH}_3}{|}}{\underset{\underset{\text{CH}_3}{|}}{\text{C}}}\text{CH}_2\text{SK} + 2\text{ClCH}_2\overset{\overset{\text{CH}_3}{|}}{\underset{\underset{\text{CH}_3}{|}}{\text{C}}}\text{CH}_3 \xrightarrow[95\text{C}°]{\text{DMSO}} \text{CH}_3\overset{\overset{\text{CH}_3}{|}}{\underset{\underset{\text{CH}_3}{|}}{\text{C}}}\text{CH}_2\text{SCH}_2\overset{\overset{\text{CH}_3}{|}}{\underset{\underset{\text{CH}_3}{|}}{\text{C}}}\text{CH}_2\text{SCH}_2\overset{\overset{\text{CH}_3}{|}}{\underset{\underset{\text{CH}_3}{|}}{\text{C}}}\text{CH}_3 \quad (9)$$

(7)

$$\text{VII} + \text{H}_2\text{O}_2 \xrightarrow{\text{HAc}} \text{CH}_3\overset{\overset{\text{CH}_3}{|}}{\underset{\underset{\text{CH}_3}{|}}{\text{C}}}\text{CH}_2\text{SO}_2\text{CH}_2\overset{\overset{\text{CH}_3}{|}}{\underset{\underset{\text{CH}_3}{|}}{\text{C}}}\text{CH}_2\text{SO}_2\text{CH}_2\overset{\overset{\text{CH}_3}{|}}{\underset{\underset{\text{CH}_3}{|}}{\text{C}}}\text{CH}_3 \quad (10)$$

(8)

Table 7 summarizes the results of the thermal stability studies and indicates that the 1,3-neopentyl disulfone structure is stable to at least 260–270°C. The corresponding 1,3-disulfide developed a yellow color on similar treatment, but again showed no loss in weight.

Table 7

Thermal Stability 1,3-Neopentylene Disulfone and Disulfide
(Heating cycle: → 260°C/30 min; 260–270°C/1 hr; N$_2$ purge)

Structure	Wt. loss, %	Final state
$\text{CH}_3\overset{\overset{\text{CH}_3}{|}}{\underset{\underset{\text{CH}_3}{|}}{\text{C}}}\text{CH}_2\text{SO}_2\text{CH}_2\overset{\overset{\text{CH}_3}{|}}{\underset{\underset{\text{CH}_3}{|}}{\text{C}}}\text{CH}_2\text{SO}_2\text{CH}_2\overset{\overset{\text{CH}_3}{|}}{\underset{\underset{\text{CH}_3}{|}}{\text{C}}}\text{CH}_3$ (mp, 125–126°C)	0.01	mp = 125.5–126.5°C
$\text{CH}_3\overset{\overset{\text{CH}_3}{|}}{\underset{\underset{\text{CH}_3}{|}}{\text{C}}}\text{CH}_2\text{SCH}_2\overset{\overset{\text{CH}_3}{|}}{\underset{\underset{\text{CH}_3}{|}}{\text{C}}}\text{CH}_2\text{SCH}_2\overset{\overset{\text{CH}_3}{|}}{\underset{\underset{\text{CH}_3}{|}}{\text{C}}}\text{CH}_3$	0.00	Yellow

Whether a beta-elimination reaction is in fact a mechanism of sulfide and sulfone decomposition, in systems with a high carbon–sulfur bond dissociation energy, is still uncertain, although the enhanced thermal stability of neopentyl-based sulfides and sulfones is in accord with such a mechanism. The effectiveness of the beta-*gem*-dimethyl and related groups in retarding a base-catalyzed beta-elimination reaction is clearly demonstrated, however, by virtue of the ability to obtain condensation polymers of the type listed in Table 4, under the prescribed conditions. In addition, unlike sulfur systems with beta-hydrogen atoms, neopentyl-type systems would also be expected to be more stable to radical-induced decomposition.

References

1. W. K. Busfield and K. J. Ivin, *Trans. Faraday Soc.*, **57**, 1044 (1961).
2. W. K. Busfield, K. J. Ivin, H. Mackle, and P. A. G. O'Hare, *Trans Faraday Soc.*, **57**, 1064 (1961).
3. G. W. Fenton and C. K. Ingold, *J. Chem. Soc.*, **1928**, 3127.
4. J. L. Kice, in *The Chemistry of Organic Sulfur Compounds*, Vol. II, N. Kharasch and C. Meyers, Eds., Pergamon Press, New York, 1966, Chap. 5.
5. C. S. Marvel and W. H. Sharkey, *J. Org. Chem.*, **9**, 113 (1944).
6. A. H. Sehon and B. De B. Darwent, *J. Am. Chem. Soc.*, **76**, 4806 (1954).
7. C. A. Kingsbury and D. J. Cram, *J. Am. Chem. Soc.*, **82**, 1810 (1960).
8. E. M. Fettes and F. O. Davis, in *Polyethers*, Part 3 (High Polymers Ser., Vol. 13), N. G. Gaylord, Ed., Wiley, New York, 1962, Chap. 15.
9. R. E. Cook, F. S. Dainton, and K. J. Ivin, *J. Polymer Sci.*, **26**, 351 (1957).
10. F. S. Dainton and K. J. Ivin, *Nature*, **162**, 705 (1948).
11. F. S. Dainton and K. J. Ivin, *Trans. Faraday Soc.*, **46**, 331 (1950).
12. F. S. Dainton and K. J. Ivin, *Proc. Roy. Soc. (London), Ser. A*, **212**, 96 (1952).
13. M. A. Naylor and A. W. Anderson, *J. Am. Chem. Soc.*, **76**, 3962 (1954).
14. F. S. Dainton and K. J. Ivin, *Proc. Roy. Soc. (London), Ser. A*, **212**, 207 (1952).
15. E. Gipstein, E. Wellisch, and O. J. Sweeting, *J. Org. Chem.*, **29**, 207 (1964).
16. G. W. Fenton and C. K. Ingold, *J. Chem. Soc.*, **1930**, 705.
17. H. Drews, E. K. Fields, and S. Meyerson, *Chem. Ind. (London)*, **1961**, 1403.
18. R. N. Johnson, A. G. Farnham, R. A. Clendenning, W. F. Hale, and C. N. Merriam, *J. Polymer Sci.*, *A-1*, **5**, 2375 (1967).
19. W. F. Hale, A. G. Farnham, R. N. Johnson, and R. A. Clendenning, *J. Polymer Sci.*, *A-1*, **5**, 2399 (1967).
20. J. M. Crafts, *Ber.*, **20**, 712 (1887).
21. R. Otto, *Ber.*, **12**, 1177 (1879).
22. M. P. Cava and A. A. Drana, *J. Am. Chem. Soc.*, **81**, 4266 (1959).
23. E. C. Leonard, *J. Org. Chem.*, **27**, 1921 (1962).
24. E. M. La Combe and B. Stewart, *J. Am. Chem. Soc.*, **83**, 3457 (1961).
25. W. Pryor, *Mechanisms of Sulfur Reactions*, McGraw-Hill, New York, 1962.
26. E. S. Huyser and J. D. Taliaferro, *J. Org. Chem.*, **28**, 1676 (1963).
27. W. E. Truce and J. R. Norell, *J. Am. Chem. Soc.*, **85**, 3236 (1963).
28. W. H. Urry and N. Nicolaides, *Am. Chem. Soc.*, *118th Meeting, Sept. 1950, Abstract of Papers.*
29. C. G. Overberger and M. B. Berenbaum, *J. Am. Chem. Soc.*, **74**, 3293 (1952).
30. F. H. Senbold, *J. Am. Chem. Soc.*, **76**, 3732 (1954).
31. G. L. Brode, *Symp. Polymerization Cyclic Ethers*, Am. Chem. Soc., Div. Polymer Chem., September, 1965. *Polymer Preprints*, **6**, No. 2, 626 (1965).
32. G. L. Brode, Paper presented at the Princeton Conference on Sulfur Chemistry, Princeton University, July, 1966.
33. S. Searles, *J. Am. Chem. Soc.*, **73**, 4515 (1951).
34. C. S. Marvel and A. Kotch, *J. Am. Chem. Soc.*, **73**, 481 (1951).
35. S. Searles, H. R. Hayes, and E. F. Lutz, *J. Org. Chem.*, **28**, 93 (1962).
36. R. W. Bost and M. W. Conn, *Ind. Eng. Chem.*, **25**, 526 (1933).
37. V. S. Foldi and W. Sweeny, *Makromol. Chem.*, **72**, 208 (1964).
38. H. D. Noether, U.S. Pat. 2,534,366 (1950).

Some New Monosulfide Polymers

R. H. GOBRAN, M. B. BERENBAUM, and
S. W. OSBORN

Thiokol Chemical Corporation, Trenton, New Jersey

INTRODUCTION

Historically, interest in sulfur-containing polymers has centered primarily on polysulfide elastomers and on polysulfide vulcanizates of the various types of rubber. Monosulfide polymers, by contrast, have received relatively little attention. Although descriptions of ethylene monosulfide condensation polymers have been in the literature for over a century, chemical instability, combined with low molecular weight, served to limit the utility of the early monosulfide polymers. Within the past several years many of the problems associated with these polymers have begun to be overcome. New synthetic techniques have emerged and the potential usefulness of some of the monosulfide polymers has become apparent. A number of review articles (1–5) dealing with monosulfide polymers and the materials for their preparation have been published recently.

In this paper the synthetic methods for making monosulfide polymers, and the properties of these polymers, are considered with particular emphasis on high molecular weight poly(ethylene sulfide) thermoplastic polymers and poly(1,2-propylene sulfide) elastomers.

METHODS OF SYNTHESIS OF MONOSULFIDE POLYMERS

Monosulfide polymers can be prepared by polycondensation, polyaddition, or ring opening polymerization reactions. The first two methods lead to polymers of relatively low molecular weight, whereas ring opening reactions can lead to high molecular weight materials under particular circumstances which will be described. We will consider the synthetic procedures in order.

Polycondensation Methods

Historically the earliest preparations of monosulfide polymers were the result of polycondensations of divalent metal sulfides or bis-mercaptides with alkyl or aryl dihalides. Both the alkylene monosulfides and the arylene monosulfides were first prepared via this route. Where polycondensation was the only method of synthesis available, additional chain extension processes have been required to prepare useful materials, and for some systems, particularly in the case of phenylene sulfides, chain extension procedures have been developed.

The earliest monosulfide polymer, that of ethylene sulfide, was prepared in 1839 by Loewig and Weidmann (6), and the polymeric products were studied further by Crafts (7) and by Meyer (8) in the latter part of the 19th century. These workers employed the condensation of an ethylene dihalide with an alkali metal sulfide or with an ethylenebis mercaptide.

$$Br—CH_2—CH_2—Br + K_2S \longrightarrow —[C_2H_4S]—_n \qquad (1)$$
$$\text{m.p. } 113–160°$$

The condensation polymers were of very low molecular weights as indicated by their melting points, and they were thermally unstable. When unreacted halogens or acid catalysts were present the polymers decomposed almost quantitatively into 1,4-dithiane.

The acid catalyzed polycondensation of certain mercaptoalcohols represents a second method of synthesis (9–11). The utility of this reaction depends upon the enhanced reactivity of a thiol group located either α or β to a hydroxyl group. Thus:

$$nHO—CH_2—CH_2—SH \xrightarrow{H^+} —[CH_2—CH_2—S]—_n + nH_2O \qquad (2)$$

The polycondensation polymers of ethylene sulfide have been reviewed in detail elsewhere (1) and will not be discussed in this report.

Methylene sulfide polymers prepared by either base- or acid-catalyzed polycondensations have been described (11,12). In these processes aqueous formaldehyde and H_2S are reacted to form a mixture of hydroxymethylene thiols:

$$H_2S + nCH_2{=}O \longrightarrow HO—[CH_2—S]—_nH + nH_2O \qquad (n = 1 \text{ or more}) \quad (3)$$

Either ammonia (or amines) or mineral acids are then used as catalysts in a dehydration step to extend the polymer chains. In this way, crystalline high melting polymers have been prepared.

Poly(arylene sulfides) have been prepared by the condensation of aryl dihalides with alkali metal sulfides or aryl dimercaptans (13). These relatively low molecular weight products can be chain extended by heat treatment in an inert atmosphere to prepare high melting phenylene sulfide resins (14).

Polyaddition Polymers

The addition of thiols to olefins has also been reviewed in considerable detail (1). The reaction between a dimercaptan and a diolefin, catalyzed free radically by ultraviolet light or peroxide, has been studied in detail by C. S. Marvel and co-workers and by others. Examples are the reaction of butadiene with 1,2-ethanedithiol (15) and the reaction of 1,6-hexamethylenedithiol with 4-vinyl-1-cyclohexene (16) (eq. 4). Emulsion

$$HS(CH_2)_6SH + \underset{}{\bigcirc}{-}CH{=}CH_2 \xrightarrow[\text{peroxide}]{\text{benzoyl}} \left[-S(CH_2)_6S-\underset{}{\bigcirc}{-}CH_2{-}CH_2- \right]_n$$

(4)

polymerization methods are particularly effective for the preparation of these polymers.

Poly(hexamethylene sulfide) polymers with molecular weights as high as 60,800 were prepared by the polyaddition method (17).

Ring-Opening Polymerization

Polymerization by ring-opening reactions represents an effective route to useful monosulfide polymers in that, theoretically at least, much higher molecular weights are attainable. All of the principal types of mono-sulfide polymers except the (linear) tetramethylene sulfide polymers and the phenylene sulfide polymers have been obtained in this way.

Methylene sulfide polymers have been prepared from *sym*-trithiane by Lewis acid catalysis (18,19) and by radiation polymerization (20,21). Recently the polymer has been prepared in a much simpler manner from the cyclic tetramer of thioformaldehyde, 1,3,5,7-tetrathiocyclooctane, which ring opens either thermally or by the means of cationic reagents (22). In either case the polymers obtained are high melting crystalline resins. The molecular weights of methylene sulfide polymers prepared from cyclic monomers are difficult to determine because of their extreme insolubility in conventional solvent, and melt viscosity data are difficult to evaluate because of thermal decomposition reactions which begin to take place at or near the melting point.

The three- and four-membered rings containing a single sulfur atom undergo a somewhat different type of ring-opening polymerization, the main driving force of which is the ring strain energy present in the monomer.

The three-membered ring, thiirane (I), and the four-membered thietane (II) have the structures illustrated. The calculated strain energy of the thiirane ring is -19.4 kcal/mole based on the standard heats of combustion and of formation as tabulated by Mackle and O'Hare (25). The strain energy of thietane, similarly derived, is -14.6 kcal/mole, while that of the five-membered ring (thiolane) is only -1.3 kcal/mole. The six-membered ring, thiane, is considered to be strain-free.

(I) (23)   (II) (24)

The ease of polymerization follows the same order of reactivity, decreasing from thiirane to thiolane with all types of catalysis.

Mackle has further shown (26) that the heat of polymerization of thiirane, $\Delta H_{(p)}$, is -20 ± 2 kcal/mole. Thus the heat of the ring-opening polymerization is essentially equal to the ring strain energy.

Ethylene sulfide (thiirane) is readily polymerized with a variety of methods, including both cationic and anionic catalysis. Cationic catalysts that have been used are the mineral acids, which produce rapid, highly exothermic polymerizations in aqueous media, and Lewis acids (2). The latter include zinc chloride, BF_3 and BF_3 complexes, $AlCl_3$, $SnCl_4$, and PF_5 (27). The molecular weight of poly(ethylene sulfide) polymers prepared from thiiranes by acidic catalysts is not directly measurable because of the ease with which such polymers are degraded by traces of residual acid. The extreme insolubility of ethylene sulfide polymer prevents quantitative removal of the catalyst, but even in the case of soluble polymers (i.e., propylene sulfide polymer), molecular weights generally do not exceed 1000 and are frequently much lower, suggesting the possibility of acid degradation during the polymerization step.

The anionic polymerization of ethylene sulfide using sodium hydroxide in methanol, ammonia, or amine catalysis was studied by Ohta, Kondo, and Ohi, who found that the molecular weights of the polymer were extremely low (28).

The anionic polymerization of episulfides has also been studied by Dermer (2) and later in great detail by Boileau and Sigwalt (4,29). Sodium hydroxide, sodium methylate, and amines, both primary and tertiary, yield ethylene sulfide polymers which melt between 180 and 205–208°. Molecular weights of these polymers as determined by Boileau and Sigwalt were less than 1000.

By the use of sodium naphthalene in tetrahydrofuran, Boileau, Sigwalt, and co-workers (31) prepared ethylene sulfide polymer with a reported melting point of 208–210°C. Using propylene sulfide they obtained elastomers with molecular weights of 70,000–320,000 by the use of high purity reagents and the rigid exclusion of air and moisture (32).

In 1959, Furukawa, Saegusa, Tsuruta, and co-workers in a series of papers (33–35) described the catalysis of epoxide polymerization by a catalyst comprising certain metal alkyls reacted with a cocatalyst. The metal alkyls used were those of aluminum, zinc, cadmium, and lithium. The cocatalysts were alumina and silica-alumina, as well as oxygen, water, alcohols, and the epoxides themselves. In particular the molecular weight of propylene oxide polymers produced by these catalysts were found to be quite high.

In 1960 it was discovered in our laboratories that a catalyst formed by the reaction of diethylzinc with water readily produced ethylene sulfide polymers which melted at 208–212°C. Although these polymers have melting points similar to those prepared by other methods of catalysis, they were found to have higher melt viscosities than any polymers prepared up to that time (36,37). The melt viscosity was determined by capillary flow plasto-meter according to modified ASTM method D-1238-57T. This technique proved to be the only reliable way of estimating relative molecular weight in view of the insolubility of the polymer in solvents which would permit direct molecular weight determination by solution measurements.

Further study of the metal alkyl/cocatalyst process indicated that both zinc and cadmium alkyls could be used. But, unlike the epoxide systems, aluminum or lithium alkyls could not be used to make active catalysts for episulfide polymerization in our laboratories with any of the cocatalysts described below, although there is at least one report that trialkyl-aluminum/water systems are effective (38). Furthermore, the use of cadmium alkyls frequently resulted in the formation of yellow products, rather than the white polymers obtained with zinc. Thus, from a practical viewpoint, diethylzinc was found to be the metal alkyl of choice.

A variety of cocatalysts could be used in the episulfide systems. The catalyst/cocatalyst ratio had to be kept relatively low for the preparation of highly active catalysts, but to obtain the maximum molecular weight polymer this ratio had to be greater than 1. Water, alcohols, glycols, and oxygen were all found to be useful cocatalysts. In addition, hydrogen sulfide, mercaptans, and sulfur were also found to be active cocatalysts for episulfide polymerization. All the cocatalysts found to be useful for diethylzinc-based catalyst systems had one feature in common—they were capable of reacting with the metal alkyl to form new Zn—O (or Zn—S) bonds. Ultimately, even finely divided zinc oxide and other metal oxides were used to prepare polymers of ethylene sulfide and 1,2-propylene sulfide, which were of very high molecular weight as shown by viscosity measure-ments (39). Zinc sulfide was similarly effective as a catalyst and the use of both cadmium and cobalt mercaptides has also been reported (40,41). A more active form of zinc oxide was prepared by the stoichiometric hydrolysis of zinc acetylacetonate in benzene, followed by careful removal of the liberated 1,3-diketone. Zinc carbonate was effective as an episulfide catalyst. Moreover, both the oxides and carbonates of zinc and cadmium are effective in aqueous polymerization media as well as in the nonpolar organic media commonly used (42).

It should be noted that cadmium can replace zinc in all the catalyst systems for episulfides that have been studied to date, although minor differences in the polymers can sometimes be noted. Apart from the yellow color imparted by cadmium, a higher degree of stereoregularity has been observed in poly(1,2-propylene sulfide) using cadmium salt catalysis (42).

Unlike true anionic ring-opening polymerizations which are inhibited by traces of impurities such as air and moisture, dialkylzinc/cocatalyst polymerizations are affected by these impurities only to the extent that the catalyst/cocatalyst ratio is substantially altered.

The mechanism of catalysis of thiirane polymerization using dialkylzinc/cocatalyst systems or the corresponding metal oxide catalysts remains speculative. However, it would appear to involve coordination of the monomer sulfur atom to the metal oxide catalyst followed by ring-opening rearrangement and coordination of the next monomer unit at the active catalyst site.

The chemistry of thietanes has also been the subject of a recent review (43). By contrast to the thiiranes, thietanes are much less readily polymerized. Whereas the three-membered ring systems polymerize readily with cationic or anionic reagents, as well as with the coordination catalysts, the four-membered monosulfide ring systems polymerize only with cationic reagents. Thietanes react vigorously with Lewis acids, such as $AlCl_3$, $SnCl_4$, and PF_5 (27,44). They also polymerize to a limited extent with triethylaluminum/water systems (27). Amines and other anionic catalysts have been reported ineffective for the ring-opening polymerization of thietanes. Trimethylene sulfide polymer, a low melting solid, has also been prepared by condensation polymerization from 1,3-dimercaptopropanol and 1,3-dibromopropane (43,45).

THE PHYSICAL PROPERTIES OF HIGH MOLECULAR WEIGHT
ALKYLENE MONOSULFIDE POLYMERS

The properties which sulfur linkages confer on hydrocarbon polymers include: chemical and solvent resistance, low absorption of moisture, and chain flexibility. The physical state of monosulfide polymers is controlled by the structure of the hydrocarbon linkages. Methylene sulfide, ethylene sulfide, and phenylene sulfide polymers are generally highly crystalline, thermoplastic solids. They exhibit chemical, solvent, and oil resistance as well as the improved chemical stability expected of monosulfide, as compared with polysulfide, polymers. The high melting points and high rigidity of the crystalline monosulfide polymers result in some processing difficulties, but these same properties make them attractive for use as tough, dimensionally stable molding resins. To varying degrees, they are susceptible to thermal and/or oxidative degradation during molding and at high temperatures during use, and they require the addition of stabilizers to achieve maximum utility.

The polymers of substituted ethylene sulfides, trimethylene sulfide, and the copolymers of these materials, are generally amorphous elastomers, although in some cases a portion of the crystalline properties are retained. Like the crystalline resins, they exhibit the solvent and chemical resistance expected of monosulfide polymers, and they also require stabilization against oxidative attack.

Poly(ethylene Sulfide)

All the ethylene sulfide homopolymers have sharp, crystalline melting points. For the high molecular weight polymers prepared by ring opening of ethylene episulfide, melting points generally lie above 205°C. Molecular weights of polymers melting above 205°C are further differentiated on the basis of melt viscosity.

The lack of solubility of poly(ethylene sulfide) in common solvents has prevented accurate molecular weight determinations by solution properties measurements. A few solvents are known which dissolve the homopolymer, but only at temperatures above 140°C. These solvents include α-methyl naphthalene and dimethyl sulfoxide. However, at these temperatures, thermal degradation of the polymer takes place, resulting in inaccurate estimates of molecular weight. In the case of dimethyl sulfoxide, an oxygen interchange reaction between the solvent and the polymer takes place at the high temperature, as judged by the noticeable odor of dimethyl sulfide.

The crystalline structure of poly(ethylene sulfide) was determined by Boileau and Sigwalt (29) from x-ray diffraction studies. The unit cell is hexagonal with $a = 4.92$ Å and $c = 6.74$ Å. After comparison of these values to the theoretical repeat distance of the monomer unit, it was concluded that the polymer chain is not in full linear extension and that two repeat monomer units exist along the c axis. The calculated density based on the unit cell is 1.42. High molecular weight poly(ethylene sulfide) prepared in our laboratory using coordination catalysts has a degree of crystallinity of $80 \pm 5\%$ as estimated from x-ray studies (30). The polymer when properly stabilized can be injection molded at elevated temperatures to form a tough thermoplastic with excellent physical properties.

Poly(methylene Sulfide)

Methylene sulfide polymers prepared by condensation or ring-opening mechanisms are also highly crystalline resins with melting points in the range of 243–260°C for the high molecular weight polymers. These polymers begin to decompose in air above their melting points. The polymer is insoluble in most organic solvents except in α-bromonaphthalene and a solvent mixture of tetramethylene sulfone and α-chloronaphthalene above 210°C (18).

The crystalline structure of poly(methylene sulfide) was determined by Lando and Stannett (20) and by Carazzolo and Mammi (21) using x-ray diffraction techniques. According to Carazzolo and Mammi, the polymer structure consisted of helices 17/9 (17 —CH$_2$—S— units and 9 turns of the helix in c axis length) packed in a hexagonal unit cell with parameter a = 5.07 Å and c = 36.52 Å.

Poly(propylene Sulfide)

High molecular weight polymers of propylene sulfide were prepared by ring-opening mechanisms using anionic or coordination catalysts. The resulting polymers were amorphous or partially crystalline. Adamek, Wood, and Woodhams (42) found that when cadmium salts were used as catalysts, isotactic or crystalline polymers were formed whose melting points varied according to molecular weight and degree of tacticity. Machon and Sigwalt (38) using ZnEt$_2$–H$_2$O as catalyst and benzene as a solvent obtained partially crystalline polymers of propylene sulfide. The stereoregular fraction of the polymer, insoluble in methyl ethyl ketone at 100°C, reached a maximum of 58% at a catalyst ratio (H$_2$O : ZnEt$_2$) of 0.92.

Vulcanization of poly(propylene sulfide) with conventional sulfur recipes can be accomplished when a small concentration of an unsaturated episulfide comonomer is incorporated with propylene sulfide. Unsaturated episulfides used for this purpose include allyl thioglycidyl ether (ATGE) and monoepisulfides of 1,4-pentadiene, 1,5-hexadiene, and vinyl cyclohexene (37,42).

Table 1 gives the properties of a sulfur-vulcanized propylene sulfide–ATGE copolymer prepared in our laboratory. The glass transition temperature of poly(propylene sulfide) is reported to be −52.5°C (42). However, in our laboratory T_g values of −40°C were observed for the sulfur-vulcanized, carbon black filled copolymer described in Table 1. The physical properties of elastomers based on propylene sulfide were improved by substituting ethylene sulfide for part of the propylene sulfide. Thus, it was found that terpolymers of propylene sulfide–ethylene sulfide–ATGE in which the ethylene sulfide content was in the range of 30–40 mole% gave the best

Table 1

Properties of Sulfur-Vulcanized Propylene
Sulfide–ATGE Copolymer

Polymer composition (mole %, initial charge)	
Propylene sulfide	90
Allyl thioglycidyl ether	10

Vulcanization recipe (parts by weight)	
Copolymer	100
Stearic acid	1
Philblack O	50
ZnO	5
Sulfur	1
Ethyl selenac	2

Cure cycle	
Time, minutes	20
Temperature, °C	150

Vulcanizate properties	
Tensile strength (psi)	1550
Elongation (%)	225
Hardness (Shore A)	80
Tear strength, lb/in.	125

Solvent resistance (% volume swell, 7 days at room temperature)	
Ethyl acetate	75
MEK	101
Hexane	10
Toluene	173

Table 2

Effect of Varying Ethylene Sulfide Content on Elastomer Properties

Polymer composition (mole %, initial charge)			Tensile (psi)	Elongation (%)	Hardness (Shore A)	Tear (lb/in.)
PS	ES	ATGE				
80	10	10	1550	368	72	240
70	20	10	1835	380	75	255
60	30	10	2020	350	81	365
55	35	10	2230	390	87	435
50	40	10	2380	300	95	520

balance of properties. Table 2 gives the properties of various compositions vulcanized in the same manner as described in Table 1. Substantial improvements are observed in physical properties as well as solvent resistance. The glass transition temperature of the vulcanizates of the terpolymers is about $-40°C$, which is the same as for vulcanized propylene sulfide–ATGE copolymer. This might indicate that block rather than random copolymers are obtained.

The aging characteristics of the vulcanized monosulfide elastomers appear to be good. Slight changes in physical properties have been reported (42) after heat aging in air for 3 days at $120°C$ in the presence of 2% phenyl-β-naphthylamine.

References

1. F. O. Davis and E. M. Fettes, "Polyalkylene Sulfides," in *Polyethers* (High Polymer Ser., Vol. 13, Part III), N. G. Gaylord, Ed., Wiley, New York, 1962, Chap. 12.
2. O. C. Dermer, "Copolymers of Olefin Sulfides," Wright Air Develop. Center Tech. Rept. No. 55-447, ASTIA Doc. No. AD110496, June 1956.
3. M. Sander, "Thiiranes," *Chem. Rev.*, **66**(3), 297 (1966).
4. P. Sigwalt, "High Polymers and Copolymers of Episulfides," *Chim. Ind. Gen. Chim.*, **96**, 909 (1966).
5. R. H. Gobran and M. B. Berenbaum, in *The Polymer Chemistry of Synthetic Elastomers*, Vol. II, J. P. Kennedy and E. Tornqvist, Eds., Interscience, New York, in press.
6. C. Loewig and S. Weidmann, *Ann.*, **46**, 81 (1839).
7. J. M. Crafts, *Ann.*, **124**, 110 (1862).
8. V. Meyer, *Ber.*, **19**, 325 (1886).
9. G. M. Bennett, *J. Chem. Soc.*, **1912**, 1583.
10. M. B. Berenbaum, E. Broderick, and R. C. Christina (Thiokol Chemical Corp.), U.S. Pat. 3,317,486 (May 2, 1967).
11. J. Harmon (E. I. du Pont de Nemours) U.S. Pat. 3,070,580 (Dec. 25, 1962); (du Pont) Brit. Pat. 972,820 (Aug. 23, 1962).
12. L. Credali, L. Mortillaro, M. Russo, and C. DeChecchi, *Polymer Previews*, **2**, 96 (1966).
13. A. D. Macallum (Dow Chemical Co.) U.S. Pat. 2,513,188 (June 27, 1950); *Chem. Abstr.*, **44**, 8165 (1950) and U.S. Pat. 2,538,941 (Jan. 23, 1951); *Chem. Abstr.*, **45**, 5193 (1951).
14. H. A. Smith (Dow Chemical Co.), Belg. Pat. 644,106 (Sept. 2, 1965); *Chem. Abstr.*, **63**, 5841 (1965).
15. D. D. Coffman (E. I. du Pont de Nemours), U.S. Pat. 2,347,182 (Apr. 25, 1944).
16. C. S. Marvel and C. S. Roberts, *J. Polymer Sci.*, **6**, 717 (1951).
17. C. S. Marvel and A. H. Markhart, *J. Polymer Sci.*, **6**, 711 (1951).
18. E. Gipstein, E. Wellisch, and O. J. Sweeting, *J. Polymer Sci.*, B, **1**, 237 (1963).
19. K. Kullmar, E. Fisher, and K. Weissermel (Farbwerke Hoechst A.G.), U.S. Pat. 3,218,300 (Nov. 16, 1965).
20. J. B. Lando and V. Stannett, *J. Polymer Sci.*, B, **2**(4), 375 (1964).
21. G. Carazzolo and M. Mammi, *J. Polymer Sci.*, B, **2**, 1057 (1964).

22. M. Russo, L. Mortillaro, C. DeChecchi, G. Valle, and M. Mammi, *J. Polymer Sci., B*, **3**, 301 (1965).
23. G. L. Cunningham, A. W. Boyd, R. J. Myers, and W. D. Gwinn, *J. Chem. Phys.*, **19**, 676 (1951).
24. D. W. Scott, M. L. Finke, W. N. Hulbard, J. P. McCullough, C. Katz, M. E. Gross, J. F. Messerly, R. E. Pennington, and G. Waddington, *J. Am. Chem. Soc.*, **75**, 2795 (1953).
25. H. Mackle and P. A. G. O'Hare, *Tetrahedron*, **19**, 961 (1963).
26. H. Mackle, Paper presented at the Sulphur Symposium, University of Alberta, Calgary, Alberta, Canada, March 18, 1965.
27. J. K. Stille and J. A. Empen, *150th Natl. Meeting, Am. Chem. Soc., Sept. 1965, Polymer Preprints*, p. 619; *Abstr.* p. 8W.
28. M. Ohta, A. Kondo, and R. Ohi, *Nippon Kagaku Zasshi*, **75**, 985 (1954); *Chem. Abstr.*, **51**, 14668 (1957).
29. S. Boileau and P. Sigwalt, *Compt. Rend.*, **252**, 882 (1961).
30. B. Post, private communication.
31. S. Boileau, J. Coste, J. Raynal, and P. Sigwalt, *Compt. Rend.*, **254**, 2774 (1962).
32. S. Boileau, G. Champtetier, and P. Sigwalt, *Makromol. Chem.*, **69**, 180 (1963).
33. J. Furukawa, T. Tsuruta, R. Sakata, T. Saegusa, and A. Kawasaki, *Makromol. Chem.*, **32**, 90 (1959).
34. J. Furukawa, T. Saegusa, T. Tsuruta, and G. Kagokawa, *Makromol. Chem.*, **36**, 25 (1959).
35. R. Sakata, T. Tsuruta, T. Saegusa, and J. Furukawa, *Makromol. Chem.*, **40**, 64 (1960).
36. Thiokol Chemical Corporation, Brit. Pat. 1,034,346 (June 29, 1966).
37. Thiokol Chemical Corporation, Brit. Pat. 1,036,091 (July 13, 1966).
38. J. P. Machon and P. Sigwalt, *Compt. Rend.*, **260**, 549 (1965).
39. S. W. Osborn, T. F. Wells, and E. L. Kutch, Can. Pat. 698,782 (Apr. 24, 1964).
40. A. Noshay and C. C. Price, *J. Polymer Sci.*, **54**, 533 (1961).
41. Y. Ishii, M. Obara, and Y. Fuzita, *Kogyo Kagaku Zasshi*, **67**, 616 (1964); through *Chem. Abstr.*, **61**, 16160e (1964).
42. S. Adamek, B. B. J. Wood, and R. T. Woodhams, *Rubber Age*, **96**, 581 (1965).
43. M. Sander, *Chem. Rev.*, **66**(3), 341 (1966).
44. Y. K. Yuriev, S. V. Dyatlovitskava, and I. S. Levin, *Vestn. Mosk. Univ. 7(12) Ser. Fiz. Mat. Estestven. Nauk*, **8**, 55 (1952); *Chem. Abstr.*, **49**, 281 (1955).
45. J. Lal, *J. Polymer Sci.*, **50**, 13 (1961).

On the Oxidation of Polyvinyl Mercaptan

C. G. OVERBERGER* and J. A. MOORE

Institute of Polymer Research, Polytechnic Institute of Brooklyn,
Brooklyn, New York

INTRODUCTION

The oxidation of mercaptans has been a fruitful field of study for many years. Some of the more interesting work has been done on the aerobic oxidation (autoxidation) of mercaptans to disulfide catalyzed by metals, since this is presumably the predominant process occurring in living systems. Much of this work is concentrated on multifunctional compounds, i.e., those containing other functionalities than mercaptan (cysteine (1–6), thioglycolic acid (7,8)). Any generalities concerning the conditions which affect the oxidizability of a thiol group are masked by complicating factors such as inductive effects, partial net charges, etc. In addition, information obtained from low molecular weight thiols is only approximately applicable to the large molecules encountered in biological systems. We therefore felt that a more realistic approach would be to study polymeric mercaptans in comparison to suitable low molecular weight models.

RESULTS AND DISCUSSION

The polymer chosen was polyvinyl mercaptan and the models selected were 2,4-pentane-, 2,5-hexane-, and 2,6-heptanedithiols.

Barron (9) had reported that the oxidizability of a series of dithiols is inversely proportional to the distance between sulfur atoms. These results were different from those of Whittaker (10), who indicated that the rates of oxidation of dithiols were insensitive to this parameter.

Using a spectrophotometric procedure we determined the relative rates of oxidation of a series of dithiols based on the observed rate of reduction of a dye, sodium 2,6-dichlorobenzeneoneindophenol in dimethylformamide (DMF) (11,12). (See Table 1.)

---

* Present address: Department of Chemistry, The University of Michigan, Ann Arbor, Michigan.

Table 1

Relative Oxidizabilities of Thiols in DMF

Thiol	Observed oxidation rate μmole ml^{-1} min^{-1} per —SH × 10^5	$k \times 10^3$	Rel. rate

1. CH$_3$—CH—(CH$_2$)$_3$—CH—CH$_3$
       | |
      SH   SH
	0.328	0.0547 ± 0.002	1.0

2. HO—CH$_2$—CH$_2$—SH	1.70	0.233 ± 0.010	5.2

3. CH$_3$—CH—(CH$_2$)$_2$—CH—CH$_3$
       | |
      SH   SH
	3.90	0.650 ± 0.030	11.9

4. CH$_3$—CH—CH$_2$—CH—CH$_3$
       | |
      SH   SH
	9.70	1.62 ± 0.10	28.7

5. CH$_3$—CH—CH—CH$_3$
       | |
      SH SH
	20.1	3.35 ± 0.20	61.2

6. $+$CH$_2$—CH—CH$_2$—CH—CH$_2 +_{n/2}$
         | |
       SH   SH
	91.4	15.2 ± 0.60	280

These results apparently verified Barron's work. Shortly after this work was published, two papers (13a,13b) appeared which showed that in addition to the oxidation reaction a competing reaction was occurring in which mercaptan added to the olefin portion of the dye (reactions 1A and 1B). The initial rate of disappearance of mercaptan is thus a *sum* of two proc-

$$\frac{-d(\text{SH})}{dt} = a(\text{Vox}) + b(\text{Vadd'n})$$

esses, oxidation and addition. The relative magnitudes of the coefficients, a and b, would determine the validity of our previous conclusions.

In view of these difficulties, we chose a system consisting of dimethyl sulfoxide (DMSO) as solvent, ferric ion as catalyst, and molecular oxygen as oxidant. Dimethyl sulfoxide is known to be an efficient oxidizing agent for mercaptans at temperatures greater than 100°C (14a,14b), but at room temperature the rate of this reaction is very much smaller than that catalyzed by ferric ion.

The solubility of the catalyst in DMSO has been shown (15) to be due to the formation of a solvent–iron complex, where the oxygen atoms of the sulfoxide molecules are the binding sites.

For the initial 30% of reaction the stoichiometry, as measured by the amount of O_2 absorbed compared to the amount of mercaptan reacted, was determined by direct titration of unreacted mercaptan (16) to be

$$4 \text{ SH/O}_2 \quad \text{or} \quad 2 \text{ dithiol/O}_2$$

Table 2 compares percent reaction calculated from oxygen uptake and from mercaptan titration. Figure 1 shows typical examples of our data

Table 2

Comparison of Percent Reaction Calculated from Oxygen Uptake and Mercaptan Titration

	SH, mole/liter	Fe^{3+}, mole/liter $\times 10^3$	Initial rate $\times 10^3$	Reaction, % Oxygen uptake, μmole $ml^{-1} min^{-1}$	Titration
Poly(vinyl mercaptan) $[\eta] = 4$	0.021	0.025	0.73	9.3	10.1
	0.021	0.025	0.68	16.5	15.8
	0.021	0.025	0.69	22.1	23.5
	0.021	0.025	0.72	37.2	30.0
2,5-Hexanedithiol	0.371	0.703	2.75	5.0	4.6
	0.371	1.406	4.95	9.9	9.9
	0.371	2.109	7.66	11.8	12.0
	0.188	2.310	...	27.5	30.5
2,6-Heptanedithiol	0.182	1.198	1.90	9.1	9.4
	0.182	2.396	4.05	18.8	18.5
	0.182	3.593	5.93	28.3	24.5
	0.182	4.791	8.40	36.5	30.0

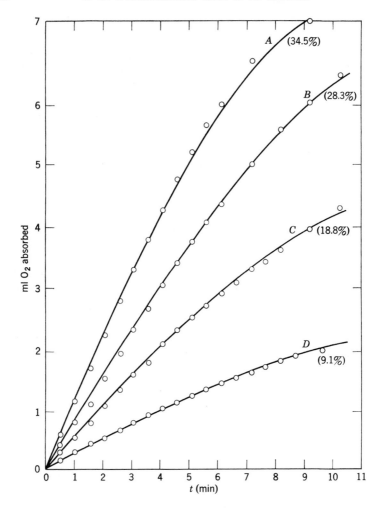

Fig. 1. Oxidation of 2,6-heptanedithiol: O_2 uptake vs. time. $[SH]_0 = 0.1824M$; $[Fe^{+3}] = (A) 1.198 \times 10^{-3}M$; $(B) 2.396 \times 10^{-3}M$; $(C) 3.593 \times 10^{-3}M$; $(D) 4.791 \times 10^{-3}M$.

where O_2 uptake is plotted against time. The initial slopes of these lines are taken as being proportional to the rates of oxidation.

Figure 2 shows the effect of iron concentration on the rate of oxidation at various mercaptan concentrations in DMSO. Curve A is for 2,6-heptanedithiol, curve B is for 2,5-hexanedithiol, and curve C is for 2,4-pentanedithiol. From these curves it can be seen that varying the

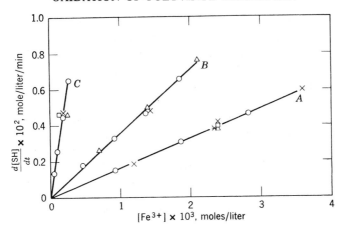

Fig. 2. Effect of ferric sulfate concentration on rate of oxidation at various mercaptan concentrations in DMSO. Curve A: 2,6-Heptanedithiol. Concentrations in moles SH/liter: ($\times$) 0.1824, ($\square$) 0.3649, ($\bigcirc$) 0.3595, (*) 0.7190, ($\triangle$) 0.0912. Curve B: 2,5-Hexanedithiol. Concentrations in moles SH/liter: ($\bigcirc$) 0.1885, ($\triangle$) 0.3714, ($\times$) 0.7429. Curve C: 2,4-Pentanedithiol. Concentrations in moles SH/liter: ($\bigcirc$) 0.0384, ($\square$) 0.1152, ($\triangle$) 0.0768, ($\times$) 0.1919.

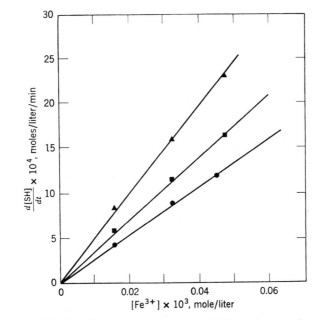

Fig. 3. Effect of ferric sulfate concentration on oxidation rates at various mercaptan concentrations. $[SH]_0$: ($\bullet$) 0.02 mole/liter; ($\blacksquare$) 0.05 mole/liter; ($\blacktriangle$) 0.10 mole/liter. $[\eta] = 0.4$.

concentration of mercaptan at a fixed concentration of iron does not affect the initial rate of oxidation. Figure 3 is a similar plot for polyvinyl mercaptan. Note, however, that mercaptan concentration *does* affect the rate in this case. The effect of varying mercaptan concentration on the rate of oxidation for polyvinyl mercaptan as compared to 2,4-pentanedithiol is illustrated in Figure 4.

Several differences in behavior are apparent when comparing the oxidation of polyvinyl mercaptan with its models. For the same iron concentration the polymer oxidizes faster than 2,4-pentanedithiol. In addition, as the molecular weight of the polymer is reduced, the fractional order of reaction with respect to mercaptan concentration approaches zero.

$[\eta]$	Reaction order
0.45	0.32
0.21	0.26
0.09	0.19

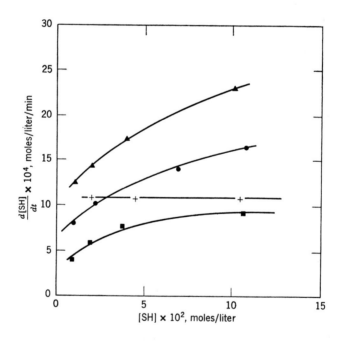

Fig. 4. Effect of mercaptan concentration on oxidation rate at various iron concentrations. Pentanedithiol $[Fe^{+3}]$: ($+$) 0.032×10^{-3} mole/liter. Poly(vinyl mercaptan) $[Fe^{+3}]$: ($\blacksquare$) 0.016×10^{-3} mole/liter; ($\bullet$) 0.032×10^{-3} mole/liter; ($\blacktriangle$) 0.047×10^{-3} mole/liter.

The effects can best be rationalized in terms of the schematic pathway shown in reactions 2 and 3. Although the slow step is the reduction of the

$$[Fe(DMSO)_6]^{+3} + nRSH \xrightarrow[]{k} \overset{Fe(III)}{[Fe(DMSO)_{n-1}(RSH)_n]} \qquad (2)$$

$$Fe(III) \xrightarrow{slow} Fe(II) + RS\cdot \qquad (3)$$

ferric–mercaptan complex, the magnitude of K must be considered. For the model compounds K is large and therefore initial zero-order dependence on mercaptan concentration is observed. For the polymer, complex formation and reaction to produce disulfide tend to increase the rigidity of the polymer coil, thereby shielding or masking SH functions from attack and effectively decreasing the magnitude of K. This shielding effect would be expected to increase directly as the molecular weight of the polymer increases.

This tentative explanation is being examined and extended at the present time and will be published at a future date.

References

1. L. J. Harris, *Biochem. J.*, **16**, 739 (1922).
2. L. Michaelis and E. S. G. Barron, *J. Biol. Chem.*, **83**, 191 (1929).
3. B. K. Cannon and G. W. Richardson, *Biochem. J.*, **23**, 1242 (1929).
4. M. Schubert, *J. Am. Chem. Soc.*, **54**, 4077 (1932).
5. D. L. Leussing, J. P. Mislan, and R. J. Gold, *J. Am. Chem. Soc.*, **64**, 1070 (1960).
6. J. E. Taylor, J. F. Yan, and J. Wang, *J. Am. Chem. Soc.*, **88**, 1663 (1966).
7. D. L. Leussing and L. Newman, *J. Am. Chem. Soc.*, **78**, 552 (1956).
8. H. Lamfrom and S. O. Nielsen, **79**, 1966 (1957).
9. E. S. G. Barron, Z. B. Miller, and G. Kalnitsky, *Biochem. J.*, **80**, 5431 (1958).
10. V. P. Whittaker, *Biochem. J.*, **41**, 56 (1947).
11. C. G. Overberger, J. J. Ferraro, and F. W. Orttung, *J. Org. Chem.*, **26**, 3458 (1961).
12. C. G. Overberger and J. J. Ferraro, *J. Org. Chem.*, **27**, 3539 (1962).
13a. H. I. Hadler, M. J. Erwin, and H. A. Lardy, *J. Am. Chem. Soc.*, **85**, 458 (1963).
13b. D. S. Coffey and L. Hellerman, *Biochemistry*, **3**, 394 (1964).
14a. S. Yannios and G. Karabinos, *J. Org. Chem.*, **28**, 3246 (1963).
14b. T. S. Wallace, *J. Am. Chem. Soc.*, **86**, 2018 (1964); T. S. Wallace and J. J. Mahon, *ibid.*, **86**, 4099 (1964).
15. F. A. Cotton and R. Francis, *J. Am. Chem. Soc.*, **82**, 2986 (1960).
16. C. G. Overberger, K. H. Burg, and W. H. Daly, *J. Am. Chem. Soc.*, **87**, 4125 (1965).

The Chemistry of the Sulfur Vulcanization of Natural Rubber

M. PORTER

The Natural Rubber Producers' Research Association,
Welwyn Garden City, Herts., England

STRUCTURAL FEATURES OF SULFUR VULCANIZATES OF NATURAL RUBBER

Vulcanization involves the chemical crosslinking of long, flexible rubber chains to produce a three-dimensional network and converts the relatively weak, plastic rubber hydrocarbon into a highly elastic material of considerable strength. Sulfur has been the paramount agent for effecting crosslinking ever since the inception of vulcanization, and since practically all rubber is used in the vulcanized state the rubber industry as a whole accounts for the consumption of upwards of 100,000 long tons of sulfur annually.

Vulcanization of natural rubber is normally achieved by heating it at 100–180°C with elemental sulfur, or a sulfur donor, in the presence of one or more organic accelerators and activators—usually zinc oxide and a fatty acid. Although crosslinking is the primary aim of this process it is accompanied by chemical modification of the main chains of the rubber at sites distant from the inserted crosslinks and by the formation in the vulcanizate, but not as part of the rubber network, of transformation products of the accelerators and activators.

The various types of chemical grouping which have been identified as being generally present in accelerated sulfur vulcanizates of natural rubber are depicted schematically in Figure 1. They comprise mono-, di-, and polysulfide crosslinks (*a*, *b*, and *c*, respectively, in Fig. 1), cyclic monosulfide (*d*) and disulfide (*e*) groups, pendent sulfide groups terminated by accelerator moieties (*f*), and conjugated diene (*g*) and conjugated triene (*h*) units. There is also evidence in particular cases for some conversion of the *cis*-olefinic double bonds of the natural rubber hydrocarbon (*cis*-1,4-polyisoprene) (**1**) into the *trans* configuration, and for a limited amount of double bond movement along the chains.

The presence of these groupings in vulcanizate networks has been inferred from examination of the reaction products of the various sulfur

165

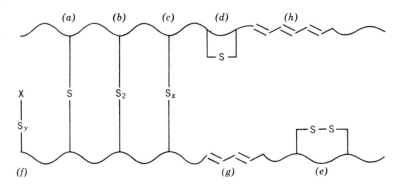

Fig. 1. Structural features of an accelerated sulfur vulcanizate of natural rubber.
(X = accelerator fragment, $x \geqslant 3$, $y \geqslant 1$.)

vulcanizing systems with olefins of low molecular weight having the structural features of **1**. The details of the intermolecular reaction products (crosslinks) have been elucidated using 2-methylpent-2-ene (**2**) as model while the intramolecular products, resulting from the involvement of neighboring olefinic double bonds in the sulfuration processes, have been identified using *trans*-2,6-dimethylocta-2,6-diene (**3**). [The more pertinent *cis*-isomer (**4**) was not readily available in quantity and in the required degree of purity.]

$$(1)$$

$$(2) \qquad (3) \qquad (4)$$

The structural characterization of actual rubber networks has been achieved by two methods. The first of these, which provides only an overall measure of network complexity in terms of the sulfurated groupings present, involves the determination of the crosslinking efficiency (E), which is defined as the number of sulfur atoms combined in the network per chemical crosslink present:

$$E = S_c/[2M_{c,\text{chem}}]^{-1}$$

where S_c = g-atoms of sulfur per gram rubber hydrocarbon in the network and $[2M_{c,\text{chem}}]^{-1}$ = "moles" of chemical crosslinks per gram of rubber hydrocarbon in the network.

The large variation in crosslinking efficiency, and therefore in network complexity, obtainable in natural rubber vulcanizates is illustrated by contrasting observed E values of 40–55 combined sulfur atoms per chemical crosslink for networks obtained by heating natural rubber with sulfur alone (1) with the E values of 2–3 observed (2) for networks prepared under conditions leading to very efficient use of sulfur for crosslinking.

The distribution of the combined sulfur among the various groupings illustrated in Figure 1 is determined by the second method, by which the networks are treated with reagents ("chemical probes") which react quantitatively with specific sulfurated groups. Thus, measurement of the crosslinking efficiency before (E) and after (E') treatment with triphenylphosphine, which converts di- and polysulfidic groups into monosulfides:

$$R—S_x—R + (x - 1)Ph_3P \longrightarrow R—S—R + (x - 1)Ph_3PS$$

allows estimates to be obtained of (1) the total amount of sulfur combined in the various main-chain modifications (Fig. 1) (given by $E' - 1$) and (2) the amount of di- and polysulfidic sulfur in the network (given by $E - E'$) (3).

Other chemical probes have been devised which enable the relative contributions of mono-, di-, and polysulfide crosslinks to the total degree of crosslinking to be determined. Sodium di-n-butyl phosphite in benzene solution cleaves di- and polysulfide links* but not monosulfide links (4), e.g.:

$$(Bu^nO)_2PO^- + R—S—S—R \longrightarrow (Bu^nO)_2\overset{\displaystyle O}{\overset{\displaystyle \|}{P}}SR + RS^-$$

while piperidinium propane-2-thiolate in n-heptane breaks polysulfide links under conditions (0.4M reagent; 2 hr at 20°C) which leave di- and monosulfide links essentially intact (5), e.g.:

$$Me_2\overset{\delta-}{C}HS\cdots H\cdots\overset{\delta+}{H}N\left\langle\bigcirc\right\rangle + R—S—S—S—R \longrightarrow$$

$$Me_2CHS \cdot SR + Me_2CHS \cdot SCHMe_2 + RS^- + S^{2-}$$

Changes in degree of chemical crosslinking caused by these two reagents separately allow di- and polysulfide crosslinks to be determined. Monosulfide crosslinks are then estimated by difference (provided carbon–carbon crosslinks are absent, as has been found to be the case in accelerated sulfur vulcanization).

---

* *Note added in proof.* A preferred alternative method for breaking di- and polysulfide links, involving treatment with a solution of n-hexanethiol in piperidine, has now been developed (22).

THE COURSE OF SULFUR VULCANIZATION

There is now very good evidence that the reactions leading to sulfuration and crosslinking of rubber take the course shown in Figure 2 in which natural rubber hydrocarbon is denoted by RH, where H is an α-methylenic or α-methylic hydrogen atom.

The active sulfurating agent formed by reaction of sulfur with an accelerator complex or from a sulfur donor and zinc oxide reacts directly with the rubber hydrocarbon to give a rubber-bound polysulfidic pendent group terminated by a fragment derived from the accelerator or sulfur donor. Such pendent groups are the immediate precursors to polysulfidic crosslinks which they form either by direct reaction with another rubber hydrocarbon molecule or by disproportionation with a second pendent group on a neighboring rubber chain. Polysulfide crosslinks are thermally unstable and chemically reactive and are subject to a number of competing reactions, the relative rates of which depend on the detailed structure of the crosslink termini, the concentration in the vulcanizate of various zinc-containing entities, and the temperature of vulcanization. These reactions have been termed "network maturing reactions" and they lead

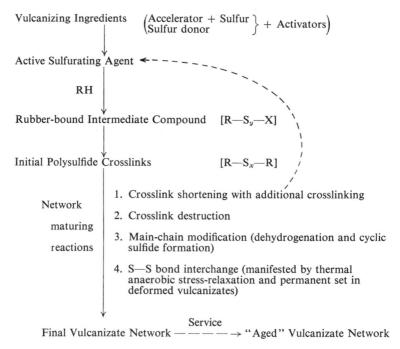

Fig. 2. Overall course of sulfur vulcanization.

to the final vulcanizate, i.e., the vulcanizate in the state in which it is removed from the press and which may contain the plethora of groupings indicated in Figure 1. Network maturing may continue during the service life of the vulcanizate, particularly if this takes place at an elevated temperature, and its effects are then superimposed on the oxidative aging reactions of the vulcanized network.

Formation of the Active Sulfurating Agent

It is now generally recognized that the initial step in sulfur vulcanization is the reaction of molecular sulfur with a species derived from the accelerator and activators. This species is usually a complex (**5**) of zinc benzothiazole-2-thiolate (ZMBT) or of a zinc dialkyldithiocarbamate (ZDC) formed *in situ*.

$$X = R_2N-\overset{\overset{\textstyle S}{\|}}{C}- \quad \text{or} \quad \text{benzothiazolyl-}C-$$

ZMBT and ZDC are themselves sparingly soluble in rubber but are rendered very soluble through coordination with nitrogen bases (either added as accelerator or present in the raw natural rubber) or zinc carboxylates. Examples of such complexes are (**6**) (6) and (**7**) (7) and the less well-defined substances formed from ZMBT and zinc carboxylates (8,9). In the following discussion these complexes are, for simplicity, collectively represented by X—S—Zn—S—X.

(6)   (7)

The action of these zinc mercaptide complexes on sulfur is not well understood. It does not give rise to isolable products but zinc perthiomercaptides (8) are believed to be formed in a series of equilibria which probably lie well on the side of mercaptide complex and free sulfur.

$$\underset{\substack{\text{S} \\ \diagdown \text{S} \\ \diagup \\ \text{S}_6}}{\overset{\delta- \quad \delta++ \quad \delta-}{XS \cdots Zn \cdots SX}} \;\; \rightleftharpoons \;\; XS-S_8-ZnSX \;\; \overset{XSZnSX}{\rightleftharpoons} \;\; XS-S_x-Zn-S_x-SX \tag{8}$$

The nucleophilic activity of amine and zinc carboxylate complexes of ZMBT toward sulfur has been demonstrated in their ability to catalyze disulfide interchange reactions and the insertion of sulfur into diethyl disulfide (9).

The average value of x in **8** will be controlled by the relative concentrations of sulfur and *soluble* zinc mercaptide. Species analogous to **8** may be formed from sulfur donors and zinc oxide (or zinc carboxylates); for example, tetramethylthiuram disulfide (TMTD) and zinc oxide give a mixture of thiuram polysulfides and zinc dimethyldithiocarbamate (ZD$_M$C) which may then exchange sulfur to give **8** in which X is specifically

$$-\overset{\overset{\text{S}}{\|}}{\text{C}}-\text{NMe}_2$$ (10,11). In such cases x will always be small.

$$\cdots Zn^{++}\cdots O^=\overset{\overset{\text{S}}{\|}}{\text{C}}-\text{S}-\text{S}-\overset{\overset{\text{S}}{\|}}{\text{C}} \longrightarrow \cdots Zn^{++}\cdots O^--\overset{\overset{\text{S}}{\|}}{\text{C}} \;\; + $$

$$\underset{\text{NMe}_2}{} \quad \underset{\text{NMe}_2}{} \qquad \qquad \underset{\text{NMe}_2}{}$$

$$\overset{\overset{\text{S}}{\|}}{\text{C}}-\text{S}-\text{S}^-\text{S}-\overset{\overset{\text{S}}{\|}}{\text{S}}-\overset{\overset{\text{S}}{\|}}{\text{C}} \longrightarrow \overset{\overset{\text{S}}{\|}}{\text{C}}-\text{S}-\text{S}-\text{S}-\overset{\overset{\text{S}}{\|}}{\text{C}}, \text{ etc.} + {}^-\text{SC}(\text{:S})\text{NMe}_2$$

$$\underset{\text{NMe}_2}{} \quad \underset{\substack{\text{C:S} \\ | \\ \text{NMe}_2}}{} \underset{\text{NMe}_2}{} \quad \underset{\text{NMe}_2}{} \qquad \underset{\text{NMe}_2}{}$$

Formation of the Rubber-Bound Intermediate Compound and its Conversion into Crosslinks

The zinc perthiomercaptides (8) are believed to be the actual sulfurating agents. Their reaction with rubber hydrocarbon gives rise to the rubber-bound intermediate which is the precursor to sulfur crosslinking.

Evidence for this intermediate is most definitive for the TMTD–zinc oxide vulcanizing system. Vulcanization of pure *cis*-1,4-polyisoprene by this system takes the course shown in Figure 3 (12), from which it is seen that quite high amounts of nitrogen and sulfur are combined with the rubber after short cure times but these are both reduced to limiting values as crosslinking reaches a maximum. The nitrogen and sulfur thus removed from the network appear as ZD$_M$C which attains a final yield of 72% of the initial TMTD (Fig. 4) (12). Figure 4 further illustrates the observation (13)

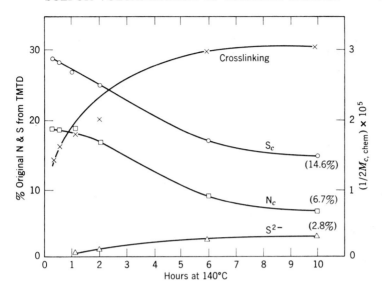

Fig. 3. Dependence of percentage of original nitrogen and sulfur in TMTD which is combined in the network (N_c and S_c) or as zinc sulfide (S^{2-}) and of the degree of chemical crosslinking $[2M_{c,chem}]^{-1}$ on the cure time at 140°C for cis-1,4-polyisoprene(100)–TMTD(4.0)–zinc oxide(4.0) vulcanizates.

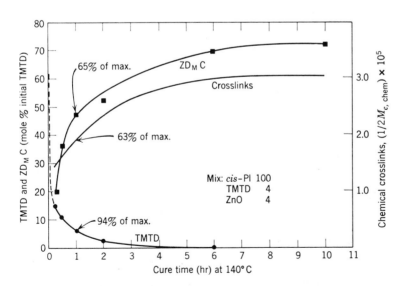

Fig. 4. Rates of reaction of TMTD and of formation of ZD_MC and crosslinks during vulcanization of cis-1,4-polyisoprene with TMTD and zinc oxide at 140°C.

that the rate of consumption of TMTD is faster than the rate of formation of ZD_MC and crosslinks, indicating that TMTD is rapidly transformed into an intermediate which then undergoes a slow reaction to give crosslinks and ZD_MC. Confirmation that this intermediate is combined with the rubber and is a precursor to crosslinks (12,14) is given by Figure 5, which shows the effect of reheating undercured *cis*-1,4-polyisoprene vulcanizates which have been freed from all extra-network material except zinc oxide and small amounts of zinc sulfide. Each new crosslink produced is accompanied by the formation of one molecule of ZD_MC.

The chemical nature of the rubber-bound intermediate has been determined (15) using the model monoolefin 2-methylpent-2-ene (**2**). The nitrogenous substances obtained in addition to crosslinked sulfides by treatment of (**2**) with TMTD and zinc oxide at 140°C (Table 1) were identified as **9**, **10**, and **11**, and the presence of a fourth compound (**12**) was inferred. Not all of these give rise to crosslinks on further reaction and implication of **9** in crosslink formation was deduced from the changes in yields of the various products on extended reaction (Table 1). Confirmation that **9** is indeed the precursor to crosslinks was obtained: (i) by isolating the nitrogenous material formed after reaction for 1 hr and heating it with olefin and zinc oxide for 4 hr at 140°C when crosslinked sulfides

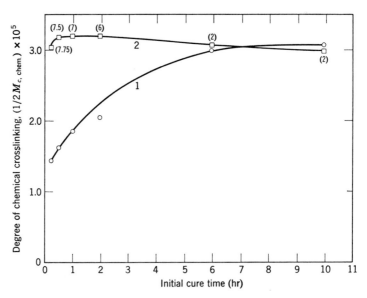

Fig. 5. Increase in crosslinking induced by reheating extracted undercured *cis*-1,4-polyisoprene–TMTD–zinc oxide vulcanizates. Figures in parentheses on curve *2* are the heating periods (hr in vacuum at 140°C) for the extracted vulcanizates of curve *1*.

Table 1

Changes in Yields of Nitrogenous Compounds and Crosslinked Sulfides during Reaction of 2-Methylpent-2-ene with TMTD and Zinc Oxide at 140°C

(Yields as mole % of initial TMTD)

Yield after 10-hr reaction		Compound	Yield after 1-hr reaction		
0		RSSC(:S)NMe$_2$(9)	18		0
12	Extended	RSC(:S)NMe$_2$(10)	12	Olefin, ZnO 4hr, 140°C	13
2.8	reaction	RSC(:O)NMe$_2$(11)	1.3		0.8
4.3		[RC(:S)NMe$_2$(12)]	2.3		2.1
24		RS$_x$R	12		14

R =

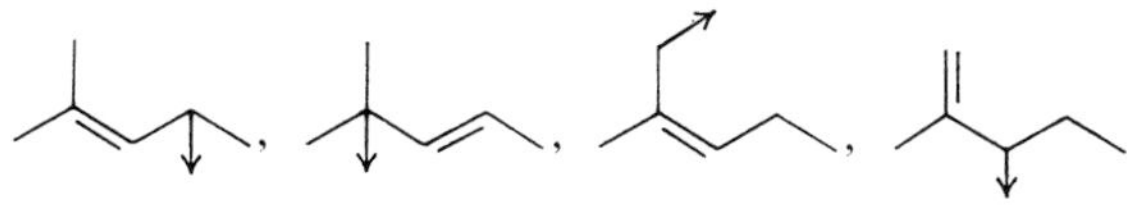

(A$_1$) (A$_2$) (B$_1$) (B$_2$)

were formed and the concentration of **9** was reduced to zero while those of **10–12** were little changed (Table 1); (ii) by heating synthetic examples of **9** (R = Et, Me$_2$C : CH·CHMe—) with olefin and zinc oxide when cross-linked sulfides and ZD$_M$C were formed in good yield. The rubber-bound intermediate compound in TMTD–zinc oxide vulcanization is thus identified as **13** and further experiments with **9** (R = Et) have demonstrated that crosslinks may be formed either by coupling of two molecules of **13** or by its reaction with another rubber molecule, both routes requiring the presence of zinc.

$$2RS_x—C(:S)—NMe_2$$
$$(13)$$
$$RS_x—C(:S)NMe_2 + RH$$
$$\xrightarrow{[ZnO]} RS_yR + ZD_MC + [H_2O]$$

where RH = polyisoprene in which H is α-methylenic or α-methylic and $x \geqslant 2$.

The mechanism by which the rubber-bound intermediate is formed from a zinc perthiomercaptide complex (**8**) and rubber hydrocarbon is not known with certainty but a process (16) which is consistent with the known features of the reaction (and which rationalizes other features of sulfur vulcanization) involves nucleophilic attack of a terminal perthiomercaptide sulfur atom on an α-methylenic or α-methylic carbon atom with concomitant displacement of hydrogen as an incipient hydride ion and formation of zinc sulfide.

$$
\begin{array}{ccc}
& \overset{\delta++\;\;\delta-}{\underset{}{Zn\cdots S}} & ZnS \\
\overset{\delta-}{XS_xS^-}\Big) \quad S{-}S_yX & \longrightarrow & XS_xSR \qquad HSS_yX \\
R{-}H & & \Big\downarrow ZnO \\
(14) & & XS_xZnS_xX + H_2O
\end{array}
$$

In this process the rate and course of the reaction (in terms of whether α-methylenic or α-methylic substitution takes place) will depend on the balance between the making of the C—S bond and the breaking of the C—H bond. It has been argued elsewhere (16) that bond making will depend upon the nucleophilicity of the sulfur atoms attached to zinc and the steric accessibility of the α-carbon atom in R, while bond breaking will be controlled by no-bond contributions (R^+H^-) to the polarization of the C—H bond and by the electrophilicity of the penultimate sulfur atoms in the perthiomercaptide. Under conditions where the bond-making step is important, substitution should consequently occur at the sterically more accessible α-methylic carbon atom; conversely, where bond breaking is important, substitution should occur at the more polarized α-methylenic position. Coordination of electron-donating ligands (such as $R \cdot CO \cdot O—$ and RNH_2) to the zinc atom will weaken the Zn—S bonds, increasing the charge on the terminal sulfur atoms and making them more nucleophilic while reducing the electrophilicity of the penultimate sulfur atoms. This will both facilitate C—S bond formation and hinder C—H bond cleavage, thus promoting substitution at α-methyl groups relative to α-methylene groups in the rubber. This effect is seen for the case of the TMTD–zinc oxide vulcanizing system in Table 2.

Table 2
Effect of Ligands in the Zinc Mercaptide Complex (5) on the Structure
of the Crosslinks Formed from 2-Methylpent-2-ene (2)

Sulfurating system (olefin in large excess)	BS— : AS— group ratio in (2)
TMTD (4), ZnO (4)	1.7
TMTD (4), ZnO (4), piperidine (0.64)	2.3
TMTD (4), ZnO (4), propionic acid (0.55)	3.7

The Structure of the Initial Polysulfide Crosslinks and its Influence on the Composition of the Final Vulcanizate Network

As has been described above, sulfuration of 2-methylpent-2-ene (**2**) by accelerated sulfur systems or by sulfur donors normally occurs exclusively by α-methylenic or α-methylic substitution and thus leads initially to the formation of allylic crosslinked polysulfides.

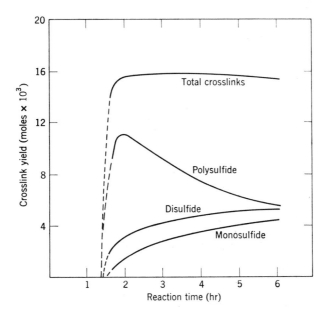

As reaction proceeds, the average value of x decreases from about 4 to a value close to 1 due to the progressive replacement of polysulfides by di- and monosulfides (Fig. 6). This crosslink-shortening is accompanied by changes in the positions of sulfur attachment to the olefin moieties; initially, the polysulfides contain effectively only A_1S—* and B_1S— groups but

Fig. 6. Yields of individual types of crosslink during reaction of 2-methylpent-2-ene with an accelerated sulfur system at 140°C. [Sulfur(2.5)–N-cyclohexyl-benzothiazole-2-sulfenamide (CBS)(0.6)–zinc oxide (4.0)–zinc propionate (3.0)–olefin (20 parts by weight).]

* This nomenclature, which is adopted for simplicity, is defined in Table 1.

the isoallylic groups A_2S— and B_2S— intrude as reaction time is increased.

Experiments with model di- and trisulfide crosslinks (17) have revealed that the crosslink-shortening process is catalyzed by ZMBT and ZDC and their complexes (e.g., **6** and **7**) and is accompanied by the formation of additional crosslinked sulfides and zinc sulfide (Table 3). It is also

Table 3

Product Yields on Reaction of Methylpentenyl Di- and Trisulfides with ZD_MC–Pyridine Complex (**7**) in the Presence of 2-Methylpent-2-ene and Zinc Oxide at 140°C for 4 hr (moles × 10^3)

Reactant	Sulfidic products			Loss (−) or gain (+) of sulfides	Methyl-penta-dienes	Zinc sulfide
	RSR	RS_2R	RS_3R			
A_1SSA_1 (4.37)	1.54	2.48	0.16	−0.19	0.9	1.40
B_1SSB_1 (4.37)	4.09	0.88	0.16	+0.76	<0.2	2.23
A_1SSSA_1 (5.00)	3.79	1.96	0.44	+1.19	0.5	4.44
B_1SSSB_1 (5.00)	5.56	1.48	0.37	+2.41	<0.2	5.16

evident that allylic rearrangements of A_1S— and B_1S— groups to A_2S— and B_2S— groups occur during desulfuration (Table 4), thus affording at least a partial explanation for the presence of the rearranged groups during the later stages of 2-methylpent-2-ene sulfuration (eq. 2).

$$RS_3R \xrightarrow{\text{XSZnSX}} RS_2R \xrightarrow{\text{XSZnSX}} RSR + RSR' + XSS_xZnS_xSX$$

Additional crosslinks   (2)

$$R= \quad (A_1) \quad \text{or} \quad (B_1) \qquad R'= \quad (A_2) \quad \text{or} \quad (B_2)$$

This extrusion of sulfur is believed to occur by complex formation between the di- or polysulfide and the zinc mercaptide, followed by S_Ni or S_Ni' attack of one of the mercaptide groups on carbon, e.g., equation 3.

The reactivities of the sulfides B_1SSB_1 and B_1SSSB_1 in this process are similar but are greater than the reactivities of A_1SSA_1 and A_1SSSA_1

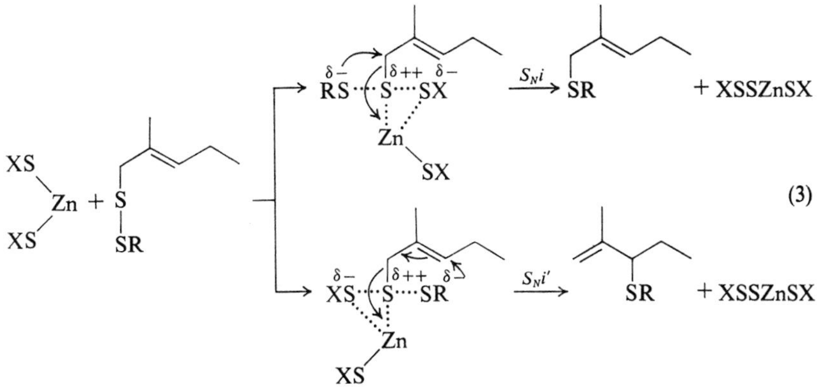

(Table 3) (17). An appreciation of this difference in reactivity is fundamental to an understanding of the well-known differences in behavior of the various sulfur vulcanizing systems in natural rubber and of the reasons for the wide range of vulcanizate properties and aging performance obtainable. This applies because of the control exercised by the rate of desulfuration over the extent of other network-maturing reactions itemized in Figure 2.

Although desulfuration of A_1SSA_1 leads, in the presence of olefin, to the formation of fresh crosslinked sulfides (as illustrated by the formation

Table 4

Composition of Mono- and Disulfides formed on Reaction of Methylpentenyl Di- and Trisulfides with ZD_MC–Pyridine Complex (7) in the Presence of 2-Methylpent-2-ene and Zinc Oxide at 140°C for 4 hr

(Wt % of sulfidic products)

	From			
Products	A_1SSA_1	B_1SSB_1	A_1SSSA_1	B_1SSSB_1
A_1SB_2	—	6.2	2.0	9.5
A_1SA_2	11.1	—	6.7	—
A_1SA_1	15.7	4.2	21.4	7.2
B_1SB_2	4.0	46.3	7.8	20.0
A_2SB_1	2.6	—	5.3	5.4
A_1SB_1	3.3	7.0	10.6	13.4
B_1SB_1	1.3	7.6	3.2	16.0
A_1SSA_2	—	—	0.8	—
A_1SSA_1	56.1	3.8	24.7	7.8
A_1SSB_1	2.6	5.3	8.6	10.5
B_1SSB_1	—	12.2	1.2	3.9

of sulfides containing B groups, Table 4) there is a reduction in the total number of crosslinks due to competing thermal decomposition with formation of conjugated dienes (eq. 4). The rate of this elimination

$$\text{(structure)} \longrightarrow \text{(structure)} + [RS_xH] \xrightarrow{ZnO} \tfrac{1}{2}(RS_{2x-1}R + H_2O + ZnS) \quad (4)$$

reaction is only appreciable for di- and polysulfides and although it appears to be faster for B-type sulfides than for A-type, the much more rapid desulfuration of the former quickly reduces the concentration of di- and polysulfides and thus effectively reduces elimination from B-type sulfides (Table 3).

The pathway by which sulfur is diverted from crosslinks into cyclic monosulfide and cyclic disulfide groups is not yet known; indeed, the detailed structures of these groups have not been completely elucidated. Nevertheless, there is evidence from experiments (18) with the model diisoprene (3) that formation of cyclic sulfurated groups accompanies crosslink destruction and the formation of conjugated dienes and trienes. It should therefore be subject to control by the same structural features in the crosslinks. This is seen to be the case in the data of Table 5 which shows the relative yields of crosslinked sulfides, conjugated dienes and trienes, and cyclic mono- and disulfides derived from 3 in the presence of two accelerated sulfur systems which give mainly A-type and mainly B-type, sulfides, respectively.

Table 5

Correlation of Type of Crosslink Terminus with Relative Molar Yields of Main-Chain Modifications Formed by Sulfuration of *trans*-2,6-Dimethylocta-2,6-diene (3)

Vulcanizing system[a]	BS—: AS— group ratio in (2)	Crosslinks	Relative molar yields from (3)			
			Conjugated dienes	Conjugated trienes	Cyclic monosulfides	Cyclic disulfides
1	0.5	1.0	0.4	1.1	1.9	0.9
2	4.8	1.0	0.3	0.1	0.07	0.14

[a] 1: Sulfur, 2; ZD$_M$C, 2; zinc oxide, 2; 3, 20 parts by weight. Heated 90 hr at 100°C.
2: Sulfur, 0.4; *N*-cyclohexylbenzothiazole-2-sulfenamide (CBS), 6; zinc oxide, 5; propionic acid, 0.55; 3, 20 parts by weight. Heated 2 hr at 140°C.

There are thus essentially two competing reactions which initially formed polysulfide crosslinks may undergo: (1) they may be desulfurated, eventually to form unreactive and thermally stable monosulfide crosslinks, and the extruded sulfur used to produce more crosslinks; or (2) they may be decomposed thermally to give cyclic mono- and disulfides and conjugated dienes and trienes. If the vulcanizing conditions are such that desulfuration proceeds rapidly, then the final vulcanizate network will be highly crosslinked, the crosslinks will be mainly monosulfidic, and there will be relatively few main-chain modifications of cyclic sulfide or olefinic type; such a network is *efficiently crosslinked* (low E value). If, on the other hand, the reaction conditions lead to slow desulfuration, thermal decomposition of the polysulfides ensues, leading to loss of crosslinks (modulus reversion) and to final vulcanizate networks containing much modification of the main chains; furthermore, the remaining crosslinks will still be largely di- and/or polysulfidic and will therefore be susceptible to further decomposition. The vulcanizates will consequently be subject to deterioration during service, particularly if it involves exposure to elevated temperatures. Such networks are *inefficiently crosslinked* (high E values).

Factors Controlling the Structure of the Initial Polysulfide Crosslinks

The relation between vulcanization efficiency and the structure of the initial polysulfide crosslinks is illustrated well by the two extreme accelerated sulfur vulcanization systems itemized in Table 5. System 1 which, with 2-methylpent-2-ene, yields a preponderance of the more slowly desulfurated A-type polysulfides, makes very inefficient use of sulfur for crosslinking natural rubber ($E \sim 25$) whereas system 2, which gives mostly B-type sulfides with 2-methylpent-2-ene, is very efficient ($E \sim 4$). Most practical vulcanizing systems for natural rubber (which have been developed empirically) lie between these two extremes.

Appreciation of the course of sulfur vulcanization as depicted in Figure 2, of the mechanisms of the individual stages, and, particularly, of the importance of the exact points of attachment of the sulfur crosslinks to the main rubber chains, now enables rational explanations to be advanced for the differences in vulcanizate structure brought about by the use of the various vulcanizing systems and the different vulcanizing conditions.

The principal role in determining vulcanizate structure is played by the zinc mercaptide complex (5), derived from the accelerator and activators, because it is involved both in the initial sulfuration of the rubber hydrocarbon to form the rubber-bound intermediate compound and in the desulfuration of di- and polysulfide crosslinks to monosulfide crosslinks. Particularly important are the nature of 5 and its concentration *in the rubber phase*, and in both of these the presence of ligands exerts a large influence.

The influence of the nature of the complex on the structure of the cross-link termini has already been described. The effect of its concentration is illustrated by the contrast between Figures 7 and 8. In the vulcanizing system of Figure 7 the concentration of the accelerator, *N*-cyclohexyl-benzothiazole-2-sulfenamide (CBS), is low and that of its derived complex (probably **6**) will also be low. Hence the average sulfur chain length, *x*, in the active sulfurating agent (**8**) will be long and will give rise initially to long polysulfidic crosslinks which, because of the low concentration of de-

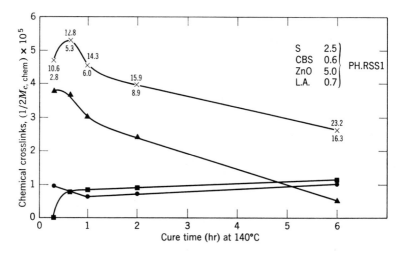

Fig. 7. Course of the CBS-accelerated sulfur vulcanization of natural rubber at 140°C with a high sulfur : accelerator ratio (2.5 : 0.6). (×) Total crosslinks. (▲) Poly-sulfide. (■) Monosulfide. (●) Disulfide. The upper and lower figures on the curve relating to total crosslinks are values of E and E', respectively.

sulfurating agent, will be shortened in length only slowly. There will thus be ample opportunity for these crosslinks to undergo thermal decomposition—with consequent reduction in crosslink density accompanied by extensive main-chain modification. These features are clearly shown in Figure 7, the extents of main-chain modification by sulfurated groupings being given by the numbers of sulfur atoms per chemical crosslink combined other than in the crosslinks, i.e., by $E' - 1$. With high concentrations of accelerator (Fig. 8) (or with sulfur donors such as TMTD) the sulfur chain length in **8**, and hence in the initial crosslinks, will be short and will be rapidly reduced still further by the plentiful desulfurating agent. Competitive thermal destruction of crosslinks is therefore limited and main-chain modification minimized (low values of $E' - 1$) (Fig. 8).

The presence of a high concentration of accelerator is, in itself, of little avail if much of its zinc derivative remains insoluble. This is especially obvious in the case of vulcanizing systems containing 2-mercaptobenzo-thiazole (MBT) or the corresponding disulfide (MBTS) unactivated by nitrogen bases (19). The poor hydrocarbon solubility of the ZMBT formed from these accelerators gives only a low equilibrium concentration in the rubber and inefficient vulcanization results (Fig. 9) (20). Extremely efficient vulcanization can nevertheless be obtained from them if nitrog-

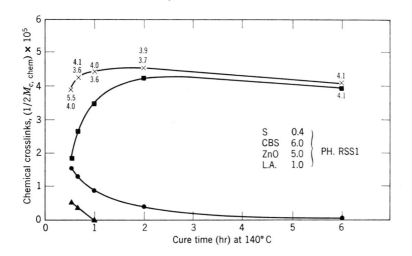

Fig. 8. Course of the CBS-accelerated sulfur vulcanization of natural rubber at 140°C with a low sulfur : accelerator ratio (0.4 : 6.0). (×) Total crosslinks. (■) Mono-sulfide. (▲) Polysulfide. (●) Disulfide. The upper and lower figures on the curve relating to total crosslinks are values of E and E', respectively.

enous activators or zinc carboxylates are included to render the ZMBT soluble by complex formation (Fig. 9). Complementary to this, vulcanizing systems based on MBT or MBTS alone are very sensitive to small varia-tions in the concentrations of the nitrogenous bases and fatty and resin acids which occur in natural rubber (16).

The use of the principles discussed above to develop vulcanizing systems and conditions which will afford natural rubber vulcanizates of particular structure, especially of the type exemplified by the vulcanizates of Figure 8 which show good resistance to thermal and thermooxidative aging, is currently being pursued and will be described elsewhere (21).

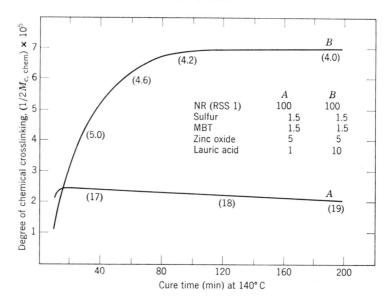

Fig. 9. Effect of fatty acid concentration on the yield of crosslinks in the MBT-accelerated sulfur vulcanization of natural rubber at 140°C. The figures on the curves are values of E.

Acknowledgment

I wish to pay tribute to the fact that the work on which this review is based was carried out under the initiative and direction of Professor C. G. Moore. I wish to thank him and Drs. B. Saville, B. R. Trego, and A. A. Watson, who were concerned with me in its execution.

References

1. C. G. Moore, L. Mullins, and P. McL. Swift, *J. Appl. Polymer Sci.*, **5**, 293 (1961).
2. C. G. Moore, *Proceedings of the Natural Rubber Producers' Research Association Jubilee Conference Cambridge, 1964*, L. Mullins, Ed., Maclaren, London, 1965, p. 188.
3. C. G. Moore and B. R. Trego, *J. Appl. Polymer Sci.*, **5**, 299 (1961).
4. C. G. Moore and B. R. Trego, *J. Appl. Polymer Sci.*, **8**, 1957 (1964).
5. C. G. Moore, B. Saville, and B. R. Trego, to be published.
6. B. Milligan, *J. Chem. Soc.*, **1966A**, 34.
7. G. M. C. Higgins and B. Saville, *J. Chem. Soc.*, **1963**, 2812.
8. A. Y. Coran, *Rubber Chem. Technol.*, **37**, 679 (1964).
9. B. Milligan, *Rubber Chem. Technol.*, **39**, 1115 (1966).
10. Y. Kawaoka, *J. Soc. Rubber Ind. Japan*, **16**, 755 (1943) and previous papers.
11. C. G. Moore, B. Saville, and A. A. Watson, *J. Appl. Polymer Sci.*, **3**, 373 (1960).
12. C. G. Moore and A. A. Watson, *J. Appl. Polymer Sci.*, **8**, 581 (1964).

13. W. Scheele, *Rubber Chem. Technol.*, **34**, 1306 (1961), and references there cited.
14. J. R. Dunn and J. Scanlan, *J. Appl. Polymer Sci.*, **1**, 84 (1959).
15. C. G. Moore and A. A. Watson, forthcoming publication.
16. L. Bateman, C. G. Moore, M. Porter, and B. Saville, in *Chemistry and Physics of Rubber-like Substances*, L. Bateman, Ed., Maclaren, London, 1963, Chap. 15.
17. A. A. Watson, Ph.D. thesis, University of London, 1965.
18. G. M. C. Higgins and M. Porter, unpublished work.
19. B. C. Barton and E. J. Hart, *Ind. Eng. Chem.*, **44**, 2444 (1952).
20. C. G. Moore and M. Porter, *J. Appl. Polymer Sci.*, in press (1967). Cf. ref. 2, p. 182.
21. T. D. Skinner and A. A. Watson, *Rubber Age*, in press.
22. D. S. Campbell and B. Saville, Proc. Intern. Rubber Conf., 1967, in press.

Role of Disulfide Interchange in Keratin Fiber Deformation

HANS-DIETRICH WEIGMANN
and
LUDWIG REBENFELD
Textile Research Institute, Princeton, New Jersey

INTRODUCTION

A complete understanding of wool fiber deformation in terms of the native configuration and structural rearrangements can only be obtained by identifying the specific influences of the bonds and interactions involved. The disulfide bond, one of the few covalent bonds involved in the maintenance of the tertiary structure in keratin fibers, occupies a unique place. Although a covalent bond it has been found to be rather unstable, and structural changes involving these bonds can occur without apparent changes in the disulfide concentration. This so-called disulfide interchange mechanism is catalyzed by sulfhydryl groups:

$$R—S—S—R + R'—S—S—R' \underset{\longleftarrow}{\overset{R''—S^{(-)}}{\rightleftharpoons}} 2R'—S—S—R \qquad (1)$$

In protein fibers such as human hair and wool containing high amounts of disulfide crosslinks and small concentrations of sulfhydryl groups, it would appear reasonable to expect an interchange between these groups under appropriate conditions. Burley (1) was the first to postulate that such an interchange mechanism plays a part in length changes in wool. Several years later the importance of SH groups in the second stage of supercontraction of keratin fibers was found (2,3) and recently the participation of these groups in the setting mechanism for wool fibers has been discussed (4–7). The disulfide interchange mechanism and its participation in the deformation of keratin fibers has been the subject of an intensive investigation at Textile Research Institute during the past several years. The results which have been obtained in these studies are presented and reviewed in this paper.

STRESS–STRAIN BEHAVIOR

When a wool fiber is stretched in water the stress–strain curve reveals three distinctly different regions (8) as shown in Figure 1. In the Hookean region the stress is approximately linearly related to the fiber strain,

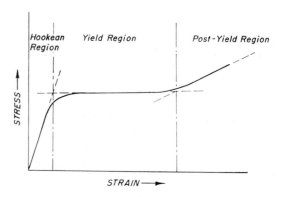

Fig. 1. Schematic stress–strain curve of a single keratin fiber.

reflecting a bond angle deformation in the microfibrils. At a certain strain, usually 1–2%, the fiber yields and the α-helices in the microfibrils start to unfold (9,10). This process of unfolding requires only small amounts of additional stress and would go on until the α–β transformation is completed, leading to an extension of over 100%. At an extension of $\sim 30\%$, however, the stress suddenly increases sharply and the fiber breaks at an extension between 50 and 60%, i.e., well before the α–β transformation is complete. Considerable disagreement exists about the structural and molecular interpretation of this part of the stress–strain curve, the so-called post-yield region (11–15). It has been shown, however, that modification of the disulfide content, or changes in the SH content of the fibers, has a strong effect on the deformation behavior of the fibers in this region. Up to the beginning of the post-yield region the deformation of the fiber in water is completely reversible unless the stretching occurs at elevated temperatures or unless the fiber is held at this strain level for long periods of time. If this extension is exceeded, however, an increasing element of irreversibility becomes apparent which does not necessarily result in a permanent deformation but manifests itself in a decrease in work necessary to reextend the fiber in a second extension–contraction cycle (16,17).

An investigation of the temperature dependence of the stress–strain curve of wool in water shows a transition temperature for the extension at which the yield region turns over into the post-yield region (18,19). The extension at which this turnover occurs is relatively temperature independent up to 60–70°C, when it starts to increase rapidly (Fig. 2). Other physical properties of extended wool fibers show changes in their temperature dependence in the same temperature range, e.g., the ability of the fiber to achieve permanent set (20), and the loss of reversibility of the α–β

transformation (19). If the concentration of free SH groups in the fiber is increased the transition temperature is drastically lowered and reaches room temperature at an SH content of approximately 200 μmole/g (Fig. 3). This dependence of the transition temperature on the SH content is shown in Figure 4 (21).

It must be kept in mind that an increase in the SH content always requires a decrease in the disulfide content which apparently also plays a significant part in determining the transition temperature. For fiber modification XXXIX, for instance, in which a considerable number of disulfide bonds have been broken (19.1%), and after most of the free SH groups have been methylated (leaving only 14.4 μmole/g free SH), the transition temperature is considerably lower than for the untreated fiber which has a comparable SH content. The effects of a stepwise elimination of the free SH groups, first by methylation and then by blocking all SH groups with N-ethylmaleimide (NEMI), are shown in Figure 5. The presumably complete elimination of SH groups with NEMI increases the stability of the disulfide bonds to such an extent that the extension at the turnover point becomes completely temperature independent up to 85°C. There is a slight but significant increase in the extension at the turnover point at temperatures above 85°C, indicating a transition at this temperature. This is true for all the fiber modifications that have been investigated

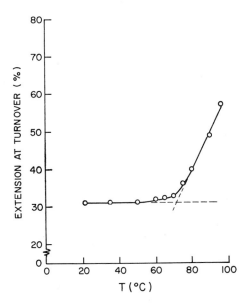

Fig. 2. Extension at turnover point of BA fleece wool fibers in buffer pH 6.98.

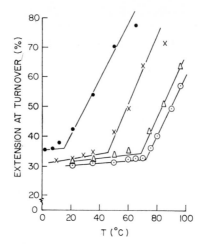

Fig. 3. Extension at turnover point of reduced BA fleece wool fibers in buffer pH 6.98.

	Sample	SH content, μmole/g	Trans. temp., °C
(⊙)	Untreated	12.4	72
(△)	XXXVIII	25.4	68
(×)	XL	72.3	46
(●)	XXXIX	200.9	15

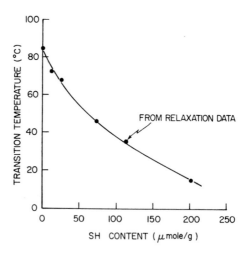

Fig. 4. Apparent second-order transition temperature of BA fleece wool fibers in buffer pH 6.98 as a function of sulfhydryl content.

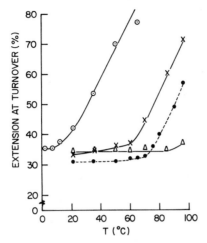

Fig. 5. Extension at turnover point of reduced BA fleece wool fibers in buffer pH 6.98. Samples and SH content: (⊙) Reduced (XXXIX), 200.9 μmole/g. (×) Reduced and methylated, 14.4 μmole/g. (△) Reduced and methylated, NEMI added, 0.0 μmole/g. (●) Untreated, 12.4 μmole/g.

in the presence of NEMI, as shown in Figure 6. It is interesting to note that the transition temperature is the same for all levels of disulfide decrease. The extension at which the turnover point occurs increases slightly with decreasing disulfide content, as shown in Figure 7. The transition temperature in the absence of SH groups, and its independence of the decrease in disulfide content, may be associated with hydrolysis of the disulfide

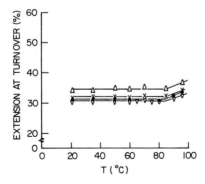

Fig. 6. Extension at turnover point of reduced BA fleece wool fibers in buffer (pH 6.98) + NEMI. Sample and % decrease in cystine: (▽) Untreated, 0%. (●) XXXVIII, 1.4%. (×) XL, 6.0%. (△) XXXIX, 19.1%.

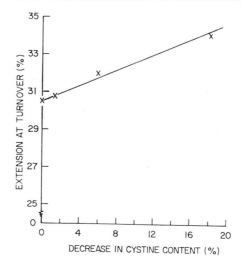

Fig. 7. Extension at turnover point of reduced BA fleece wool fibers in buffer (pH 6.98) + NEMI.

bonds at this temperature. The dependence of the transition temperature on the SH content of the fibers indicates that this transition is connected with the stability of the disulfide bonds. The rate of the disulfide inter-change, which determines the relative stability of the disulfide bonds, depends on the concentration of the catalyst, i.e., the SH group in the fiber.

In an untreated fiber the disulfide crosslinks reach such a degree of instability at 72°C that the restrictions for mobility of the chain segments are decreased to a critical level, and the viscoelastic behavior of the fiber shows a rapidly increasing flow component with increasing temperature. This is closely related to what is postulated to happen in the rubbery flow region (22) which, in crosslinked polymers, is connected with changes in chemical structure caused by oxidative scission, depolymerization, bond interchange, etc. Polysulfide rubbers undergo interchange reactions, catalyzed by mercaptide ions (23,24), involving disulfide or polysulfide bonds in this region in a manner analogous to wool.

Where, in the rather complex morphological structure of the keratin fiber, does this reaction occur? It is well known that the matrix contains a comparatively high amount of disulfide crosslinks and therefore appears to be the logical location of the plastic flow phenomenon. If this is the case, there must be a close interrelation between matrix and the crystalline microfibrils, since in the same temperature range these crystalline regions lose their ability to undergo a reversible α–β transformation (19) and the fiber becomes increasingly elastomeric. These two phenomena in the matrix and the microfibrils seem to be interrelated since the suppression of the flow component in the matrix, as shown by an increase in the transition temperature for fibers where the SH groups have been eliminated by blocking, apparently restores the reversibility of the α–β transformation even at high temperatures (7) as will be shown later.

STRESS RELAXATION

Depending on the rate at which a fiber is stretched, a certain amount of stress relaxation occurs during the stretching process, and it is obvious that the stress–strain properties of polymers are closely interrelated with their stress relaxation behavior. The breakdown of the various bonds involved in the stretching process is reflected in the stress relaxation curves. Stress relaxation of keratin fibers was first investigated by Speakman and his co-workers (8,25), who found that two stages can be clearly distinguished. The first stage involves the breakdown of secondary bonds such as H bonds, salt linkages, and van der Waals interactions (26–28).

The second stage of stress relaxation is much slower and is connected with the scission of disulfide bonds. The stress-supporting disulfide bonds can be broken by the addition of reducing agents, and stress relaxation in the presence of reducing agents has indeed been used to study their reaction with disulfide bonds in keratin assuming that the rate of relaxation is equal to the rate of bond breakdown (29–32). There seems to be a close analogy between the reductive scission of disulfide bonds in the presence of reducing agents and the sulfhydryl-catalyzed interchange between disulfide bonds. Disulfide interchange in connection with stress relaxation was first discussed by Tobolsky and his co-workers (23,24,33) and by Fettes and co-workers (34) to explain the chemical relaxation of polysulfide rubbers at elevated temperatures. It was pointed out that the chemical stress relaxation is markedly affected by traces of mercaptan and that polysulfide rubbers free from mercaptan and especially mercaptide groups should be quite stable toward chemical stress relaxation. Such a dependence on sulfhydryl groups was also found in the case of keratin fibers (35,36), which show a remarkable stability against the second-stage stress relaxation in the presence of reagents which block sulfhydryl groups.

In Figures 8 and 9 the relaxation modulus is shown as a function of time for various temperatures in the absence and presence of an SH-blocking reagent, and it is clearly indicated that the presence of the blocking reagent suppresses the second stage of stress relaxation. Apparently a structural rearrangement occurs in this second stage of stress relaxation which involves disulfide bonds. These disulfide bonds support the stress,

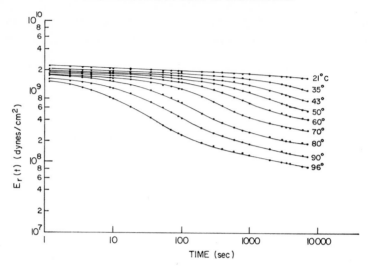

Fig. 8. Relaxation modulus as a function of time and temperature for untreated BA fleece wool fibers from 20% strain in phosphate buffer at pH 7.0.

and during rearrangement they are moved into stress-free positions by a disulfide interchange mechanism. In the presence of a blocking reagent the interchange mechanism cannot proceed and the structural rearrangement does not occur.

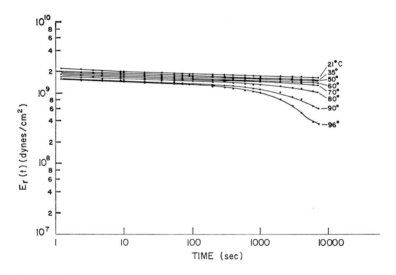

Fig. 9. Relaxation modulus as a function of time and temperature for untreated BA fleece wool fibers from 20% strain in phosphate buffer (pH 7.0) + NEMI.

An investigation of the temperature dependence of the relaxation modulus at a time of 10 sec reveals a transition temperature at approximately 70°C indicated by a deviation from a linear temperature–modulus relationship, as shown in Figure 10. In the presence of the sulfhydryl group blocking reagent the deviation from linearity at 70°C does not take place and the relaxation modulus decreases linearly over the entire temperature range. This is another clear indication of the strong effect of SH groups on the stability of the stressed disulfide bonds in keratin fibers.

The temperature of 70°C at which the deviation from linearity occurs in the absence of NEMI is quite close to the transition temperature which was found from investigating the temperature dependence of stress–strain curves, as discussed previously. Apparently the measurement of the temperature dependence of the relaxation modulus is another means of determining this SH-dependent transition. Since this transition is connected with the interchange between disulfide bonds, and therefore with the rate of this reaction, the temperature at which the transition is observed depends on the time at which the modulus is measured. With increasing time the transition temperature decreases. The observation that the transition temperature determined from stress–strain measurements coincides with that determined from the temperature dependence of the relaxation modulus at 10 sec is due to the fact that comparable times are involved in both cases.

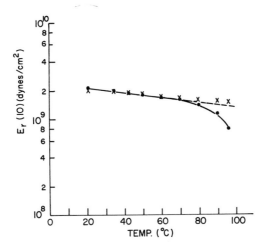

Fig. 10. Relaxation modulus at 10 sec as a function of temperature for untreated BA fleece wool fibers from 20% strain in phosphate buffer at pH 7.0. (●) Without NEMI. (×) With NEMI.

KINETIC ANALYSIS

Tobolsky and co-workers (37) have shown that the following expression holds for the disappearance of stress supporting network chains in interchanging polysulfide rubbers:

$$-\frac{dN(t)}{dt} = kmN(t) \tag{2}$$

where $N(t)$ is the number of moles of network chains per unit volume supporting stress at time t, k is a specific rate constant for the interchange reaction, and m is the number of bonds per network chain capable of undergoing interchange.

Since the stress decay in the second stage of stress relaxation in keratin fibers is controlled by disulfide bonds and their removal from stress-supporting positions by an interchange reaction, this equation appears to be suitable for the quantitative description of this process. If an expression for the concentration of the catalyst, n, i.e., the mercaptide ion in the fiber, is introduced, the following expression is obtained.

$$\frac{N(t)}{N(0)} = \exp\left(-\frac{t}{\tau_{ch}}\right) = \frac{f(t)}{f(0)} \tag{3}$$

where $\tau_{ch} = 1/kmn$. Since this equation describes only the II stage of stress relaxation, the initial stress $f(0)$ must be replaced by a stress value taken at a time when the I stage of stress relaxation is completed and the interchange reaction has not yet begun. Since the elimination of SH groups with NEMI apparently stops the interchange reaction but does not interfere with the I stage of stress relaxation controlled by the breakdown of secondary bonds the stress value in the presence of NEMI at 1.2 sec was chosen as a substitute for $f(0)$.

In Figures 11 and 12 are shown families of curves of $S_t/S_{NEMI\,1.2}$ as a function of the logarithm of time for the various temperatures at the 20 and 40% strain levels, respectively, where S_t is the stress at any time t in the absence of NEMI, and $S_{NEMI\,1.2}$ is the stress in the presence of NEMI after 1.2 sec of relaxation. Since the rate constant k is a function of the temperature alone, plots of $S_t/S_{NEMI\,1.2}$ vs. log t should be superimposable by horizontal translation along the log t axis. While this is true in a limited way, the curves tend to level off at increasingly higher stress values with decreasing temperature, particularly at the 20% strain level.

The activation energy of the interchange reaction may be determined from the temperature dependence of the chemical relaxation time τ_{ch}. Such relationships are shown in Figure 13 where it may be seen that the

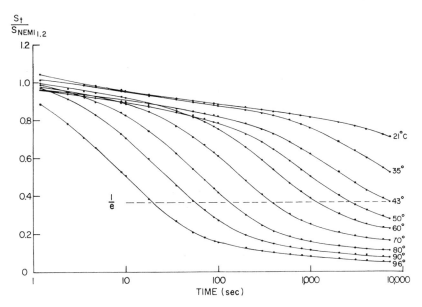

Fig. 11. Stress relaxation from 20% strain for untreated BA fleece wool fibers in phosphate buffer at pH 7.0 at various temperatures. Stress normalized by the stress in the presence of NEMI after 1.2 sec.

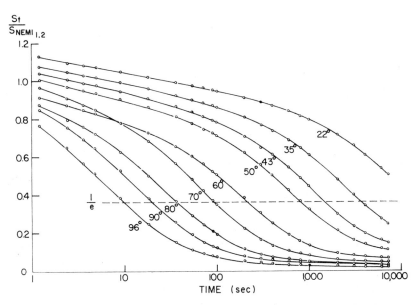

Fig. 12. Stress relaxation from 40% strain for untreated BA fleece wool fibers in phosphate buffer at pH 7.0 at various temperatures. Stress normalized by the stress in the presence of NEMI after 1.2 sec.

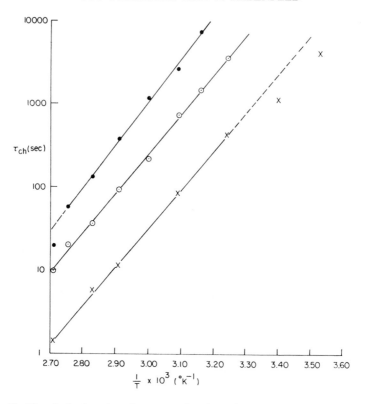

Fig. 13. Chemical relaxation times as a function of the reciprocal of the absolute temperature for untreated and reduced BA fleece wool fibers. (●) Untreated, 20% strain at 500%/min. (☉) Untreated, 40% strain at 1000%/min. (×) Reduced, 20% strain at 500%/min.

points fall quite satisfactorily on straight lines when τ_{ch} is plotted as a function of $1/T$, where T is the absolute temperature. Calculations of the slopes of these lines by the method of least squares resulted in activation energies for the untreated fibers of 23.6 ± 1.0 kcal/mole for 20% extension and 21.8 ± 0.4 kcal/mole for 40% extension.

In the case of the reduced sample (with a tenfold increase in the concentration of the catalyst), the expected shift to shorter relaxation times can be observed. The activation energy in this case is almost identical (21.3 kcal/mole) with that of the untreated fibers, indicating that the rate-controlling mechanism is the same. These activation energies are in good agreement with those found in other polymer systems whose viscoelastic behavior is largely controlled by disulfide interchange reactions (37,38).

REVERSIBILITY OF DEFORMATION

As has been shown, an extended keratin fiber undergoes a structural and molecular rearrangement above the transition temperature. The rate of this rearrangement increases with increasing temperature as can be seen in Figure 8 where the relaxation modulus can be taken as an indication of the extent of the rearrangement. At 96°C it is complete within a few minutes. Various other properties change irreversibly in the same period of time, i.e., the x-ray pattern of the α-keratin and the birefringence (39). Another indication for disordering and irreversible rearrangements of the native keratin structure is the longitudinal swelling of the fibers. In water at 96°C longitudinal swelling increases within a few minutes after extension of the fiber and reaches a maximum value which depends on the strain level and is then relatively time independent (39–42). If the fiber is released after this structural rearrangement, contraction occurs under entropic forces (18) to an equilibrium length which is determined by the bonds formed in the rearranged configuration of the fibers and their stability under the conditions of release. One of the bonds formed in the rearranged extended configuration is the disulfide bond which, during the rearrangement, is removed from stress-supporting into stress-free positions by an interchange mechanism as indicated. Upon release of the fiber these newly formed disulfide bonds come under stress again and, unless prevented from doing so, they are again removed from these stressed positions into energetically favored positions via an interchange mechanism. This second rearrangement during the contraction can also be prevented by elimination of the catalyst for the reaction which dominates the rearrangement, i.e., by adding a reagent which effectively blocks the mercaptide groups. If the blocking reagent is added shortly before the fiber is released, the disulfide bonds which are now in positions in which they oppose contraction become stable and the rearranged extended configuration is "frozen in." By interrupting the "setting" process at various times the rearrangement of the disulfide bonds can be followed, as is manifested by the increase in fiber length which is referred to as "permanent set" (Fig. 14). As expected from the classical experiments of Astbury and Woods (43), the "water curve" shows supercontraction at short setting times and increasing amounts of permanent set as the setting times increase. If NEMI is added 2 min before the fibers are released from extension, this curve changes completely. As the rearrangement of the polypeptide chain proceeds, and the disulfide bonds are being displaced, the amount of permanent set one can get by stopping the rearrangement at different times increases until a maximum is reached where the structural rearrangement is complete. The slope of this "NEMI curve" is initially steep and later levels off similar to that of the stress-relaxation curve which is also shown in Figure 14.

The inflexion in the "NEMI curve" cannot be observed in the stress-relaxation curve and has not been found at other extensions. It appears that the "NEMI curve" and the stress-relaxation curve illustrate the same molecular rearrangement from different viewpoints. Stress relaxation shows the displacement of the stress-supporting disulfide bonds, and the

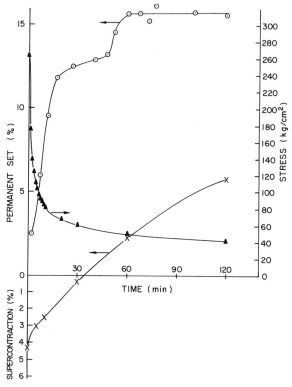

Fig. 14. (×) Change in length of fibers held at 20% extension in water at 96°C for various times. (▲) Stress relaxation of fiber after 20% extension in water at 96°C. (⊙) Change in length of fibers held at 20% extension in water at 96°C for various times; NEMI added 1 min before release from extension.

"NEMI curve" shows that they are displaced into positions that support the extended configuration. The relative rate for the rearrangement appears to be independent of the strain level as indicated by Figure 15 which shows the "NEMI and WATER curves" for extensions varying from 10 to 60%.

If the proposed interchange mechanism is correct, changes in the SH concentrations in the fibers should have considerable effects on the rate at which the molecular rearrangements occur. As expected, and in accord with stress relaxation data (35), the reduced sample (32.3 μmole SH/g)

shows a more rapid approach, and the blocked sample (0 μmole SH/g) a
slower approach to the completely rearranged structure (Fig. 16) (untreated fiber 12.4 μmole SH/g). The "water curves" for the three fiber
modifications show clearly that the rate at which the extended configuration is stabilized depends considerably upon the concentration of the SH

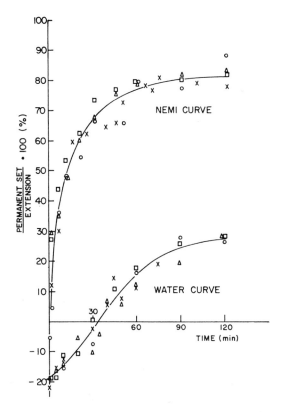

Fig. 15. Relative change in length of fibers extended in H₂O at 96°C (5%/min).
Extension: (○) 10%; (×) 20%; (△) 40%; (□) 60%.

groups in the fibers. This indicates that the stabilization process is not a
mere crystallization of the extended β form for which the conditions are
unchanged (time, temperature) but that there has to be an additional
stabilization by chemical bonds, the formation of which depends upon the
SH concentration. It is possible that these bonds are the thioether crosslinks of the amino acid lanthionine which is formed under these conditions
(4) and the formation of which appears to depend upon the SH concentration (44).

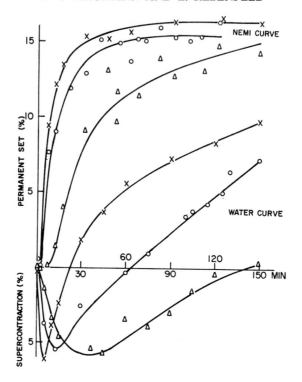

Fig. 16. Changes in length of modified fibers in H_2O at 96°C. 20% extension. 100%/min rate of extension. (△) Blocked I_B. (○) Untreated. (×) Reduced XXXVII.

Since the structural and molecular rearrangements which occur during irreversible deformations are controlled by interchange between disulfide bonds and SH groups, the presence of an SH-blocking reagent should prevent this rearrangement, and one would expect completely reversible deformation behavior. The data in Tables 1 and 2 indicate that this is exactly what happens in the presence of NEMI. There is no disorientation as indicated by a lack of supercontraction or setting and the longitudinal swelling, another indication of irreversible disorientation, remains unchanged for the entire 2-hr period. The birefringence is essentially unchanged after 2 hr, indicating that there have been no structural changes during this rather strong treatment (2-hr set and 2-hr slack at 96°C in aqueous NEMI solution). This behavior could be predicted from the transition temperature under these conditions, which would be expected to be higher than 96°C. The inability of keratin fibers which have been treated with 1-fluoro-2,4-dinitrobenzene (45,46) or iodine (4) to be permanently

Table 1

Set and Swelling of B.A. Fleece Wool Fibers at 96°C

(Setting rate = 100%/min; setting strain = 20%)

Time of setting (min)	Set in water		Set in NEMI soln.	
	Perm. set (%)	Long. swell (%)	Perm. set (%)	Long. swell (%)
0	0.0	1.7	−0.5	1.6
5	−3.8	4.5	−0.1	1.5
15	−5.1	4.4	0.6	1.6
30	−2.5	4.9	−0.1	1.5
60	−0.3	5.0	0.0	1.6
90	2.5	5.1	−0.8	1.7
120	5.1	4.9	−0.1	1.6

set in boiling water or steam must also be attributed to a similar increase in their transition temperature which is due to an elimination of free SH groups in the fibers by these chemical treatments.

In general, it can be concluded that in the presence of an effective SH-blocking reagent the disulfide bond becomes a stable crosslink and the mechanism for the irreversible deformation is suppressed. There is, of course, no absolute stability for any bonds and in the presence of SH-blocking reagents the slow hydrolysis of disulfide bonds will weaken the native structure and thereby introduce an element of irreversibility as indicated by the data on the mechanical properties in Table 2.

Table 2

Properties of B.A. Fleece Wool Fibers Set for 2 hr at 96°C

(Setting rate = 100%/min; setting strain = 20%)

	Set in water		Set in NEMI soln.	
	Before	After	Before	After
Birefringence	0.0117	0.0083	0.0117	0.0112
Permanent set (%)	—	5.3	—	−0.1
Long. swelling (%)	1.59	4.88	1.50	1.62
Energy to 25% exten. (kg/cm²)	119.5	49.5	120.2	69.0
Elastic modulus (mg/cm²)	27.0	3.0	26.3	16.6
Stress at yield pt.	0.42	0.033	0.44	0.20

References

1. R. W. Burley, *Proc. Intern. Wool Text. Res. Conf., Australia, 1955*, D88.
2. W. G. Crewther and L. M. Dowling, *J. Textile Inst.*, **51**, T775 (1960).
3. H.-D. Weigmann and L. Rebenfeld, *Textile Res. J.*, **33**, 985 (1963).
4. H. Zahn, F. W. Kunitz, and H. Meichelbeck, *Colloque "Structure de la Laine," Inst. Text. France 1961*, p. 227.
5. J. B. Caldwell, S. J. Leach, A. Meschers, and B. Milligan, *Textile Res. J.*, **34**, 627 (1964).
6. B. Milligan, J. B. Caldwell, and S. J. Leach, *III Cirtel, Paris 1965*, Sect. 2, 309.
7. H.-D. Weigmann, L. Rebenfeld, and C. Dansizer, *III Cirtel, Paris 1965*, Sect. 2, 319.
8. J. B. Speakman, *Proc. Roy. Soc. (London)*, **103B**, 377 (1928).
9. E. G. Bendit, *Nature*, **179**, 535 (1957).
10. E. G. Bendit, *Textile Res. J.*, **30**, 547 (1960).
11. M. Feughelman and A. R. Haly, *Biochim. Biophys. Acta*, **32**, 596 (1959).
12. M. Feughelman and A. R. Haly, *Kolloid Z.*, **168**, 107 (1960).
13. M. Feughelman and A. R. Haly, *Colloque "Structure de la Laine," Inst. Text. France, Paris 1961*.
14. M. Feughelman, A. R. Haly, and P. Mason, *Nature*, **196**, 957 (1962).
15. A. R. B. Skertchly, *J. Textile Inst.*, **55**, T154 (1964).
16. J. B. Speakman, *J. Textile Inst.*, **38**, T102 (1947).
17. J. B. Speakman and L. Jagger, *Nature*, **164**, 190 (1949).
18. M. Feughelman and T. W. Mitchell, *Textile Res. J.*, **29**, 404 (1959).
19. M. Feughelman, A. R. Haly, and B. J. Rigby, *Textile Res. J.*, **29**, 311 (1959).
20. A. J. Farnworth, *Textile Res. J.*, **27**, 632 (1957).
21. H.-D. Weigmann, L. Rebenfeld, and C. Dansizer, *Textile Res. J.*, **35**, 604 (1965).
22. A. V. Tobolsky, *Properties and Structure of Polymers*, Wiley, New York, 1960, p. 72.
23. M. Mochulsky and A. V. Tobolsky, *Ind. Eng. Chem.*, **40**, 2155 (1948).
24. M. D. Stern and A. V. Tobolsky, *J. Chem. Phys.*, **14**, 93 (1946).
25. J. B. Speakman and S. Y. Shah, *J. Soc. Dyers Colourists*, **57**, 108 (1941).
26. G. C. Wood, *J. Textile Inst.*, **45**, T462 (1954).
27. B. J. Rigby, *Australian J. Phys.*, **8**, 176 (1955).
28. M. Feughelman and B. J. Rigby, *Proc. Intern. Wool Textile Res. Conf. Australia, 1955*, D62.
29. S. M. Katz and A. V. Tobolsky, *Textile Res. J.*, **20**, 87 (1950).
30. E. T. Kubu, *Textile Res. J.*, **22**, 765 (1952).
31. E. T. Kubu and D. J. Montgomery, *Textile Res. J.*, **22**, 778 (1952).
32. C. E. Reese and E. Eyring, *Textile Res. J.*, **20**, 743 (1950).
33. A. V. Tobolsky, *J. Appl. Phys.*, **27**, 673 (1956).
34. E. M. Fettes, F. O. Davis, and E. Bertozzi, *J. Polymer Sci.*, **19**, 17 (1956).
35. H.-D. Weigmann, L. Rebenfeld, and C. Dansizer, *Textile Res. J.*, **36**, 535 (1966).
36. M. Feughelman, *III Cirtel, Paris 1965*, Sect. 2, p. 245.
37. A. V. Tobolsky, W. J. MacKnight, and M. Takahashi, *J. Phys. Chem.*, **68**, 787 (1964).
38. A. V. Tobolsky, *Properties and Structure of Polymers*, Wiley, New York, 1960, Chap. V, Sect 8.
39. M. Feughelman, A. R. Haly, and J. W. Snaith, *Textile Res. J.*, **32**, 913 (1962).
40. H. Zahn and H. Brauckhoff, *Biochem. Z.*, **318**, 401 (1948).

41. A. R. Haly and J. W. Snaith, *Textile Res. J.*, **33**, 872 (1963).
42. H.-D. Weigmann, L. Rebenfeld, and C. Dansizer, *Textile Res. J.*, **35**, 412 (1965).
43. W. T. Astbury and H. J. Woods, *Phil. Trans. Roy. Soc.* (*London*), **232**, 333 (1933).
44. H. Zahn, F. W. Kunitz, and D. Hildebrand, *J. Textile Inst.*, **51**, T740 (1960).
45. A. J. Farnworth and J. B. Speakman, *Nature*, **161**, 890 (1948).
46. J. B. Speakman, *Textile Rec.*, **81**, 46 (1963).

Polymerization of Fluorothiocarbonyl Compounds

W. H. SHARKEY

E. I. du Pont de Nemours and Company, Wilmington, Delaware

The preparation and chemistry of fluorothiocarbonyl compounds (1–3) has been investigated in some detail in the past several years. The parent compound in this class is thiocarbonyl fluoride, $CF_2\!\!=\!\!S$. It has been prepared by a number of routes, which are outlined below.

$$Cl_2C\!\!=\!\!S \xrightarrow{hv} Cl_2C\diagup{\overset{S}{\underset{S}{}}}\diagdown CCl_2 \longrightarrow F_2C\diagup{\overset{S}{\underset{S}{}}}\diagdown CF_2 \xrightarrow{\Delta} CF_2\!\!=\!\!S^4$$

$$CF_2ClSCl \xrightarrow{Sn} CF_2\!\!=\!\!S^5$$

$$(CF_3S)_2Hg + SiH_3I \longrightarrow SiH_3SCF_3 \longrightarrow SiH_3F + CF_2\!\!=\!\!S^6$$

One of the most unusual features of $CF_2\!\!=\!\!S$ is the ease with which it polymerizes in anionic systems. Addition of a trace of dimethylformamide, or of a number of other mild bases, to a solution of $CF_2\!\!=\!\!S$ in dry ether that is cooled to $-78°C$ promotes a very rapid polymerization (2). The product is a high molecular weight polymer that has a number average molecular weight of 300,000–400,000 and a weight average molecular weight in excess of 1 million. It is a tough elastomer that is surprisingly resistant to acids and aqueous alkali. For example, the polymer can be boiled in nitric acid without apparent damage. It also can be boiled in 40% aqueous alkali for 24 hours or longer without suffering diminution of molecular weight, although some weight is lost. The elastomeric poly-(thiocarbonyl fluoride) can be cured by mixing into it divinylbenzene along with a small amount of a free-radical initiator followed by heating to 100°C in a positive pressure mold. The cured product has good snap and is a strong, resilient, and highly abrasion-resistant rubber.

Not all properties of poly(thiocarbonyl fluoride) are good ones. For example, although it is elastomeric as isolated and when formed into films by melt-pressing, the polymer does slowly crystallize at temperatures below 35°C to a nonrubbery, plastic form. Also, the polymer is not stable above 175°C. Furthermore, it is quickly and completely destroyed by amines.

It became desirable to determine the structure of the polymer in order to develop approaches toward improving stability and to devise means for copolymerization. This was done by chemical and spectral studies on poly(thiocarbonyl fluoride), which indicated that the polymer is composed mainly of long chains of $CF_3S-(-CF_2-S-)_n-CF=S$. Reaction with methanol-C^{14} established that there is approximately one methanol reactive group per polymer chain. Degradation of the polymer by reaction with antimony pentafluoride gave low molecular weight oils composed of $CF_3S-(-CF_2-S-)_{\bar{x}}CF_3$ in which x varied from about 3 to about 25. These oils show strong infrared absorption at 13.1 μ and fluorine NMR resonance at 37.6 ppm higher field than that of CCl_3F used as an external standard. That these values are representative of CF_3S- was indicated by comparison with values obtained using $CF_3SCF=S$ as a model. This compound also has fluorine NMR resonance at 71.5 ppm lower field than the standard which has been assigned to the fluorine in $SCF=S$. These same values can be discerned in low molecular weight poly(thiocarbonyl fluoride) obtained by anionic polymerization at the relatively high temperature of $-25°C$. A resume of the infrared and chemical data is shown in the following table.

End group	IR absorption at	
CF_3S-	13.1 μ	IR band unaffected by reaction with methanol
$-SCF=0$	5.4 μ	IR band removed by reaction with methanol
$-SCF=S$	8.2 μ	IR band removed by reaction with methanol

Initiation with dimethylformamide gives polymer that does not contain initiator fragments. Use of dimethylformamide tagged with C^{14} established this fact. Also, from end group studies it became evident that there is a chain-transfer factor of at least 10 in this polymerization. It is believed the polymerization may occur as follows:

Initiation:

$$DMF + \begin{Bmatrix} \text{monomer} \\ \text{solvent} \\ \text{impurity} \end{Bmatrix} \longrightarrow B^{\ominus}$$

$$B^{\ominus} + CF_2=S \longrightarrow BCF_2S^{\ominus}$$
$$F^{\ominus} + CF_2=S \longrightarrow CF_3S^{\ominus}$$

Propagation:

$$BCF_2S^{\ominus} + nCF_2{=}S \longrightarrow BCF_2S{\left(CF_2S\right)}_{n-1}CF_2S^{\ominus}$$

$$CF_3S^{\ominus} + nCF_2{=}S \longrightarrow CF_3S{\left(CF_2S\right)}_{n-1}CF{=}S^{\ominus}$$

Termination:

$$BCF_2S{\left(\text{-}SCF_2S\right)}_{n-1}CF_2S^{\ominus} \longrightarrow BCF_2S{\left(CF_2S\right)}_{n-1}CF{=}S + F^{\ominus}$$

$$CF_3S{\left(CF_2S\right)}_{n-1}CF_2S^{\ominus} \longrightarrow CF_3S{\left(CF_2S\right)}_{n-1}CF{=}S + F^{\ominus}$$

One of the consequences of the structure of the polymer is instability to heat. It has been mentioned that poly(thiocarbonyl fluoride) decomposes above 175°C. The product from this decomposition is $CF_2{=}S$ monomer, which can be recovered almost quantitatively. The heat decomposition has been rationalized as probably involving hydrolysis of the unstable end to form a chain that could eliminate carbon oxysulfide as shown in Scheme I.

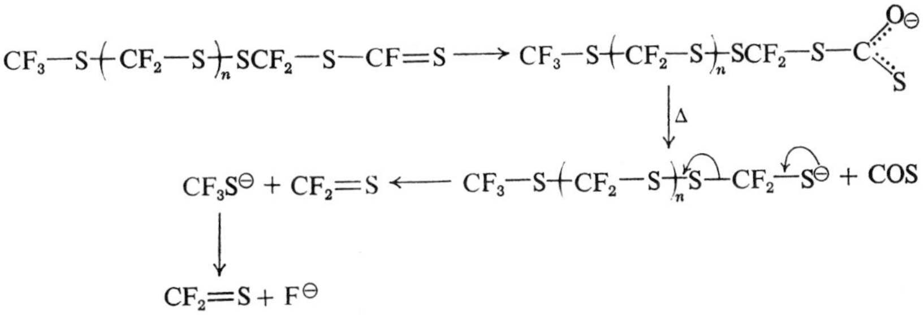

Scheme I

Decomposition by triethylamine is also visualized as a consequence of the unstable end of the polymer. In this case, the first step could be reaction of the amine together with traces of water that might be present in the polymer as follows.

$$\sim SCF_2{-}S{-}CF{=}S + 2R_3N + H_2O \longrightarrow \sim SCF_2{-}S{-}C(\cdots O^{\ominus})(\cdots S)\ R_3NH^{\oplus} + R_3NHF$$

One of the surprising aspects of fluorothiocarbonyl compound polymerization is the susceptibility of these materials to free-radical initiation (7). In this case, the most critical feature is the use of very low polymerization temperatures. This means that the problem was development of a method for generating free radicals chemically at low temperatures in sufficient quantities to sustain polymerization. The solution to this problem was the use of the trialkylborane/oxygen redox couple. Polymerization

of CF_2=S either in bulk or in solution at $-78°C$ in the presence of a trialkylborane and oxygen led to high molecular weight poly(thiocarbonyl
fluoride). Radicals were shown to be generated via a two-step reaction.
In the first step, the trialkylborane is oxidized to boron peroxide. The
second step involves reaction of the boron peroxide with additional
trialkylborane to generate radicals.

$$R_3B + O_2 \longrightarrow R_2BOOR$$
$$R_2BOOR + 2R'_3B \longrightarrow R_2BOBR'_2 + R'_2BOR + 2R'\cdot$$

It is important to use less than one mole of oxygen per mole of trialkylborane because of the requirements of the second reaction shown above.
Because the initiation reaction occurs in two steps, the first can be carried
out prior to polymerization. A convenient procedure is to prepare standardized solutions of a peroxyborane solution and a trialkylborane solution
and use appropriate amounts of each as needed.

Most surprisingly, the free-radical polymerization system is effective in
copolymerizing CF_2=S with conventional unsaturated monomers. These
include a wide variety of C=C compounds such as olefin hydrocarbons,
polymerizable vinyl monomers, and allyl compounds. A brief list of
typical polymerizable monomers is

$$
\begin{array}{lll}
CH_2{=}CH_2 & CH_2{=}CHCl & CH_2{=}CHCH_2Cl \\
CH_3CH{=}CH_2 & CH_2{=}CHOCCH_3 & CH_2{=}CHCH_2OC{-}Cl \\
 & \quad\parallel & \qquad\parallel \\
 & \quad O & \qquad O
\end{array}
$$

There are three copolymer types that deserve particular mention. One
is the CF_2=S/propylene copolymer. In this case, there appears to be a preference to the $2:1$ CF_2=S/propylene composition. If an excess of propylene
is used in the polymerization, a $2:1$ copolymer will be obtained. This
copolymer has a crystalline melting point of $-57°C$, which is, as
expected, much lower than the $35°C$ melting point of poly(thiocarbonyl
fluoride).

A second copolymer deserving special mention is the CF_2=S/vinyl
acetate copolymer. Upon hydrolysis, this product is converted to low
molecular weight oils. This result suggests that sulfur and acetate are on
the same carbon atom as indicated in Scheme II. To form the proposed

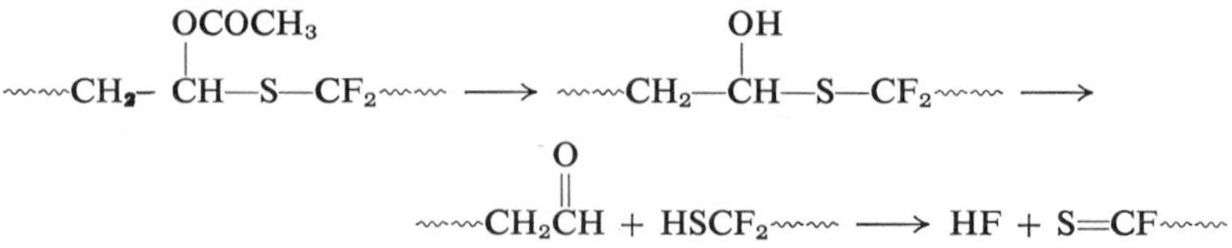

$$
\begin{array}{ccc}
OCOCH_3 & & OH \\
| & & | \\
{\sim}CH_2{-}\,CH{-}S{-}CF_2{\sim} & \longrightarrow & {\sim}CH_2{-}CH{-}S{-}CF_2{\sim} \longrightarrow
\end{array}
$$

$$
\begin{array}{c}
O \\
\parallel \\
{\sim}CH_2CH + HSCF_2{\sim} \longrightarrow HF + S{=}CF{\sim}
\end{array}
$$

Scheme II

structure, it would appear necessary for CF_2=S to react abnormally at some stage in the polymerization. Two hypothetical mechanisms to account for this behavior are:

$$R\cdot + CF_2 = S \longrightarrow RCF_2S\cdot$$

$$RCF_2S\cdot + CH_2 = \overset{\displaystyle \overset{OCOCH_3}{|}}{CH} \longrightarrow RCF_2S\overset{\displaystyle \overset{OCOCH_3}{|}}{C}H \text{---} CH_2\cdot$$

$$(1)$$

$$1 + CF_2 = S \longrightarrow RCF_2S \text{---} \overset{\displaystyle \overset{OCOCH_3}{|}}{C}HCH_2 \text{---} CF_2 \text{---} S\cdot$$

- -

$$R\cdot + S = CF_2 \longrightarrow RS \text{---} CF_2\cdot$$

$$RSCF_2\cdot + CH_2 = \overset{\displaystyle \overset{OCOCH_3}{|}}{CH} \longrightarrow RSCF_2CH_2 \text{---} \overset{\displaystyle \overset{OCOCH_3}{|}}{C}H\cdot$$

$$(2)$$

$$2 + S = CF_2 \longrightarrow RSCF_2CH_2 \text{---} \overset{\displaystyle \overset{OCOCH_3}{|}}{C}H \text{---} SCF_2\cdot$$

Decrease in molecular weight upon hydrolysis is not the fault of the acetate group. Support for this statement was obtained by copolymerization of CF_2=S with 3-butenyl acetate. The product was a high molecular weight polymer that could be hydrolyzed to give a tough, high molecular weight hydroxyl-containing copolymer.

The third special free-radical copolymerization case is the CF_2=S/allyl chloroformate copolymer. Products containing as little as 3 mole % allyl chloroformate have melting points below 0°C. Because they contain an active group, they can be crosslinked by reaction with zinc oxide. Thus, this is a thiocarbonyl fluoride polymer that can be vulcanized by means of a simple chemical reaction involving a group on the polymer chain. Furthermore, products prepared by zinc oxide vulcanization have very high resilience, being only slightly less rubbery than poly(thiocarbonyl fluoride) homopolymer.

Acknowledgments

This short paper is a brief summary of work done by W. J. Middleton, H. W. Jacobson, R. E. Putnam, D. S. Acker, A. L. Barney, J. M. Bruce, Jr., J. N. Coker, and D. G. Pye of the Central Research Department, and H. C. Walter of the Elastomer Chemicals Department of E. I. du Pont de Nemours and Co. The author is grateful for having the privilege of being the spokesman for this group.

References

1. W. J. Middleton, E. G. Howard, and W. H. Sharkey, *J. Org. Chem.*, **30**, 1375 (1965).
2. W. J. Middleton, H. W. Jacobson, R. E. Putnam, H. C. Walter, D. G. Pye, and W. H. Sharkey, *J. Polymer Sci. A*, **3**, 4115 (1965).
3. W. Sundermeyer and W. Meise, *Z. Anorg. Allgem. Chem.*, **317**, 334 (1962).
4. W. J. Middleton, E. G. Howard, and W. H. Sharkey, *J. Am. Chem. Soc.*, **83**, 2589 (1961).
5. N. N. Yarovenko and A. S. Vasil'eva, *J. Gen. Chem.* (*USSR*), **29**, 3754 (1959).
6. A. J. Downs and E. A. V. Ebsworth, *J. Chem. Soc.*, **1960**, 3516.
7. A. L. Barney, J. M. Bruce, Jr., J. N. Coker, H. W. Jacobson, and W. H. Sharkey, *J. Polymer Sci. A-1*, **4**, 2617 (1966).

Fluorinated Polysulfides

C. G. KRESPAN

E. I. du Pont de Nemours and Company, Wilmington, Delaware

Our work started not so much as an effort to prepare fluorinated poly-sulfides as it was to simply promote reaction between sulfur and various fluoroolefins. Since this goal has been realized under several sets of conditions, I shall first discuss these reactions of sulfur and fluoroolefins and then proceed to details of the preferred syntheses of polymeric fluorinated polysulfides. Although a number of fluoroolefins were used in these studies, we shall concentrate on the results with tetrafluoroethylene, since they proved to be the most interesting.

In an early study of trifluoromethyl radicals generated from CF_3I, Emeleus and Haszeldine showed that $CF_3 \cdot$ would attack elemental sulfur and that the thermal reaction at 300°C tended to give bis(trifluoromethyl) disulfide as the end product. This technique of generating fluorinated radicals can also be applied to fluoroolefins provided iodine will add to give a 1,2-diiodide. Evidence has been obtained that tetrafluoroethylene diiodide dissociates at elevated temperatures by way of a free radical inter-mediate. It was possible to take advantage of this equilibrium to obtain the fluorinated radicals needed for attack on elemental sulfur. Reaction occurs to give a polysulfide chain attached to a fluorinated residue on one end and terminated by a thiyl radical at the other end. This radical can continue the chain by adding another molecule of tetrafluoroethylene. By repetition of such reactions, polymers can be formed containing iodine end groups and varying amounts of sulfur, depending upon the relative amount of iodine initially present (eq. 1). However, molecular weights tend

$$ICF_2CF_2I \rightleftharpoons ICF_2CF_2 \cdot + I \cdot \rightleftharpoons CF_2{=}CF_2 + I_2$$

$$\Big\downarrow S_x$$

$$ICF_2CF_2S_x \cdot \xrightarrow{CF_2=CF_2} ICF_2CF_2S_xCF_2CF_2 \cdot \longrightarrow \text{etc.}$$

(1)

to be low, the products are gross mixtures of polymers, and the presence of iodine contributes to thermal and photochemical instability. A mode of initiation not involving iodine was therefore sought.

As is well known, the eight-membered rings present in elemental sulfur at ordinary temperatures dissociate on heating to temperatures above

150°C. This thermal rupture of the sulfur rings results in formation of sulfur chains bearing radical ends. In view of the known reactivity of alkylthio radicals in additions to tetrafluoroethylene, it seemed likely that conditions for adding such sulfur chains to tetrafluoroethylene might also be found. Reaction of sulfur and tetrafluoroethylene under pressure can be promoted thermally by heating the mixture at 150°C or over provided a suitable reaction medium such as carbon disulfide is present. The diradical which must be first formed, $\cdot S_x CF_2 CF_2 \cdot$, can react in various ways to propagate a polymer chain. For example, reaction with another molecule of tetrafluoroethylene could occur by addition of the thiyl radical end or by addition of the fluorocarbon radical end to form a four-carbon chain. Repetition of such steps leads to iodine-free polymeric polysulfides, but again, mixtures of polymers which tend toward low molecular weight are obtained (eq. 2).

$$S_8 \rightleftharpoons \cdot(S_x)\cdot \xrightarrow{CF_2=CF_2} \cdot S_x CF_2 CF_2 \cdot$$

$$\downarrow CF_2=CF_2 \qquad\qquad (2)$$

$$\cdot CF_2 CF_2 S_x CF_2 CF_2 \cdot \ + \ \cdot S_x CF_2 CF_2 CF_2 CF_2 \cdot \ \longrightarrow \ \text{etc.}$$

The preferred procedure is the preparation of pure monomers and their subsequent homopolymerization in a separate step. These monomers can be obtained by carrying out the reaction at 1 atm. The simple expedient of refluxing a reservoir of sulfur (445°C) and leading tetrafluoroethylene into the hot sulfur vapor gives three monomers directly. Visualizing this reaction to proceed through the same sort of diradical intermediate as before, $\cdot S_x CF_2 CF_2 \cdot$ is formed in the vapor phase. It therefore tends to undergo preferential intramolecular cyclization by attack of the fluoro-carbon radical end on sulfur atoms at various positions in the sulfur chain. This displacement goes primarily to give the cyclic tetrasulfide, tetrafluoro-1,2,3,4-tetrathiane, in 60% yield. This material, shown by NMR to exist in a puckered configuration, is a pale yellow oil which freezes at 12.5°C. The tetrathiane can be stored provided bases are scrupulously excluded. Tetrafluoro-1,2,3-trithiolane is formed to a lesser extent by attack of the fluorocarbon radical end in the intermediate on the third sulfur atom. The smaller ring in this product has less ability than the tetrathiane to assume a nonplanar configuration, so that repulsions between the filled p-orbitals on adjacent sulfur atoms are higher. The resulting weak sulfur–sulfur bonds are so easily cleaved that the material gives extremely facile ring-opening polymerization and cannot be stored. Tetrafluoro-1,2-dithietane, which might be obtained by displacement on the second sulfur, is so unstable that it has been detected only as a transient species. Finally, small amounts of tetrafluorothiirane, the three-membered ring containing only one sulfur atom, are also obtained (eq. 3).

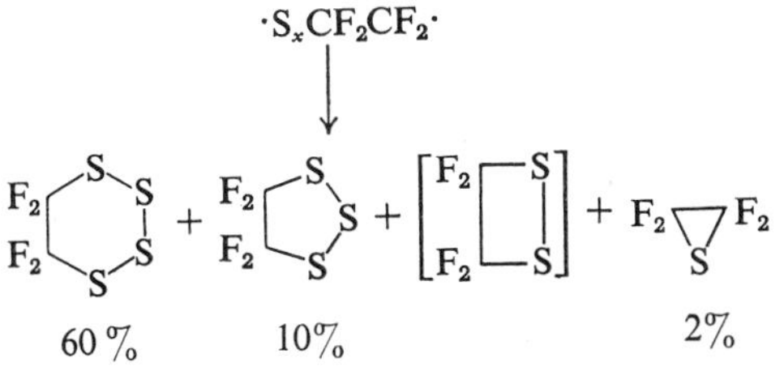

$$\cdot S_x CF_2 CF_2 \cdot$$

$$\tag{3}$$

60%   10%   2%

Considering first the tetrathiane, polymerization can be easily induced even by weak bases. For example, introduction of tetrafluorotetrathiane into acetonitrile at $-40°C$ gives a good yield of high molecular weight polymer with a very regular tetrasulfide structure. A high degree of crystallinity, shown by x-ray studies, and the course of reaction with morpholine indicate the presence of S_4 polysulfide units almost exclusively (eq. 4).

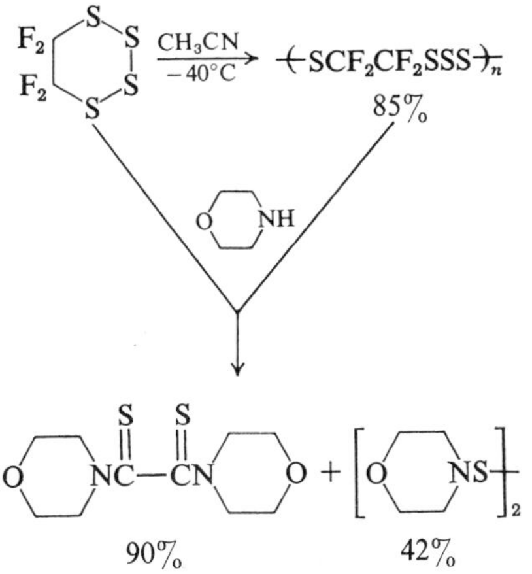

$$\tag{4}$$

90%   42%

The reaction with bases, using morpholine as the example, occurs by attack on the highly polarized sulfur–sulfur bond adjacent to the fluoroalkyl group to give a sulfur anion stabilized by its attachment to a very negative fluoroalkyl residue. As shown in the following equations, such anions readily eliminate α-fluoride to form thioacid fluorides. The latter, in turn, react rapidly with morpholine to form thioamides. Repetition of this process at the other sulfur–sulfur bond adjacent to the fluoroalkyl segment results in formation of dimorpholine disulfide and the dithiooxamide with the expected high specificity (eq. 5).

$$O\!\!\diagup\!\!\diagdown\!\!NH + F_2\!\!\diagup^{S-S}\!\!\diagdown_{S}\!\!\diagdown\!\!S \longrightarrow O\!\!\diagup\!\!\diagdown\!\!\overset{+}{N}HSSSCF_2CF_2S^- \longrightarrow$$

$$O\!\!\diagup\!\!\diagdown\!\!N\overset{\overset{S}{\parallel}}{SSSCF_2CF} \longrightarrow O\!\!\diagup\!\!\diagdown\!\!N\overset{\overset{S}{\parallel}}{SSSCF_2CN}\!\!\diagup\!\!\diagdown\!\!O \longrightarrow \quad (5)$$

$$\left[O\!\!\diagup\!\!\diagdown\!\!NS\right]_2 + \overset{S}{\overset{\parallel}{FC}}-\overset{S}{\overset{\parallel}{CN}}\!\!\diagup\!\!\diagdown\!\!O \longrightarrow O\!\!\diagup\!\!\diagdown\!\!N\overset{S}{\overset{\parallel}{C}}-\overset{S}{\overset{\parallel}{CN}}\!\!\diagup\!\!\diagdown\!\!O$$

When these reactions with base are carried out under mild conditions, the mercaptide ion formed initially has sufficient stability to give nucleophilic attack on another molecule of cyclic tetrasulfide before loss of fluoride ion occurs. Propagation of the polymerization occurs by repetition of the mercaptide ion addition to cyclic tetrasulfide. Similar considerations can be used to rationalize a consistent mode of ring opening for the cyclic trisulfide to form a linear polymer with trisulfide units (eq. 6).

As will be described later, indirect means have been found for the preparation of polymeric disulfide. The regular structure of this polymer is also indicated by its reaction with base. Attack occurs at the disulfide linkage to give a dithiooxamide and a sulfenamide. Complete dissolution of the polymer occurs, indicating few, if any, monosulfide links to be present (eq. 7).

$$F_2\!\!\diagup^{S}\!\!\diagdown_{S}\!\!\diagdown\!\!S \longrightarrow \left(SCF_2CF_2SS\right)_n \qquad (6)$$

$$\left[F_2\!\!\diagup^{S}\!\!\diagdown\!\!\diagup_{S}\right] \longrightarrow \left(SCF_2CF_2S\right)_n \xrightarrow{O\!\!\diagup\!\!\diagdown\!\!NH}$$

$$\qquad (7)$$

$$O\!\!\diagup\!\!\diagdown\!\!N\overset{\overset{S}{\parallel}}{SCF_2CN}\!\!\diagup\!\!\diagdown\!\!O + O\!\!\diagup\!\!\diagdown\!\!N\overset{S}{\overset{\parallel}{C}}-\overset{S}{\overset{\parallel}{CN}}\!\!\diagup\!\!\diagdown\!\!O$$

Synthesis of the polymeric disulfide has been accomplished indirectly by thermal reaction of the cyclic tetrasulfide with tetrafluoroethylene. At 200°C one mole of tetrafluoroethylene per mole of tetrasulfide reacts to form polydisulfide directly. In contrast to its heterolysis with base, the cyclic tetrasulfide apparently undergoes homolysis at the isolated or 2,3 sulfur–sulfur bond to give relatively stable thiyl radicals. These radicals interact with tetrafluoroethylene, perhaps with formation of an intermediate eight-membered ring adduct, to yield polymer (eq. 8). Thermal reaction of the trithiolane with tetrafluoroethylene accounts for the formation of a 1,2,5-trithiepane. This material, although quite stable toward heat and weak bases, can be polymerized with triethylamine at low temperatures (eq. 9).

$$\text{(8)} \qquad \xrightarrow[\text{CF}_2=\text{CF}_2]{200°C} \qquad \longrightarrow \ (\text{SCF}_2\text{CF}_2\text{S})_{\overline{n}}$$

$$\text{(9)} \qquad \xrightarrow[\text{CF}_2=\text{CF}_2]{200°C} \qquad \xrightarrow[-40°C]{(\text{C}_2\text{H}_5)_3\text{N}} \ (\text{SCF}_2\text{CF}_2\text{SCF}_2\text{CF}_2\text{S})_{\overline{n}}$$

Our studies with the final monomer, tetrafluorothiirane, showed that its polymerization is best carried out under free radical conditions. Initiation with peroxides, N_2F_2, or a combination of light and bis(trifluoromethyl) disulfide gives high molecular weight monosulfide polymer. The propagating step in this polymerization was shown to be attack of a free radical chain end on sulfur of the episulfide by study of the model reaction with cyclohexane. In the model system, cyclohexyl radicals were generated and found to attack the episulfide at sulfur with displacement of fluoroalkyl. The newly formed fluoroalkyl radical in turn abstracted hydrogen from cyclohexane in a chain transfer step or, in a prototype of the propagation step, attacked another molecule of episulfide at the sulfur atom. (See reaction 10.)

$$\xrightarrow[\text{or R·}]{h\nu;\ \text{CF}_3\text{SSCF}_3} \ (\text{SCF}_2\text{CF}_2)_{\overline{n}}$$

$$\xrightarrow[\text{C}_6\text{H}_{12}]{\text{R·}} \quad \langle \rangle-\text{SCF}_2\text{CF}_2\text{H} \ + \ \langle \rangle-\text{SCF}_2\text{CF}_2\text{SCF}_2\text{CF}_2\text{H} \qquad \text{(10)}$$

The synthesis of the thiirane directly from tetrafluoroethylene and sulfur gives poor yields and is more conveniently carried out in the laboratory by the unusual transfer of the difluoromethylene group from hexafluoropropylene epoxide to thiocarbonyl fluoride (eq. 11). This reaction, although erratic, could be made to give about 35% yields under carefully controlled conditions.

$$\text{F}-\overset{\text{S}}{\underset{\|}{\text{C}}}-\text{F} + \ \text{F}_2\overset{\text{CF}_3}{\underset{\text{O}}{\triangledown}}\text{F} \ \xrightarrow{175°C} \ \text{F}_2\overset{}{\underset{\text{S}}{\triangledown}}\text{F}_2 \ + \ \text{CF}_3\overset{\text{O}}{\underset{\|}{\text{CF}}} \qquad \text{(11)}$$

Moving to a consideration of the polymers themselves, the following table allows a number of qualitative comparisons to be made. Increasing amounts of sulfur cause a steady reduction in crystalline melting point and an increase in reactivity toward light, heat, and bases. While the mono-sulfide polymer is completely stable at 250°C, suffers only very slow decomposition at 300°C, and is not attacked by amines such as triethyl-amine, the polymeric tetrasulfide has sulfur–sulfur bonds which are labile at 25°C (as evidenced by slow elimination of elemental sulfur) and is vigorously attacked by triethylamine. Although the molecular weight of the tetrasulfide in toluene solution decreases on aging for a few days as a result of this instability, the freshly prepared polymers have inherent viscosities greater than 1 and mechanical properties roughly comparable to those of the monosulfide polymer. (See Table 1.)

The thermal behavior of the polytetrasulfide has been shown to be a result of the easy cleavage of the sulfur–sulfur bonds. Simple heating of this polymer at 250°C results in distillation of the monomeric cyclic tetra-sulfide along with other monomers and sulfur and with formation of residual polymer rich in fluorocarbon. An unusual reaction occurs at 300°C under pressure. Under these conditions, sulfur is slowly extruded and octafluoro-1,4-dithiane (**1**) is formed in good yield. This reaction probably involves a rare example of radical displacement on saturated carbon, in this case by thiyl radical at some stage to give the monosulfide group. (See reaction 12.)

(1)

Properties of S_4 polymer:
White, cold-drawable thermoplastic.
Unstable to heat, light, bases.

Unlike polymeric tetrasulfide, the polymeric disulfide exhibits a largely reversible dissociation on pyrolysis. When heated under vacuum at 250°C, the disulfide polymer slowly cracks and the volatiles can be collected in a cold trap. When the pyrolysis is complete, the original polymer sample is completely gone and examination of the contents of the cold trap shows it to be entirely the reformed polydisulfide. Introduction of the volatiles from such a pyrolysis into a mass spectrometer showed the highest mass to be that of a dimer of tetrafluoro-1,2-dithietane. The mass spectrum also indicated monomeric dithietane to be present. Another indication of its presence was obtained by trapping the dithietane with a different fluoro-

Table 1
Properties of Fluorinated Sulfide Polymers

	Melting pt.,°C	Molding temp.,°C	Stability	Mol. wt.
$-(CF_2CF_2S_4)_n$	55–60	100	Unstable	$\eta = 0.7–1.2$ (tough)
$-(CF_2CF_2S_3)_n$	95–100	—	Unstable	$\eta = 1.2$ (brittle)
$-(CF_2CF_2S_2)_n$	—	—	Dissociates at 250°	Brittle
$-(CF_2CF_2S)_n$	178	250	Slow decomp. at 300°	Tough (quenched)
$-(CF_2CF_2)_n$	327	380	> 400°	Tough

olefin, hexafluoropropylene. When the pyrolysis is conducted in the presence of hexafluoropropylene, a 1,4-dithiane (**2**) bearing one trifluoromethyl group is obtained (eq. 13).

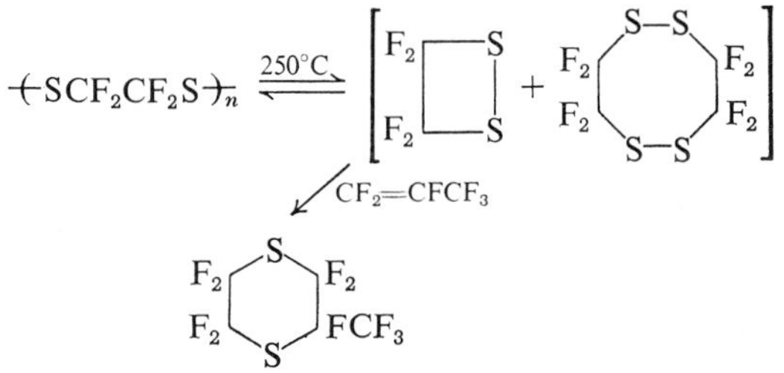

$$-(SCF_2CF_2S)_n \xrightarrow{250°C} \left[\begin{array}{c} F_2 \boxed{} S \\ F_2 \boxed{} S \end{array} + \begin{array}{c} S-S \\ F_2 \bigcirc F_2 \\ F_2 F_2 \\ S-S \end{array} \right]$$

$$\searrow CF_2{=}CFCF_3$$

(13)

$$\begin{array}{c} F_2 \overset{S}{\diagup} F_2 \\ F_2 \underset{S}{\diagdown} FCF_3 \end{array}$$

(**2**)

Properties of S₂ polymer:
White, brittle polymer.
Less sensitive than the tetrasulfide, but still cleaved by bases.

Although more stable thermally than any of the other sulfur/tetrafluoroethylene polymers, the polymonosulfide does pyrolyze readily at 350°C with the formation of three major products. The products trapped out were octafluoro-1,4-dithiane, tetrafluoroethylene, and the polydisulfide (**3**) from tetrafluoro-1,2-dithietane.

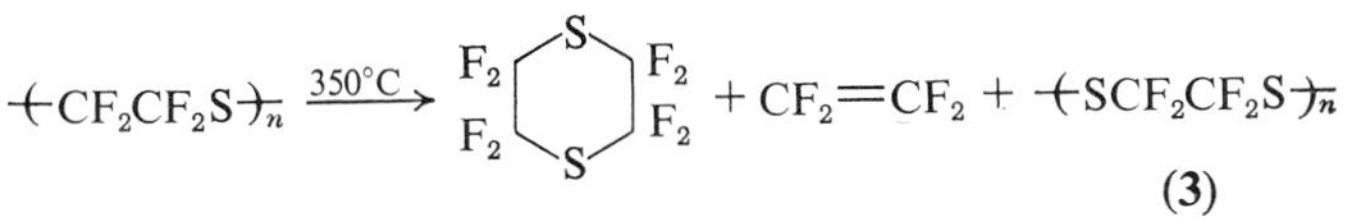

$$-(CF_2CF_2S)_n \xrightarrow{350°C} \begin{array}{c} F_2 \overset{S}{\diagup} F_2 \\ F_2 \underset{S}{\diagdown} F_2 \end{array} + CF_2{=}CF_2 + -(SCF_2CF_2S)_n \quad (14)$$

(**3**)

Properties of S polymer:
White cold-drawable thermoplastic.
Resistant to acids and bases.
Very stable to light, heat.

The probable mechanism for formation of these products involves attack of radical chain ends on monosulfide sulfur further back in the chain. Assuming homolysis occurs either at weak spots in the chain by pyrolysis of sulfur–sulfur bonds or in addition by cleavage of carbon–sulfur bonds as illustrated in reaction 15, the chain ends react as follows. Fluoroalkyl radicals can undergo a β-elimination with formation of a thiyl radical and a two-carbon fragment, tetrafluoroethylene, or they can give intramolecular displacement on sulfur with formation of octafluoro-1,4-dithiane and a fluorocarbon radical chain end. Thiyl radical chain ends give intramolecular attack on sulfur to eliminate tetrafluoro-1,2-dithietane, which as we have seen spontaneously polymerizes to the disulfide.

$$-CF_2CF_2SCF_2CF_2SCF_2CF_2SCF_2CF_2SCF_2CF_2-$$

$$\downarrow$$

$$-CF_2CF_2SCF_2CF_2SCF_2CF_2\cdot + \cdot SCF_2CF_2SCF_2CF_2-$$

$$-CF_2CF_2SCF_2CF_2S\cdot + CF_2{=}CF_2 \qquad \begin{bmatrix} F_2 & S \\ & \\ F_2 & S \end{bmatrix} + \cdot CF_2CF_2- \qquad (15)$$

and

$$-CF_2CF_2\cdot + F_2\overset{S}{\underset{S}{\bigcirc}}F_2 \qquad\qquad +SCF_2CF_2S\!\!+_n$$

These studies explain the formation of surprisingly large amounts of octafluorothiolane in copolymerizations of tetrafluoroethylene with tetrafluorothiirane. Such copolymers form but are difficult to obtain in high molecular weight. Presumably, the incorporation of tetrafluoro-thiirane by attack of the growing chain on sulfur occurs and reaction of the new intermediate with tetrafluoroethylene gives a four-carbon chain. Intramolecular attack by the resulting fluorocarbon radical chain end on sulfur is favorable. The result is conversion of the episulfide to octafluoro-thiolane in amounts far in excess of the catalyst used (eq. 16).

Copolymerization of the episulfide with hydrocarbon olefins proceeds so readily, however, that such side reactions are suppressed. For example, copolymerization with propylene tends to give 1:1 copolymer which is an elastomer of high molecular weight (eq. 17).

$$\sim CF_2\cdot + F_2\triangledown_S F_2 \longrightarrow \sim CF_2SCF_2CF_2\cdot$$

$$\sim CF_2SCF_2CF_2CF_2CF_2\cdot \xrightarrow{\quad} \sim CF_2\cdot + \underset{25\text{--}30\%}{\overset{F_2\square F_2}{F_2\underset{S}{\bigsqcup}F_2}} + \text{copolymer} \qquad (16)$$

with $CF_2{=}CF_2$

$$CH_2{=}CHCH_3 + F_2\triangledown_S F_2 \longrightarrow \left(CH_2\overset{\overset{\displaystyle CH_3}{|}}{CH}SCF_2CF_2\right)_n \qquad (17)$$

In summary, several fluorinated polysulfides of high molecular weight and regular structure have been prepared from the corresponding cyclic monomers. Among these polymers, the monosulfide polymer from tetra-fluorothiirane proved most stable due to the absence of the weak sulfur–sulfur link.

Acknowledgment

Of the many people who contributed to this work, I should like to acknowledge especially Dr. W. R. Brasen and Dr. H. N. Cripps.

Interchange Reactions in Alkyl Polysulfide Polymers

M. B. BERENBAUM

Thiokol Chemical Corporation, Trenton, New Jersey

The polysulfide elastomers, around for about forty years, are among the oldest of the synthetic elastomers. Despite this, relatively little is known of the chemistry of these polymers. Other than the information available from patents and a few papers from industrial laboratories such as Thiokol, most of the scientific effort has been carried out by Professor Tobolsky at Princeton University in his elegant studies on the chemical stress relaxation characteristics of these polymers. The interchange process at the polysulfide bonds is responsible not only for stress relaxation but for many of the unique features of the chemistry of these polymers. This paper will review the effects of polysulfide interchange on the preparation and the performance of these polymers.

POLYMER SYNTHESIS

Polymerization is a condensation reaction between an alkyl dihalide and an alkali polysulfide in an aqueous medium. In the presence of suitable dispersing agents, the product is formed as a dispersion. The most widely used system, accounting for better than 90% of current production, is bis-2-chloroethyl formal reacted to form the disulfide polymer. Trihalides such as 1,2,3-trichloropropane can be added to the system to introduce branching or crosslinking.

$$ClCH_2CH_2OCH_2OCH_2CH_2Cl + Na_2S_2 \longrightarrow \tag{1a}$$
$$-(-SCH_2CH_2OCH_2OCH_2CH_2S-)_{n}-$$

$$ClCH_2\underset{\underset{Cl}{|}}{C}HCH_2Cl + Na_2S_2 \longrightarrow -(-SCH_2\underset{\underset{\underset{+}{|}}{\overset{|}{S}}}{C}HCH_2S-)_{n}- \tag{1b}$$

If this polymerization were a conventional condensation reaction between a difunctional dihalide and a divalent polysulfide anion, then exact stoichiometry would be essential in order to obtain high molecular weight products. An excess of one of the reagents would serve as a chain stopper and limit the degree of polymerization. Hydrolytic side reactions to which organic halides are susceptible in the presence of the alkaline polysulfide solution would also result in the formation of inert terminals and limit the product molecular weight. In actual practice, however, high molecular weights are readily obtained by the use of an excess of the inorganic polysulfide to deliberately form a mercaptide-terminated intermediate molecular weight polymer, the excess polysulfide serving to drive the reaction of the dihalide to completion. Some hydroxyl-terminated chain stoppered polymer is also formed.

$$ClRCl + S_2^{-2} \text{ (excess)} \longrightarrow {}^-S(SRS)_nS^- \tag{2a}$$

$${}^-S(SRS)_nS^{-2} + {}^-OH \longrightarrow {}^-S(SRS)_nSROH \tag{2b}$$

During the polymerization, the excess polysulfide ion is continually interchanging with the polysulfide bonds present in the polymeric product. The preparation of disulfide polymers is described here but the reactions apply equally well to higher polysulfide polymers. When the interchange occurs in the middle of a relatively high molecular weight chain, as in equation 3a, then the fragments formed are still of sufficient molecular weight to be insoluble in the aqueous medium and remain in suspension. However, when the interchange occurs near a terminal carrying the chain-stopping hydroxyl group, as in 3b, soluble low molecular weight fragments are formed and these are partitioned into the aqueous phase. Equations 3c and 3d indicate that not only is the polysulfide anion interchanging but that interchange by a nucleophilic displacement also occurs between the mercaptide terminals of the polymeric fragments with polysulfide groups in other polymer segments. Again, if this occurs near a terminal, the chain stopper is solubilized, while the effect is negligible if exchange takes place to yield higher molecular weight products.

$$-SRSSRSSRSSRS- + S_2^{-2} \rightleftharpoons -SRSSRSS^- + {}^-SSRSSRS- \tag{3a}$$

$$-SRSSRSSRSSROH + S_2^{-2} \rightleftharpoons -SRSSRSS^- + {}^-SSROH \tag{3b}$$

$$-SRSSRS^- + -SRSSRSSRSSRS- \rightleftharpoons -SRSSRSSRSSRS- + {}^-SRSSRS- \tag{3c}$$

$$-SRSSRS^- + -SRSSROH \rightleftharpoons -SRSSRSSRS- + {}^-SROH \tag{3d}$$

The hydroxyl-terminated segments accumulate in the aqueous phase; when the reaction is complete, the polymer dispersion is settled and the supernatant mother liquor containing the chain stopper is decanted. The intermediate molecular weight polymer is brought to the high molecular weight stage by further washing and decantation treatments. These serve to reverse the direction of the equilibrium reaction described in equation 3a, since the equilibrium is driven to the left and therefore to a chain extension process by removal of the inorganic disulfide ion.

If the reaction with excess polysulfide and the washing process do not yield a product with a high enough degree of polymerization, then the polymer dispersion can be retreated with fresh polysulfide solution to completely convert any remaining few halogen terminals or to complete the solubilization of the residual hydroxyl groups and thereby permit the reaction to proceed to the desired molecular weight. In general practice, molecular weights of the order of 500,000 or better are readily achieved. Incidentally, the random displacement reactions in equations 3a and 3c serve to bring about the equilibration of the polymer molecular weight distribution to that appropriate to a condensation polymer. There is probably some deviation from the perfect distribution predicted by Flory since the monomeric and possibly some of the dimeric segments are solubilized in the polymerization and are lost in the washing process.

Other evidence on the randomization action of equations 3a and 3c during the polymerization can be seen by studies on the preparation of copolymers. The preparation of block copolymers had been proposed by sequential reaction of the monomers, i.e., a half mole of monomer A is added to a mole of alkali polysulfide followed by a half mole of monomer B when A has reacted completely. Random copolymers are always obtained. These are indistinguishable from the products obtained by simultaneous addition of two monomers.

Further, random copolymers can be prepared from aqueous dispersions of two or more homopolymers by addition of polysulfide ion to the blended dispersions of the polymers. This can best be seen in an experiment by Bertozzi, Davis, and Fettes (1) in which dispersions of a hard plastic ethylene disulfide polymer, $(-CH_2CH_2S_2-)_n$, and a triglycol disulfide polymer, $(-CH_2CH_2OCH_2CH_2OCH_2CH_2S_2-)_n$, chain stoppered to the liquid stage with a hydrocarbon terminal insoluble in the aqueous polysulfide medium, were blended in equimolar quantities and heated at 90°C in the presence of a small amount of sodium disulfide. The disulfide anion interchanges rapidly with the disulfide groups in the polymer as in equation 3a to form thiomercaptide-terminated intermediates which then redistribute according to equation 3c to finally give a random system. Recovery of the product yielded a homogeneous liquid polymer of significantly higher viscosity than the triglycol disulfide liquid. If the sodium disulfide was omitted so that the reactive thiomercaptide terminals were not present, then the product was an inhomogeneous mixture of fine particles of the hard ethylene disulfide polymer dispersed in the liquid triglycol polymer.

CHEMISTRY OF THE CONDENSATION REACTION

The reaction of the halides is that predicted from the reaction of simple monofunctional halides in displacement reactions. For example, primary halides are more reactive than secondary; allylic and benzyl compounds are particularly active, while aromatics are very sluggish.

On the other hand, the reactivity of the polysulfide ionic species is not yet clear. An aqueous solution of inorganic polysulfide ions is an equilibrium mixture of the monosulfide to the pentasulfide ions with the solution rank* the average value for the concentration of the various species present. We still do not know the relative reactivity of the individual polysulfide ions since they cannot be isolated long enough to permit kinetic studies. An idea of the difficulties can be seen in attempting to analyze the data in Table 1 on the condensation of bis-2-chloroethyl formal with 100% excess of sodium polysulfide of different ranks.

Table 1

Effect of Alkali Polysulfide Rank on Polymer Sulfide Rank

Na_2S_x[a] rank	$-RS_x-$ rank
1.50	1.68
2.00	1.95
2.50	2.16
3.00	2.35
3.50	2.60
4.00	3.25

[a] Sodium polysulfide; approx. molar concentration, 100% excess.

Superficially, it would appear that the disulfide ion is the most reactive species since the rank of the polymer attained tends to approach this value. For example, with sodium polysulfide of 1.5 rank, the polymer rank is 1.68 which would indicate that the disulfide is reacting more rapidly than the monosulfide ions present. Similarly, the higher rank polysulfide ions tend to give lower values of polymer rank, again implying greater reactivity of the disulfide ionic species. It is true that the monosulfide ion reacts significantly more slowly with the organic dihalide than the disulfide ion but, if anything, the higher rank ionic polysulfides react more rapidly than the disulfide. The true mechanism is obscured by the dynamic equilibrium of the polysulfide bonds in the polymer with the inorganic polysulfide ions in the aqueous mother liquor. The equilibration is effected by a nucleophilic displacement interchange at the organic polysulfide bond as in equation 4.

$$-RSS\,SR- + \,^-S_y^- \rightleftharpoons -RS\,SSy^- + \,^-SR \rightleftharpoons -RSSR- + \,^-SS_y^- \qquad (4)$$

* The rank of polysulfide compounds is defined as the number of sulfur atoms in an organic polysulfide bond or ionic species.

We find that no matter what the course of the condensation reaction, the interchange yields a polymer mixture with a rank corresponding to the equilibrium value with the ionic polysulfide environment. For example, treatment of a polymer dispersion prepared with a rank of 4 with an equimolar amount of Na_2S_4 yields a polymer with a rank of 3.1 with a corresponding increase in the rank of the polysulfide solution.

THIOL-TERMINATED POLYSULFIDE POLYMERS

The thiol-terminated liquid polymers are the most widely used of the polysulfide polymers. These are prepared from the aqueous dispersion of a high molecular weight disulfide polymer by another interchange reaction. Equations 5a and 5b describe the conversion of a disulfide group in the polymer to two thiol terminals by treatment with a sodium hydrosulfide and sodium sulfite.

$$—SRSSRSSRSSRS— + {}^-SH \rightleftharpoons —SRSSRS^- + HSSRSSRS— \quad (5a)$$

$$—SRSSRSSH + {}^{-2}SO_3 \longrightarrow —SRSSRSH + {}^{-2}S_2O_3 \quad (5b)$$

Reaction 5a, the interchange, results in reduction of molecular weight to the desired level. However, if the product is isolated by the decantation washing process, the reaction will be reversed, regenerating the original high molecular weight product. The function of the sulfite ion as described in 5b is to strip out the sulfur in the alkyl hydrodisulfide terminal, generating another thiol group and preventing the reversal of the equilibrium. Depending on the proportion of the NaSH and Na_2SO_3 used, thiol-terminated polymers can be prepared at any desired molecular weight from as low as 500 up to 50,000–100,000.

The commercial utility of the thiol-terminated liquid polymers is based on the relatively facile oxidation of these products by a wide variety of organic and inorganic oxidizing agents. Either room temperature or elevated temperature cures to high molecular weight polysulfide elastomers can readily be obtained. These liquid polymers are useful adhesives, sealants, and caulking materials. The ideal cure is of the type described in reaction 6a, in which the thiol is cleanly converted to a disulfide bond in a chain extension process. Unfortunately, with many of the metal dioxides used, reaction 6b occurs to some extent, with formation of undesirable ionic bonds in the polymer backbone.

$$RSH + PbO_2 \longrightarrow RSSR + PbO + H_2O \quad (6a)$$

$$RSH + PbO \longrightarrow RSPbSR + H_2O \quad (6b)$$

The presence of these bonds does not affect the appearance of a suitable cure but markedly affects the compression set and aging characteristics of the final products. Tobolsky and Colodny have shown (2) that the stress relaxation characteristics are dependent on the presence or absence of these ionic bonds which can readily enter into chemical relaxation processes by the interchange reactions. The effect of the mercaptide–disulfide interchange on relaxation rate can be seen in the hundredfold greater τ value for a thiol polymer cured with disocyanate, eliminating the possibility of ionic bond formation, versus a cure with lead dioxide which gave a high proportion of the weak salt bond. It is obviously important in commercial practice to select curing agents and activators that will favor the formation of polymers with predominantly disulfide bonds.

The presence of the mercaptide bond also has an adverse effect on the product thermal stability. High weight loss is observed on heat aging and the cause is believed to be the cyclic exchange reaction shown in equation 7.

$$-SSCH_2CH_2OCH_2OCH_2CH_2S-S\begin{array}{c} CH_2CH_2O \\ \diagup \qquad \diagdown \\ \qquad\qquad CH_2 \longrightarrow \\ \diagdown \qquad \diagup \\ S-CH_2CH_2O \end{array}$$

$$-SSCH_2CH_2OCH_2OCH_2CH_2S^- + \begin{array}{c} CH_2CH_2O \\ S \diagup \qquad \diagdown \\ | \qquad\qquad CH_2 \\ S \diagdown \qquad \diagup \\ CH_2CH_2O \end{array} \qquad (7)$$

The mercaptide terminal enters into a displacement reaction at the nearby disulfide bond in the polymer, with consequent evolution of the volatile cyclic disulfide and regeneration of the active terminal to propagate the cyclodepolymerization. The cyclic disulfide based on the polymer from bis-2-chloroethyl formal has been collected in significant proportions from products which have been cured to give substantial proportions of mercaptide groups in the backbone of the product. With polymers based on bis-2-chloroethyl ether, a monomer which tends to favor the ring formation reaction because of the smaller ring formed, salt like cures can yield a product which can be completely volatilized in a few days at 100°C.

INTERCHANGE AT POLYSULFIDE BOND

If polysulfide bonds of rank higher than 2 are present in the polymer, then interchange can take place at an even greater rate. Tobolsky and co-workers have shown (3) that the relaxation rate of alkyl tetrasulfide polymers is very much greater than that of the disulfide systems. In fact, the observed relaxation rate of the disulfide polymers could be explained by the presence of 6% trisulfide or tetrasulfide groups in the polymer. Since the polymer was prepared with aqueous sodium disulfide, it is probable that the product did contain high rank bonds in this proportion. This interchange process is minimized in most commercial polysulfide polymers since, in the preparation of the thiol-terminated products, the treatment with sodium sulfite not only removes the high rank sulfur from the hydrodisulfide terminals but it also removes the high rank sulfur present in polysulfide groups in the polymer backbone as in equation 8.

$$-RS\,SSR- + ^{-2}SO_3 \rightleftharpoons -RS^- + ^-O_3SS\,SR- \longrightarrow -RSSR- + ^{-2}S_2O_3$$

(8)

We suspect that the conflicting results sometimes observed in studies on the polysulfide polymers arise from the presence of relatively small amounts of polysulfide groups in the polymer backbone. This could explain the discrepancies in the results reported by Fettes and Mark (4) and Shlyakhter and his co-workers (5) on the redistribution of blends of thiol-terminated liquid polymers of different molecular weights. Both groups were studying the randomization resulting from the thiol–disulfide interchange in these bimodal blends of polymers. Fettes found that redistribution of 100°C, even in the presence of an amine, was very slow. On the other hand, Shlyakhter observed that the viscosity of blends of the thiol-terminated liquid polymers dropped even on agitation at room temperature. At 100°C, a random distribution was achieved in 6–8 hr. We have recently attempted to repeat this work in our laboratories and find that, using commercial liquid polymers, our results are in between although they fall somewhat closer to the Fettes observations.

Workers at the Natural Rubber Producers Association have developed a number of chemical probes to distinguish between various types of crosslinks in vulcanized rubber. Among these techniques is a procedure for distinguishing trisulfide and polysulfide bonds from the lower rank crosslinks. This involves the treatment at room temperature of the crosslinked rubber with a piperidine solution of isopropyl thiol. In 8–9 hr, the thiol compound has cleaved all the high rank bonds without affecting the disulfide crosslinks. The difference in reactivity between the trisulfide and disulfide bonds is of the order of 10^3. Thus even a small amount of polysulfide in a polymer would bring about the anomalous results reported in the aforementioned liquid polymer redistribution studies. We suspect that further dethionation of our commercial polymers will result in an even lower rate of exchange.

This survey on the chemistry of polysulfide polymers can only touch on the highlights of the unusual reactions encountered with these products. In every case mentioned above, the information available is preliminary and subject to confirmation by more precise experimentation. A great deal of work must be done before the chemistry of these polymers is fully understood.

References

1. E. R. Bertozzi, F. O. Davis, and E. M. Fettes, *J. Polymer Sci.*, **19**, 17 (1956).
2. A. V. Tobolsky and P. C. Colodny, *J. Appl. Polymer Sci.*, **2**, 39 (1959).
3. A. V. Tobolsky, W. J. MacKnight, and M. Takahashi, *J. Phys. Chem.*, **68**, 787 (1964).
4. E. M. Fettes and H. Mark, *J. Appl. Polymer Sci.*, **7**, 2239 (1963).
5. R. A. Shlyakhter, E. G. Ehrenburg, T. P. Nasonova, and E. P. Piskareva, *J. Polymer Sci. C*, **16**, in press.

PART III

Sulfides in Biological Systems

Electron Exchange between Thiols and Disulfides during Cell Division

HIKOICHI SAKAI*

Columbia University, New York

Cell division is usually recognized as the process of nuclear division and sequential cell cleavage. The separation of the chromosomes is involved in the function of the mitotic apparatus and the division of the cell, cytokinesis, is the constriction of the cell by the cortex.

The mitotic apparatus itself, having the nature of a gel, is a dynamic complex of the spindle, chromosomes, centrospheres, and astral rays. The spindle is composed of so-called continuous and chromosomal fibers and a vesicular matrix in which they are embedded (3,4). These fibers have been shown to be composed of microtubules (3,4,8).

On the other hand, the cell cortex is a thin layer, about 3 μ in thickness, which surrounds the cytoplasm (5,15). Essentially, theories on cell division can be divided into two. One insists on the role of the mitotic apparatus (1,2,13); the other seeks for cleavage activity of the cortex (6,7,11,12,22). It has recently been shown that the mitotic apparatus has influence upon the cortex at or after metaphase (6,7). After metaphase, the cell can divide itself without visible structure of the mitotic apparatus, which means the cell cortex becomes active to constrict the cell. Therefore, there must be some interaction between the cell cortex and the mitotic apparatus during the cleavage cycle.

A contractile protein can be extracted by $0.6M$ KCl at pH 7 from the cortex of the sea urchin egg as well as from the whole cell (18). It forms a protein thread when mixed with organic solvent. The contraction to the extent of 30–40% is induced by addition of di-, tri-, or tetravalent cations at ph 7 and the effect is reversed by EDTA, showing a cyclic shortening and elongation. ATP has no effect on it. Such a kind of protein thread, on the other hand, contracts by the action of SH oxidant. Neither alkylating agents nor mercaptide-forming reagents induce the shortening of the protein thread. In short, the contraction is induced in part by electrostatic forces and in part by the oxidation of a pair of SH groups of the protein

* Present address: Department of Biophysics and Biochemistry, University of Tokyo, Tokyo, Japan.

thread. The SH amount of this cortex protein fluctuates as a function of the stage of cell division. It increases toward the formation of the mitotic apparatus and then decreases as cell cleavage proceeds (16,17,19).

Experimentally, nuclear division can be separated from cytokinesis as was first found by Wilson in 1902 (23). An ether–seawater mixture inhibits the cell cleavage but the nuclear division does take place. Such a cell, if returned to ordinary seawater, divides into 4, 8, 16, and so on at a time. During the treatment, there is no change in the amount of SH of the cell cortex. But after returning to ordinary seawater, the amount of SH changes only with cell division (16,19). Therefore, the cell prepares the maximum contractility of the cortex just before cleavage.

The mitotic apparatus can be isolated directly from the living cell (14,21). The spindle fibers and astral rays are composed of numerous microtubules (9). Each microtubule is composed of 12–13 subfilaments, as Ledbetter and Porter reported on a plant cell (10). The subfilament is made from a single row of globular protein units, the dimension of which is about 35 Å in diameter (9). This is the protein which is a major building block of the mitotic apparatus. The microtubules are easily soluble in neutral salt. The dissolved mitotic apparatus shows three protein components (21). The 3.5S component which is a major fraction can be split into 2.5S particles by sulfite or dithiothreitol. The dimension of the 2.5S particle is almost the same as that of the protein unit of the microtubules of the mitotic apparatus (9). This protein can be extracted directly from eggs at various developmental stages as a calcium-insoluble protein fraction. The number of SH groups of this calcium-insoluble protein changes during the cleavage cycle of the sea urchin eggs, the fluctuation being just a mirror image of that of the contractile protein either from whole eggs or from the cell cortices (20). This is a sort of oxidation–reduction chemically coupled between the cortex protein and the mitotic apparatus protein during cleavage cycle.

The same reaction occurs *in vitro* between the isolated 3.5S protein of the mitotic apparatus and the contractile protein of the cortex in the presence of GSH, ascorbic acid, calcium ions, and a so-called pH 5 fraction which catalyzes the reaction (20). The decrease in the amount of SH of the contractile protein is accompanied by an increase of SH groups in the protein of the mitotic apparatus. This reaction is an oxidation–reduction, not transfer of SH radicals. The reaction depends on the amount of the pH 5 fraction as well as on the ratio between the amounts of SH groups of both the contractile protein and the calcium-insoluble protein fraction. Furthermore, the reaction is reversible; a SH-rich mitotic apparatus protein can give electrons to a SH-poor cortex protein.

This reaction provides a chemical basis for the contraction–elongation of the thread of the cortex protein. It contracts by a SH-poor mitotic apparatus protein in the presence of catalytic pH 5 fraction, GSH, ascorbic acid, and calcium ions. Conversely, the contracted thread elongates by a SH-rich mitotic apparatus protein in the presence of the same pH 5 fraction and other cofactors.

These are chemical expressions of the interaction between the cell cortex and the mitotic apparatus. The constriction of the cell is due to the cortex protein which has the highest contractility at anaphase through the reaction of electron exchange between the cortex and the mitotic apparatus.

References

1. K. Dan, *J. Fac. Sci., Imp. Univ. Tokyo, Sect. IV*, **6**, 323 (1943).
2. J. Gray, *A Textbook of Experimental Cytology*, Cambridge University Press, London, 1931.
3. P. Harris, *J. Cell Biol.*, **14**, 475 (1962).
4. P. Harris and D. Mazia, *Symp. Intern. Soc. Cell Biol.*, **1**, 279 (1962).
5. Y. Hiramoto, *Embryologia*, **3**, 361 (1957).
6. Y. Hiramoto, *Exptl. Cell Res.*, **11**, 630 (1956).
7. Y. Hiramoto, *J. Cell Biol.*, **25**, 161 (1965).
8. R. E. Kane, *J. Cell Biol.*, **15**, 279 (1962).
9. B. Kiefer, H. Sakai, A. J. Solari, and D. Mazia, *J. Mol. Biol.*, **20**, 75 (1966).
10. M. C. Ledbetter and K. R. Porter, *Science*, **144**, 872 (1964).
11. D. A. Marsland, *Intern. Rev. Cytol.*, **5**, 199 (1956).
12. D. A. Marsland and J. V. Landau, *J. Exptl. Zool.*, **125**, 507 (1954).
13. D. Mazia, in *The Cell*, Vol. 3, J. Brachet and A. E. Mirsky, Eds., Academic Press, New York, 1961, p. 77.
14. D. Mazia, J. M. Mitchison, H. Medina, and P. Harris, *J. Cell Biol.*, **10**, 467 (1961).
15. J. M. Mitchison, *Quart. J. Microscop. Sci.*, **97**, 109 (1956).
16. H. Sakai, *J. Biophys. Biochem. Cytol.*, **8**, 603 (1960).
17. H. Sakai, *J. Biophys. Biochem. Cytol.*, **8**, 609 (1960).
18. H. Sakai, *J. Gen. Physiol.*, **45**, 411 (1962).
19. H. Sakai, *Exptl. Cell Res.*, **32**, 391 (1963).
20. H. Sakai, *Biochim. Biophys. Acta*, **102**, 235 (1963).
21. H. Sakai, *Biochim. Biophys. Acta*, **112**, 132 (1966).
22. M. M. Swann and J. M. Mitchison, *Biol. Rev.*, **33**, 103 (1958).
23. E. B. Wilson, *Wilhelm Roux Arch. Entwicklungsmech. Forsch.*, **13**, 353 (1902).

The Action of Cyanogen Bromide on Protein-Bound Sulfur-Containing Amino Acids

ERHARD GROSS
National Institute of Arthritis and Metabolic Diseases, National Institutes of Health, Bethesda, Maryland

In this paper we shall concern ourselves with the chemistry of sulfur-containing amino acids as they are found in proteins.

The primary structure of human growth hormone has been established recently by Li and his associates (1). Among the 188 amino acids (Fig. 1) we find a number of sulfur-containing amino acids. There are three residues of methionine in the hormone. The heavy arrows indicate a simple chemical reagent used to bring about cleavage of the peptide bonds of these three sulfur-containing amino acids.

The type of peptide bond cleavage that we are going to discuss is known as *nonenzymatic* fragmentation of peptides and proteins (2).

H-Phe-Pro-Thr-Ileu-Pro-Leu-Ser-Arg-Leu-Phe-Asp-Asn-Ala-Met-Leu-Arg-Ileu-Leu-Ser-Leu-Glu-Leu-Ileu-
10 20

Ser-Try-Leu-Glu-Pro-Val-Glu-Phe-Ala-His-Arg-Leu-His-Gln-Leu-Ala-Phe-Asp-Thr-Tyr-Glu-Glu-Phe-
30 40

Glu-Glu-Ala-Tyr-Ileu-Pro-Lys-Glu-Gln-Lys-Tyr-Ser-Phe-Leu-Gln-Asp-Pro-Glu-Thr-Ser-Leu-Cys-Phe-
50 60

Ser-Ser-Ileu-Glu-Ser-(Asp,Pro,Pro,Thr)-Arg-Glu-Glu-Thr-Gln-Lys-Ser-Asp-Leu-Glu-Leu-Leu-Arg-Ser-
70 80 90

Val-Phe-Ala-Asn-Ser-Leu-Val-Tyr-Gly-Ala-Ser-Asn-Ser-Asp-Val-Tyr-Asp-Leu-Leu-Lys-Asp-Leu-Glu-
100 110

Glu-Gly-Ileu-Glu-Thr-Leu-Met-Gly-Arg-Leu-Glu-Asp-Pro-Ser-Gly-Arg-Thr-Gly-Gln-Ileu-Phe-Lys-Glu-Thr-
120 130

Tyr-Ser-Lys-Phe-Asp-Thr-Asn-Ser-His-Asn-Asp-Asp-Ala-Leu-Leu-Lys-Asp-Tyr-Gly-Leu-Leu-Tyr-Cys-
140 150 160

Phe-Arg-Lys-Asp-Met-Asp-Lys-Val-Glu-Thr-Phe-Leu-Arg-Ileu-Val-Gln-Cys-Arg-Ser-Val-Glu-Gly-Ser-
170 180

Cys-Gly-Phe-OH
188

Fig. 1. Primary structure of human growth hormone.

I have chosen phalloidin—for various reasons—to illustrate nonenzymatic fragmentation of peptides and proteins. This peptide is one of the highly toxic components of the mushroom *Amanita phalloides*. It has an unusual and thus far unique bicyclic structure (3). (Fig. 2). It contains several unusual amino acids, one of which is γ,δ-dihydroxyleucine. Historically it was this amino acid that first provided nonenzymatic fragmentation of a peptide bond.

We find two additional functional groups—two hydroxyl groups—in the molecule. In general, an amino acid with other functional groups than the NH_2 or COOH group will lend itself to nonenzymatic modification and fragmentation.

It may be of particular interest to the reader to stress the attachment of the *sulfur* of cysteine to the α-position of the indole nucleus of tryptophan.

In phalloidin (Fig. 3) the following chemical events take place at 100°C in $0.2N$ H_2SO_4 (30 min): protonation of the γ-hydroxyl group, carbonium ion formation (assisted by the neighboring group effect of the carbonyl function), lactonization, participation of the single electron pair of the peptide nitrogen, imino lactone formation, hydrolysis, and release of the amino group of the amino acid that was attached to γ,δ-dihydroxyleucine.

This *first* nonenzymatic cleavage of a peptide bond opened the door to the structural elucidation of phalloidin.

Some other amino acids, the peptide bonds of which are subject to nonenzymatic cleavage are tryoptophan (4), tyrosine (5), and histidine (6). The functional groups invoked here are the α,β-double bond in indole, the phenolic hydroxyl, and the imidazole ring, respectively.

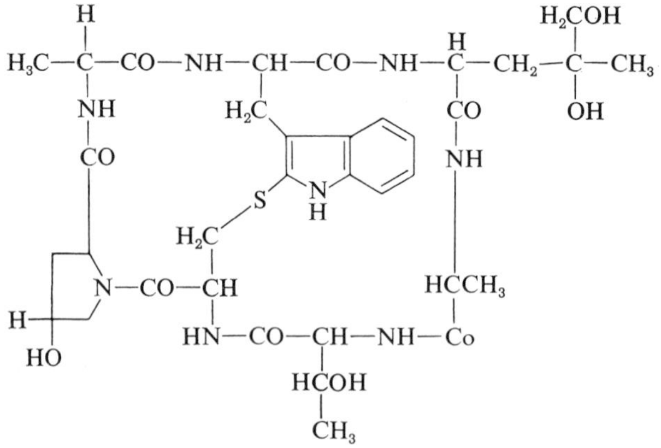

Fig. 2. The structure of phalloidin (from *Aminata phalloides*).

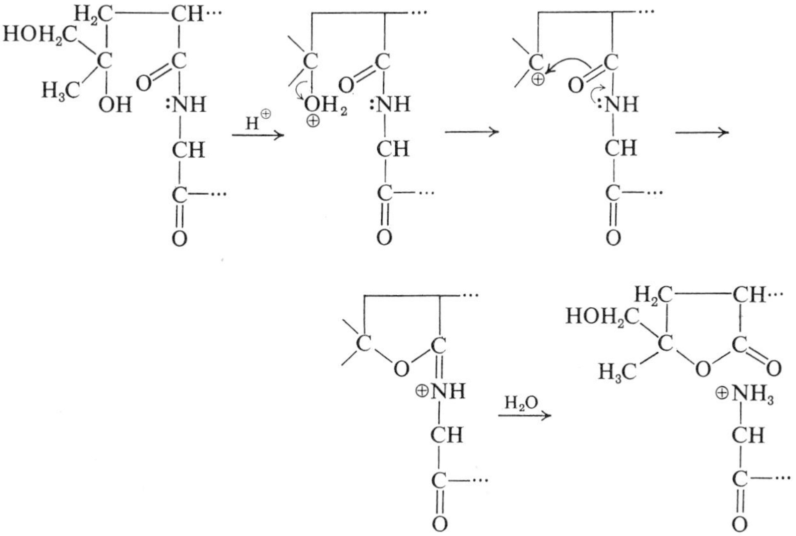

Fig. 3. Cleavage of the γ,δ-dihydroxyleucyl–peptide bond in phalloidin.

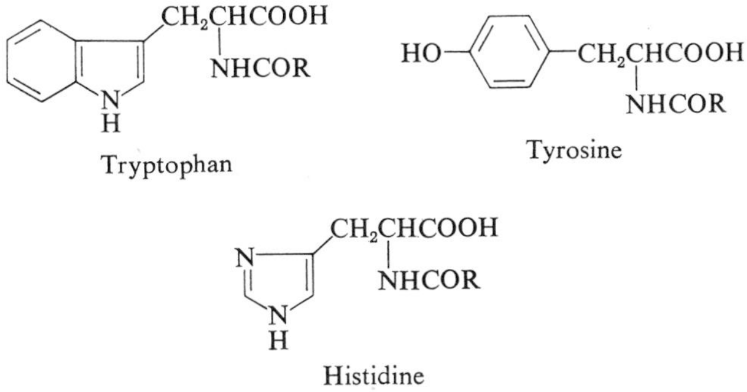

Tryptophan

Tyrosine

Histidine

The reagent for the nonenzymatic cleavage of the peptide bonds of certain sulfur-containing amino acids is cyanogen bromide. Von Braun and his associates (7) demonstrated in the early 1920's that thioethers are subject to cleavage by BrCN. Temperature requirements were 60–70°C. In retrospect we propose the mechanism shown in Figure 4. For example, the reaction products of the cleavage of propylbutyl sulfide are propyl-bromide and butylthiocyanate.

We shall discuss the action of cyanogen bromide on two amino acids which contain the structural element of a thioether: (a) methionine, and (b) the lower homolog of methionine, S-methylcysteine.

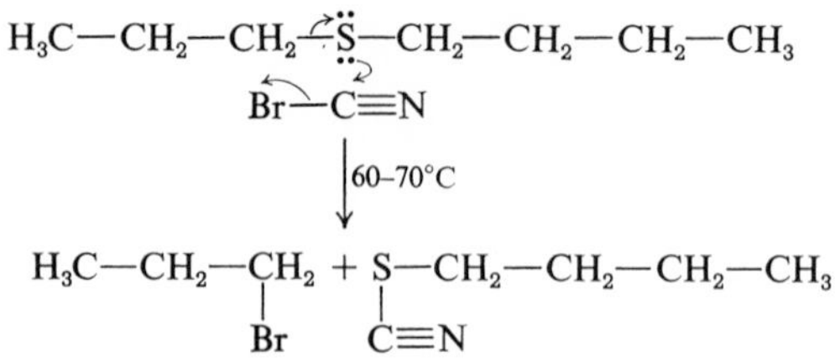

$$H_3C-CH_2-CH_2-\overset{\cdot\cdot}{S}-CH_2-CH_2-CH_2-CH_3$$
$$Br-C\equiv N$$

$$\Big\downarrow 60\text{--}70°C$$

$$H_3C-CH_2-\underset{\underset{Br}{|}}{CH_2} + \underset{\underset{C\equiv N}{|}}{S}-CH_2-CH_2-CH_2-CH_3$$

Propyl bromide   Butylthiocyanate

Fig. 4. The reaction of cyanogen bromide with sulfides (e.g., propylbutyl sulfide).

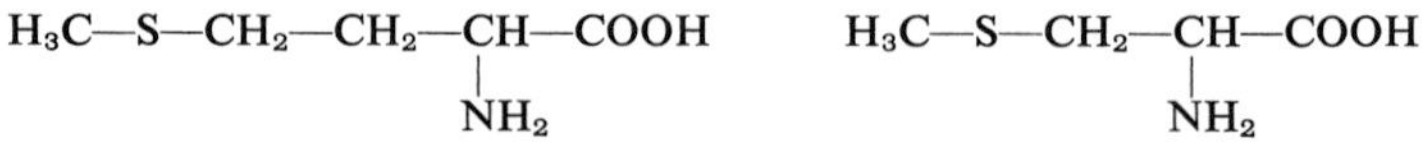

$$H_3C-S-CH_2-CH_2-\underset{\underset{NH_2}{|}}{CH}-COOH \qquad H_3C-S-CH_2-\underset{\underset{NH_2}{|}}{CH}-COOH$$

Methionine   S-Methylcysteine

Cyanogen bromide reacts with methionyl peptides in the following way (Fig. 5): BrCN is partially polarized

$$\overset{\delta\ominus}{Br}-\overset{\delta\oplus}{C}\equiv N$$

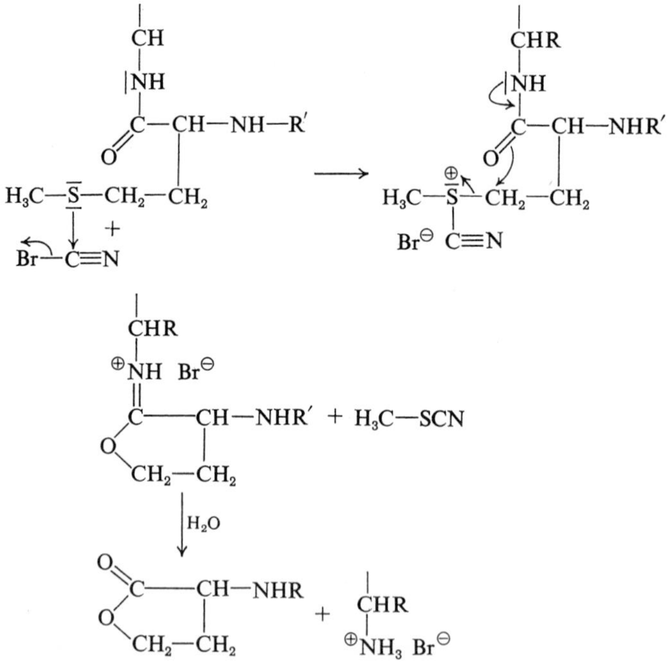

Fig. 5. Reaction mechanism of the cleavage of methionine peptides with cyanogen bromide.

The positive charge at the cyano group is attracted by the high electron density of the sulfur atom; an (intermediary) sulfonium salt (cyanosulfonium bromide) is perhaps briefly in existence. The carbonyl group exerts a strong neighboring group effect, the thiomethyl group is expelled as methylthiocyanate, and a lactone is formed. The electron deficit at the carbonyl carbon atom is compensated by the participating single electron pair of the peptide nitrogen. The resulting imino-lactone is very labile and readily hydrolyzed: homoserine lactone is formed and the amino group of the amino acid next to methionine released.

To be applicable, a method for the nonenyzmatic fragmentation of proteins has to be highly selective. That this is the case for the cyanogen bromide reaction is demonstrated by the exposure of an amino acid standard to the reagent. The chromatogram (Fig. 6, upper half) shows a mixture of all commonly occurring amino acids. The same standard mixture was treated with cyanogen bromide. The result of this exposure is shown in Figure 6 in the lower chromatogram. The only amino acid that is affected is methionine. *Two* new peaks have occurred, representing homoserine and homoserine lactone, the conversion products of methionine.

Once applied to a mixture of the methionyl peptides indicated in Figure 7, the following results were obtained: all amino acids expected are released. Please notice that from acetyl methionyl methionine we have some unaltered methionine left. With a larger excess of reagent and after a longer time of exposure to the reagent, both methionine residues are completely converted to homoserine and/or homoserine lactone (Fig. 8).

The cyanogen bromide reaction was first successfully applied to the enzyme ribonuclease (Fig. 9). There are four residues of methionine in the molecule, two of them in a unique methionylmethionyl sequence. From this sequence, cleavage with cyanogen bromide should release homoserine and/or homoserine lactone.

This was indeed the case as is shown by the chromatogram (Fig. 10) of the gel filtration over Sephadex of the reaction mixture: C-protein, C-peptide, homoserine, and homoserine lactone are the fragments which were eluted (in the order given). The capital letter C stands for cyanogen bromide; i.e., the protein and peptide, respectively, are obtained by cyanogen bromide cleavage.

Of the many applications of the cyanogen bromide reaction we shall only discuss one more in detail. In Figure 11 we see the partial sequence of chymotrypsin which contains the active serine (Ser*). The enzyme contains two residues of methionine. The one nearest to the active serine is selectively oxidized to methionine sulfoxide upon treatment with hydrogen peroxide (8). This could be shown by applying the cyanogen bromide

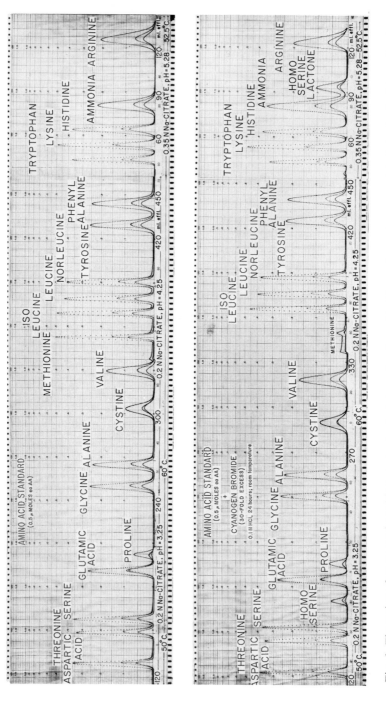

Fig. 6. The action of cyanogen bromide on a standard mixture of amino acids. Upper chromatogram: original standard mixture of amino acids. Lower chromatogram: same mixture after treatment with cyanogen bromide.

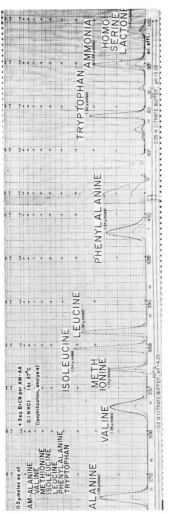

Fig. 7. Cleavage of acetylmethionyl peptides with cyanogen bromide. AM = acetylmethionyl; AM-AA = acetylmethionyl amino acid.

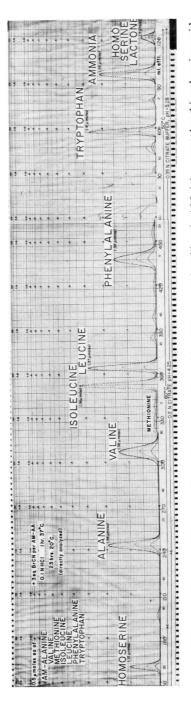

Fig. 8. Cleavage of acetylmethionyl peptides with cyanogen bromide. AM = acetylmethionyl; AM-AA = acetylmethionyl amino acid.

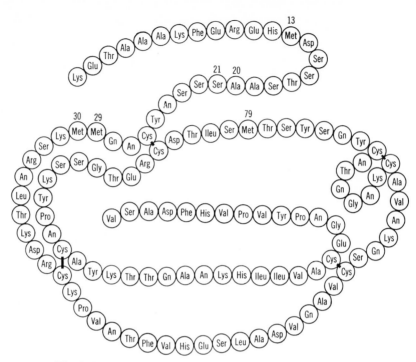

Fig. 9. The primary structure of bovine pancreatic ribonuclease.

Table 1

Applications of the Cyanogen Bromide Reaction to Peptides and Proteins

Protein	Molecular weight	Residues of methionine	Application
Pseudomonas cyto-chrome C-551	8000	2	Structural studies[a]
β-Galactosidase	135000	24	Structural studies[b] (non-identity of polypeptide chains)
Gastrin	2000	2	Structural studies[c]
Rabbit γ-globulin	140000	11	Immunologically active fragment; 52% conversion of methionine[d]

[a] D. P. Ambler, *Biochem. J.*, **89**, 349 (1963).

[b] E. Steers, Jr., G. R. Graven, C. B. Anfinsen, and J. L. Bethune, *J. Biol. Chem.*, **240**, 2478 (1965).

[c] H. Gregory, D. M. Hardy, D. S. Jones, G. W. Kenner, and R. C. Sheppard, *Nature*, **204**, 931 (1964).

[d] H. J. Cahnmann, D. Arnon, and M. Sela, *J. Biol. Chem.*, **240**, 2762 (1965).

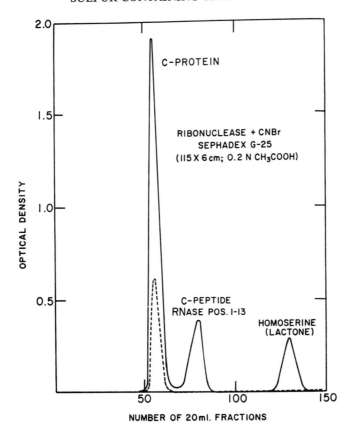

Fig. 10. Gel filtration of the products of the reaction of cyanogen bromide with bovine pancreatic ribonuclease. (——) At 570 mμ. (———) At 280 mμ.

reaction. Methionine sulfoxide does not react with cyanogen bromide. Only the peptide bond of the *distant* residue of methionine was cleaved.

A lengthy discussion of the numerous applications of the cyanogen bromide reaction is not feasible here. One table (Table 1) showing four applications may suffice. Notice that the reaction is applicable over a wide range of molecular size. Here we have molecular weights ranging from

15   3   *
Asp-Ala-Met-Ileu-Cys-Ala-Gly-Ala-Ser-Gly-Val-Ser-Ser-Cys-Met-Gly-Asp-Ser-Gly

Fig. 11. Partial primary structure of chymotrypsin; the asterisk designates the active serine.

2000 to 140,000. Please notice also that *physiologically active fragments* of proteins have been isolated subsequent to the application of the cyanogen bromide reaction, in this case an immunologically active fragment of a γ-globulin.

We shall now turn to the second thioether amino acid. *S*-Methylcysteine does not react with cyanogen bromide. The β-lactone (Fig. 12, reaction scheme a) which would result from a reaction analogous to that of methionine with cyanogen bromide does not form. However, when we acylate the amino group of *S*-methylcysteine (Fig. 12, reaction scheme b), we introduce a 1,5 relationship between the oxygen of the carbonyl group of the acyl group (and the β-carbon atom) and the reaction proceeds in this manner: (*1*) sulfonium salt formation, assisted by the neighboring group effect of the carboxyl group, (*2*) electron group participation, and (*3*) formation of an oxazolinium bromide and methylthiocyanate (9).

At low temperature the reaction proceeds via the mechanism of Figure 13. The oxazolinium bromide is readily hydrolyzed to the *O*-acyl derivative. To complete the cleavage the ester must be hydrolyzed. At high temperature β-*elimination* takes place (mechanism B, Fig. 13). The

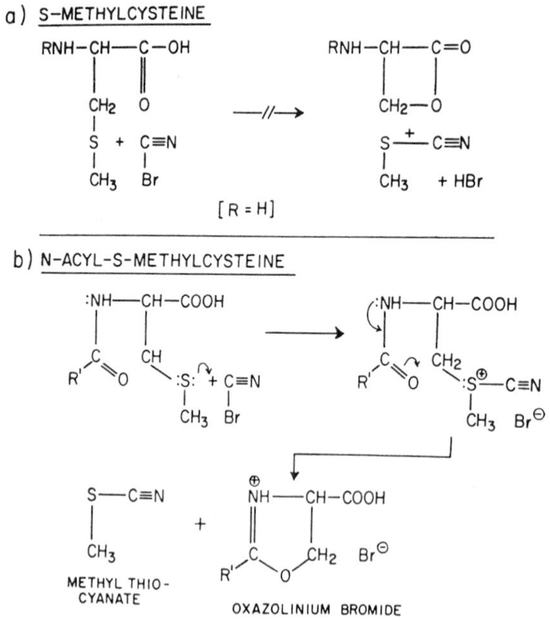

Fig. 12. Reaction of cyanogen bromide with the lower homolog of methionine, i.e., *S*-methylcysteine.

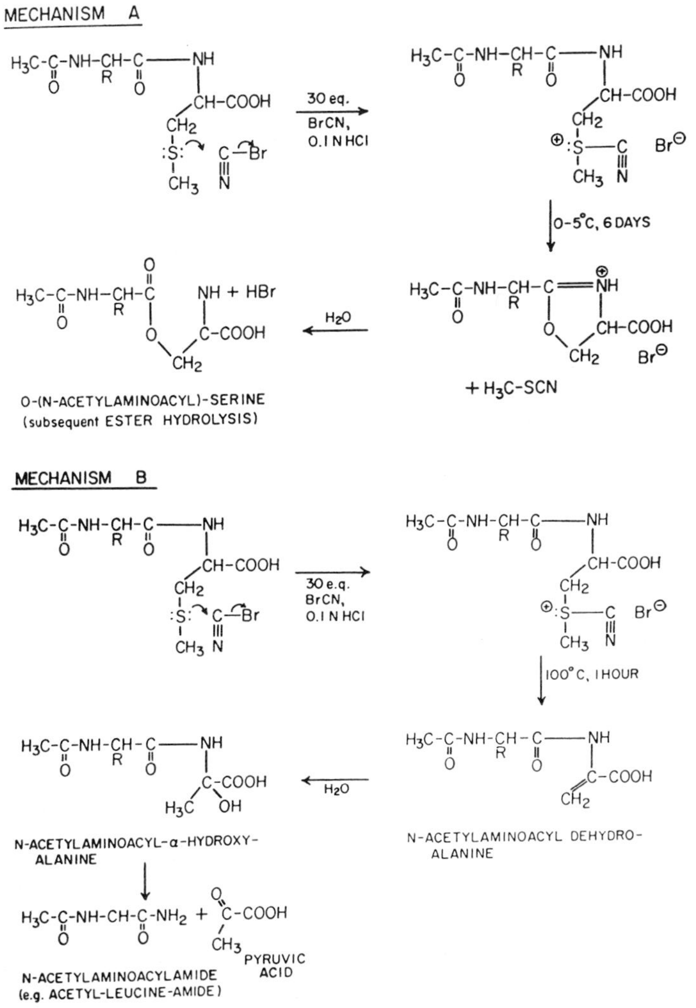

MECHANISM A

MECHANISM B

Fig. 13. The reaction of cyanogen bromide with *N*-acetylaminoacyl-*S*-methyl cysteine.

dehydroalanine derivative is formed. Water is added under formation of the α-hydroxyalanine derivative. The latter is hydrolyzed to pyruvic acid and *N*-acetylaminoacylamide.

The *S*-alkyl derivatives shown in Table 2 do not react with cyanogen bromide. The failure of *S*-methylcysteine to react with cyanogen bromide we have explained in Figure 12, reaction scheme a. Cystathionine contains

Table 2

S-Alkyl Derivatives of Cysteine which do not React with
Cyanogen Bromide

---

1. *S*-Methylcysteine

$$H_3C\!-\!S\!-\!CH_2\!-\!CH\!-\!COOH$$
$$\underset{NH_2}{|}$$

2. Lanthionine

$$HOOC\!-\!CH\!-\!CH_2\!-\!S\!-\!CH_2\!-\!CH\!-\!COOH$$
$$\underset{NH_2}{|}\qquad\qquad\underset{NH_2}{|}$$

3. Cystathionine

$$HOOC\!-\!CH\!-\!CH_2\!-\!S\!-\!CH_2\!-\!CH_2\!-\!CH\!-\!COOH$$
$$\underset{NH_2}{|}\qquad\qquad\qquad\underset{NH_2}{|}$$

4. *S*-Benzylcysteine

$$\text{⟨phenyl⟩}\!-\!CH_2\!-\!S\!-\!CH_2\!-\!CH\!-\!COOH$$
$$\underset{NH_2}{|}$$

---

the structural features of methionine and might be expected to react with cyanogen bromide. Carboxyethylcysteine does react with cyanogen bromide. In cystathionine, the β-carbon atom of the carboxyethyl group is substituted by an amino group. It is perhaps the positive charge at this amino group which interferes with the attack of cyanogen bromide at the sulfur atom.

As soon as the amino group of *S*-alkyl cysteines is acylated, reaction with cyanogen bromide will take place (cf. Fig. 12, reaction scheme b). A sampling of applications is shown in Table 3.

The following acetylaminoacyl derivatives of *S*-methylcysteine were successfully cleaved with cyanogen bromide in the yields shown in the last column of Table 4. We determined the amount of unreacted *S*-methyl-cysteine and the amount of newly formed serine. This enabled us to calculate the extent of cleavage via mechanisms A and B (Fig. 13), respectively. The results, in percent of cleavage, are shown in the fourth and fifth column of Table 4. The reaction conditions are given in the first column.

Two extremes of reaction conditions are shown in Table 4: (*a*) High temperature. In the second line the reaction proceeds predominantly via mechanism B. (*b*) Low temperature. In the last line, the reaction proceeds predominantly via mechanism A.

To apply this type of cyanogen bromide reaction to proteins there must

Table 3

N-Acyl-S-alkyl Derivatives of Cysteine which React with Cyanogen Bromide

1. N-Acetyl-S-methylcysteine

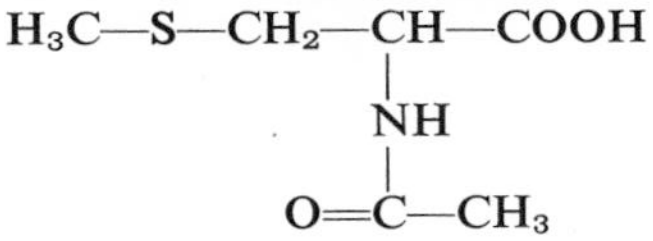

$$H_3C-S-CH_2-CH-COOH$$
$$|$$
$$NH$$
$$|$$
$$O=C-CH_3$$

3. N-Acetyl-S-ethylcysteine

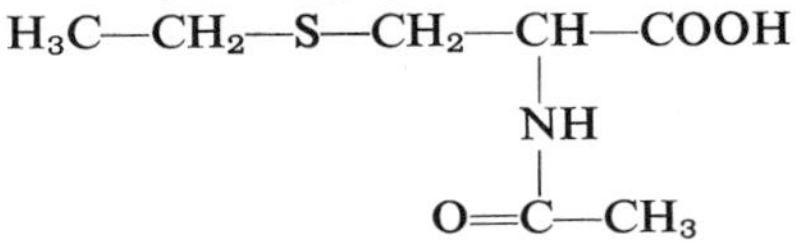

$$H_3C-CH_2-S-CH_2-CH-COOH$$
$$|$$
$$NH$$
$$|$$
$$O=C-CH_3$$

3. N-Acetyl-S-propylcysteine

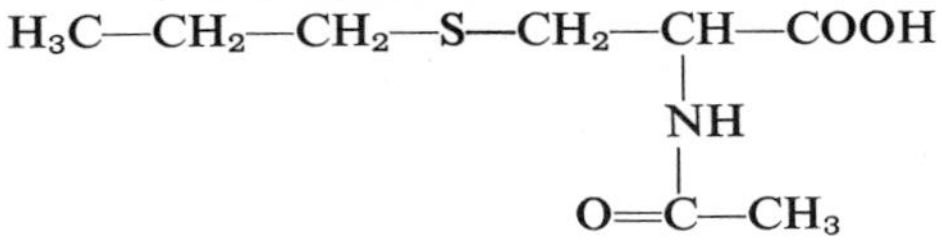

$$H_3C-CH_2-CH_2-S-CH_2-CH-COOH$$
$$|$$
$$NH$$
$$|$$
$$O=C-CH_3$$

4. N-Propionyl-S-methylcysteine

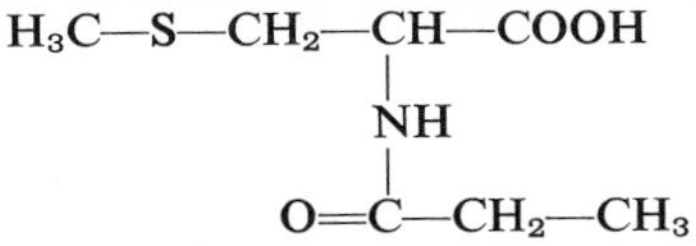

$$H_3C-S-CH_2-CH-COOH$$
$$|$$
$$NH$$
$$|$$
$$O=C-CH_2-CH_3$$

5. N-(n-Butyryl)-S-methylcysteine

$$H_3C-S-CH_2-CH-COOH$$
$$|$$
$$NH$$
$$|$$
$$O=C-CH_2-CH_2-CH_3$$

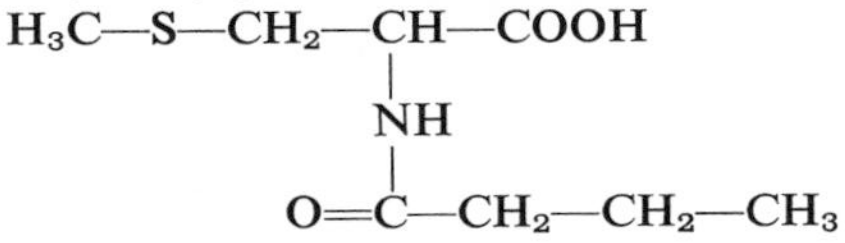

6. N-(Isobutyryl)-S-methylcysteine

$$H_3C-S-CH_2-CH-COOH$$
$$|$$
$$NH$$
$$|$$
$$O=C-CH$$

with CH_3 groups on the CH

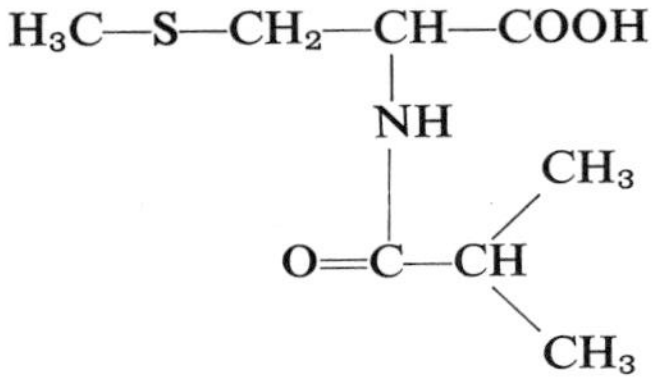

7. N-Acetyl-S-carboxyethylcysteine

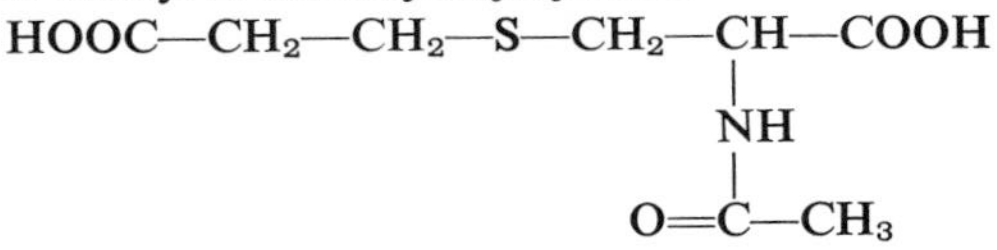

$$HOOC-CH_2-CH_2-S-CH_2-CH-COOH$$
$$|$$
$$NH$$
$$|$$
$$O=C-CH_3$$

Table 4

Cleavage with Cyanogen Bromide of Acetylaminoacyl-S-methylcysteine

Reaction	CysCH$_3$,%	Ser, %	Mechanism A, %	Mechanism B, %	Yield of cleavage, %
100°C; 1 hr; 0.1N HCl; 30 equiv BrCN	15	40	40	45	85
100°C; 1 hr; 0.01N HCl; 30 equiv BrCN	13	9	9	78	87
25°C; 48 hr; 0.1N HCl; 30 equiv BrCN	27	60	60	13	73
25°C; 76 hr; 0.1N HCl; 30 equiv BrCN	23	54	54	23	77
0°C; 120 hr; 0.1N HCl; 30 equiv BrCN	16	75	75	(9)	84

be present in the molecule either free SH groups or disulfide bonds which we will have to reduce. We have reduced the disulfide bonds of ribonuclease. First we removed selectively from the NH$_2$ terminal region a peptide of 20 amino acids. This can be done enzymatically with either subtilisin or nagarse (10,11) (Fig. 9). Then we cleaved the methionyl peptide bonds with cyanogen bromide. This was followed by reduction of the disulfide bonds

Table 5

Cleavage of N-Acetylleucyl-S-methylcysteinylglycine with Cyanogen Bromide[a]

(N-Acetylleucyl-S-methylcysteinylglycine contained 1.01 residues of leucine, 1.06 residues of S-methylcysteine, and 0.99 residues of glycine)

Amino acyl	CysCH$_3$, %	Ser, %	Leu, %	Mechanism A, %	Mechanism B, %	Yield of cleavage
Leu	5	22	100	22	73	95
Val	6	16	100	16	78	94
Phe	trace	5	100	5	95	100
Gly	5	22	100	22	73	95

[a] Reaction conditions: 100°C, 1hr, 0.1N HCl, 30 equiv BrCN.

with dithioerythritol and alkylation. After separation by gel filtration on Sephadex we again subjected the purest fragment to treatment with cyanogen bromide, this time to cleave the aminoacyl bond of cysteine (Fig. 14).

The pattern of separation on Sephadex G-25 while eluting with $0.2N$ acetic acid is presented in Figure 15: peaks I and II are representative of the methylated fragments of ribonuclease comprised of residues 31–79 and 80–124, respectively. The low peak (III) represents the fragment 22–29. The last peak is the oxidation product of dithioerythritol.

From the pure fragment (22–29) which contains one residue of S-methylcysteine two peptide fragments have been isolated, thus indicating successful cleavage of the aminoacylpeptide bond of S-methylcysteine (Table 6).

Pepsin is a protease with features which are rather strikingly different from those of other proteolytic enzymes. Of interest to us is the fact that there is present in the molecule a total of only three residues of lysine and arginine (Table 7). Therefore, the proteolytic enzyme with the highest degree of specificity, i.e., trypsin, finds only *three* peptide bonds to cleave. This leaves the structurally interested protein chemist with fragments which are difficult to handle. However, there are also present in the molecule four residues of methionine and six residues of half-cystine (Table 7).

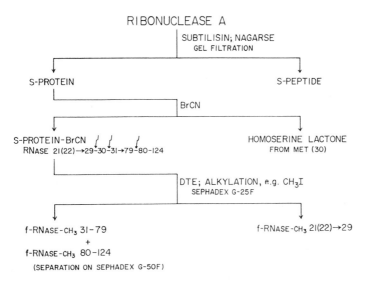

Fig. 14. Enzymatic and nonenzymatic fragmentation of bovine pancreatic ribonuclease; DTE = dithioerythritol.

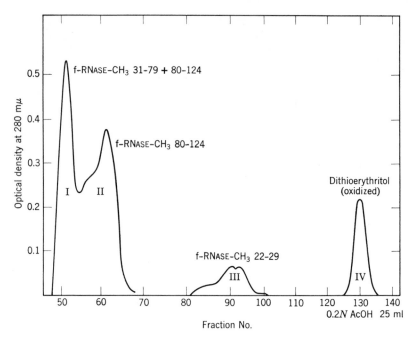

Fig. 15. Gel filtration on Sephadex G-25 of the fragments of RNase-*S*-protein obtained by cleavage of the methionyl peptide bonds with cyanogen bromide and reduction of the disulfide bonds with dithioerythritol.

Table 6

Cleavage of *S*-Methylcysteinyl Peptide Bonds with Cyanogen Bromide (f-RNase-CH₃ 22–29 designates a fragment of bovine pancreatic ribonuclease consisting of the original amino acid residues 22–29 of bovine pancreatic ribonuclease; the residue of half-cysteine in position 26 has been methylated.)

Cleavage with cyanogen bromide of f-RNase-CH₃ 22–29:

Reaction conditions:
    0.1N hydrochloric acid
    Room temperature
    24–72 hours
    Excess of BrCN
Conversion of *S*-methylcysteine: 85%
Gel filtration (Sephadex G-25, 0.2N AcOH) after lyophilization of reaction mixture:

        No starting material; two peptides isolated at higher effluent volumes

Table 7

Amino Acid Composition of Pepsin

Amino acid	Number of residues	
		Literature[a]
Aspartic acid	44	44
Threonine	27	28
Serine	43	44
Glumatic acid	27	27
Proline	17	17
Glycine	38	38
Alanine	18	18
Half-cystine	4[b]	6
Valine	23	21
Methionine	4	5
Isoleucine	26	27
Leucine	28	28
Tyrosine	17	18
Phenylalanine	15	14
Tryptophan		6
Lysine	1	1
Histidine	1	1
Ammonia		36
Arginine	2	2

[a] O. O. Blumenfeld and G. E. Perlmann, *J. Gen. Physiol.*, **42**, 553 (1959).
[b] Direct analysis.

Following *S*-methylation this will provide us with 10 peptide bonds which are amenable to nonenzymatic cleavage.

The low content of lysine and arginine in pepsin is aggravated by the fact that one of the arginines and the lysine are separated by only *three* amino acids (12) (Fig. 16). Three of the tryptic fragments will therefore be even larger.

In Figure 17 the available information on the primary structure of pepsin has been incorporated. The three disulfide bridges have been

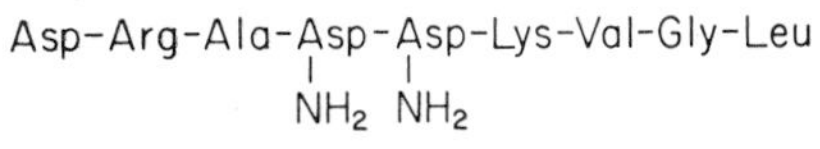

```
Asp-Arg-Ala-Asp-Asp-Lys-Val-Gly-Leu
              |   |
             NH₂ NH₂
```

Fig. 16. Pepsin fragment "enriched" in basic amino acids.

reduced (13) by treatment with dithioerythritol (14). The newly generated mercapto groups were alkylated, i.e., either methylated or carboxymethylated (13).

In the hydrolysate of reduced and S-carboxymethylated pepsin which had been treated with cyanogen bromide (13) we notice that only methionine has been converted to homoserine and/or homoserine lactone (cf. Fig. 18 for the respective locations of the peaks representing these amino acids).

Once S-methylated pepsin is treated with cyanogen bromide (13), both amino acids, methionine and S-methylcysteine, are affected (cf. Fig. 19 for the respective locations of the peaks representing the corresponding amino acids).

We have thus far seen how two thioether amino acids are utilized in the degradation in the analysis of proteins. It is likely that one of them, methionine, is removed from the NH₂ terminus of proteins at the end of *protein biosynthesis*.

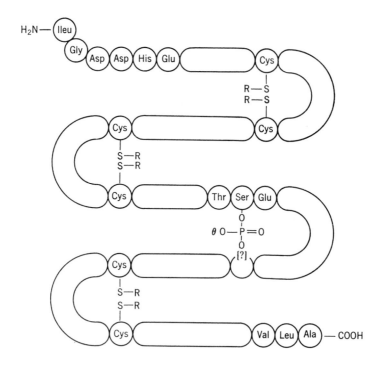

Fig. 17. Reduced and alkylated pepsin.

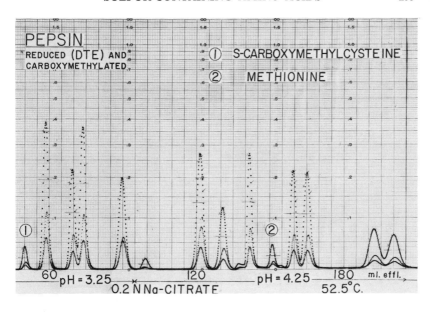

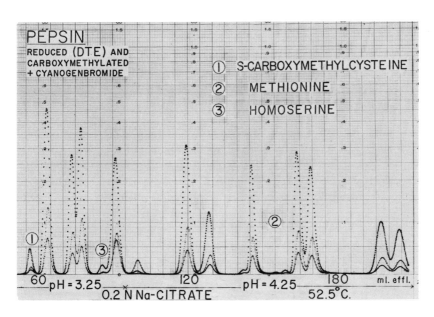

Fig. 18. The action of cyanogen bromide on reduced and carboxymethylated pepsin. Upper chromatogram: amino acid analysis of reduced and carboxymethylated pepsin. Lower chromatogram: amino acid analysis of reduced and carboxymethylated pepsin after treatment with cyanogen bromide.

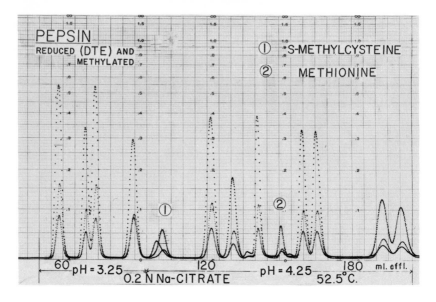

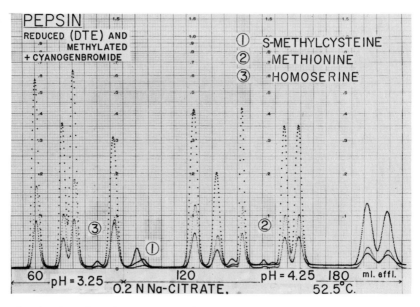

Fig. 19. The action of cyanogen bromide on reduced and methylated pepsin. Upper chromatogram: amino acid analysis of reduced and methylated pepsin. Lower chromatogram: amino acid analysis of reduced and methylated pepsin after treatment with cyanogen bromide.

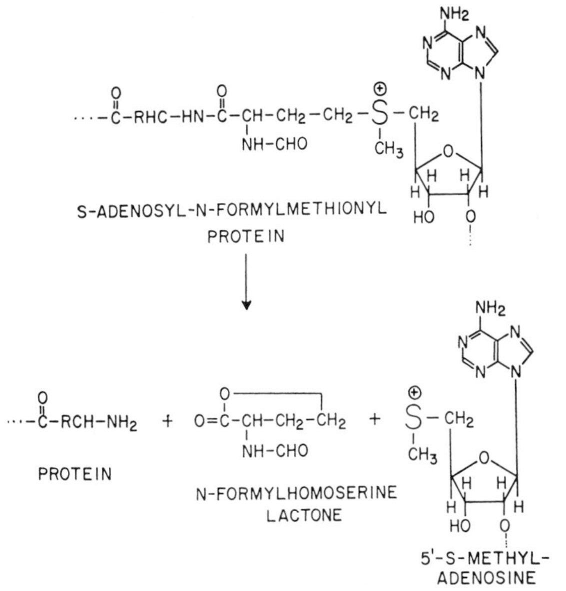

Fig. 20. Biosynthesis of proteins: chain initiation. Proposed mechanism for the removal of the chain initiator *N*-formylmethionine.

N-Formylmethionine functions as chain initiator in certain organisms, e.g., in *E. coli*.* If we form a sulfonium salt, e.g., with adenosine, we offer provisions for a mechanism that will remove the chain initiator, probably without the involvement of enzymes (Fig. 20).

* See reference 15 for a recent discussion of this topic.

References

1. C. H. Li, W. K. Liu, and G. S. Dixon, *J. Am. Chem. Soc.*, **88**, 2050 (1966).
2. B. Witkop, in *Advances in Protein Chemistry*, Vol. 16, M. L. Anson and J. T. Edsall, Eds., Academic Press, New York, 1961, p. 221.
3. Th. Wieland and W. Schön, *Ann.*, **593**, 157 (1955).
4. A. Patchornik, W. B. Lawson, E. Gross, and B. Witkop, *J. Am. Chem. Soc.*, **82**, 5923 (1960).
5. G. L. Schmir, L. A. Cohen, and B. Witkop, *J. Am. Chem. Soc.*, **81**, 2228 (1959). E. J. Corey and L. F. Haefele, *ibid.*, **81**, 2225 (1959).
6. S. Shaetiel and A. Patchornik, *J. Am. Chem. Soc.*, **85**, 2799 (1963).
7. J. von Braun and G. Engelbertz, *Ber.*, **56**, 1573 (1923).

8. D. E. Koshland, Jr., D. H. Strumeyer, and W. J. Ray, Jr., *Brookhaven Symp. Biol.*, **15**, 101 (1962).

9. E. Gross, C. H. Plato, J. L. Morell, and B. Witkop, *150th Meeting, Am. Chem. Soc., Atlantic City, N.J., 1965, Div. Biol. Chem., Abstr. 125*, p. 60C.

10. F. M. Richards and P. J. Vithayathil, *J. Biol. Chem.*, **234**, 1459 (1959).

11. E. Gross and B. Witkop, *Biochem. Biophys. Res. Commun.*, **23**, 720 (1966).

12. T. S. Kuznetzov, G. G. Novalena, and V. M. Stepanov, *Biochem. Biophys. Acta*, **118**, 219 (1966).

13. E. Gross and J. L. Morell, unpublished results.

14. W. W. Cleland, *Biochemistry*, **3**, 480 (1964).

15. M. R. Capecchi, *Proc. Natl. Acad. Sci. U.S.*, **55**, 1517 (1966).

Studies on Esters of Sulfur-Containing Acids

EMIL THOMAS KAISER

University of Chicago, Chicago, Illinois

The five-membered cyclic phosphorus-containing esters, potassium ethylene phosphate (1) and lithium propyl phostonate (2), are known to hydrolyze enormously faster than the corresponding open-chain esters. Ethylene phosphate hydrolyzes exclusively with P—O bond cleavage in alkaline solution whereas the open-chain analog, dimethyl phosphate, reacts primarily by way of C—O cleavage (3,4). When this difference in the modes of bond cleavage is taken into account, the rate enhancement for the attack at the phosphorus atom of the cyclic ester by hydroxide ion can be estimated to be greater than 10^8. Larger ring cyclic esters such as the six-membered systems do not appear to exhibit the lability of the five-membered ones but rather behave quite analogously to the open-chain compounds.

To determine whether the unusual lability of the five-membered cyclic esters is confined to the phosphorus series or if similar high reactivity might be observed in the hydrolysis of five-membered cyclic sulfur-containing esters, the comparative rates of reaction of ethylene sulfate, trimethylene sulfate, and dimethyl sulfate were measured (5). As Table 1 shows, ethylene sulfate, the five-membered cyclic species, undergoes alkaline hydrolysis at a rate which is somewhat faster but by no means enormously so than those of the other esters. However, it was not possible to measure the rate enhancement for attack at the sulfur atom since ethylene sulfate reacts with only about 14% S—O bond cleavage, and within the limits of experimental detection dimethyl sulfate and trimethylene sulfate hydrolyze exclusively with C—O cleavage.

Table 1

Relative Second-Order Rate Constants for the Alkaline
Hydrolysis of Esters of Sulfuric Acid at 25.0° (5)

Sulfate	k_2
Dimethyl	1.0
Trimethylene	0.2
Ethylene	20.

Accordingly, a kinetic study was undertaken on the hydrolysis of catechol cyclic sulfate (I) and diphenyl sulfate (II) (6).* Nucleophilic attack of
hydroxide ion at the aromatic carbon atoms in these compounds should be
extremely unlikely. Hence, the difference in the rates of hydrolysis of the
two esters should represent the difference in the rate of attack at sulfur for a
five-membered cyclic sulfate (I) compared to that for its open-chain analog
(II). Equations 1 and 2 represent the hydrolytic reactions under consideration.

$$\text{(I)} \quad \text{SO}_2 + \text{OH}^- \longrightarrow \begin{array}{c}\text{-OH}\\\text{-OSO}_3^-\end{array} \qquad (1)$$

(I)

$$\text{(II)} \quad \text{O-SO}_2\text{-O} \quad + \text{OH}^- \longrightarrow \text{-OH} + \text{-OSO}_3^- \qquad (2)$$

(II)

Of course, since the factors responsible for the unusual lability of the
phosphorus-containing five-membered cyclic esters are not entirely understood, the influence of the incorporation of an aromatic double bond into
a five-membered cyclic ester system like that in catechol cyclic sulfate could
not be predicted.

The second-order rate constant for the alkaline hydrolysis of I at 25°
was found to be 18.8 M^{-1} sec^{-1}. Extrapolation of measurements made at
higher temperatures gave a value for the second-order rate constant for the
alkaline hydrolysis of II of 8.9 × 10^{-7} M^{-1} sec^{-1} at 25.0°. A comparison then of the relative rate constants observed for the hydrolyses of
catechol cyclic sulfate (I) and diphenyl sulfate (II) which reflects the
difference in the rates of attack by hydroxide ion at sulfur in these two
compounds, shows that the five-membered cyclic ester reacts 2 × 10^7
times faster than its open-chain analog. This represents the first observation of such an enormous rate enhancement for the hydrolysis of a five-
membered cyclic ester which contains a heteroatom other than phosphorus.
The largest rate difference found previously in sulfur-containing systems
was that between the alkaline hydrolysis of catechol cyclic sulfite and diphenyl sulfite, the five-membered cyclic ester hydrolyzing only 1.5 × 10^{-3}
times more rapidly than its open-chain analog (7). The observation of this
reduced rate factor for a five-membered cyclic sulfur-containing ester in

* There is a great difference between the hydrolysis behavior of cyclic sulfites and
sulfates. For instance, ethylene sulfate releases about 6 kcal/mole more heat on
hydrolysis than does dimethyl sulfate, but the heats of hydrolysis of ethylene sulfite
and dimethyl sulfite are nearly the same (see ref. 5 and a paper by R. E. Davis in
J. Am. Chem. Soc., **84**, 599 (1962)).

which the sulfur atom is in a lower oxidation state makes it of interest to determine what structural features of the catechol cyclic sulfate system might be varied and still permit a very large rate acceleration.

An analog of catechol cyclic sulfate in which one of the ring oxygen atoms has been replaced by a methylene group is the five-membered cyclic sulfonate (III), o-hydroxy-α-toluene sulfonic acid sultone. Its rate of alkaline hydrolysis was compared to that of the open-chain analog, phenyl α-toluenesulfonate (IV) (8). As in the case of the aromatic sulfates, nucleophilic attack of hydroxide ion at the aromatic carbon atom is considered to be most unlikely.

$$\text{(III)} \qquad + \text{OH}^- \longrightarrow \qquad \qquad (3)$$

$$\text{(IV)} \qquad + \text{OH}^- \longrightarrow \qquad \qquad (4)$$

The second-order rate constant for the hydroxide ion-catalyzed hydrolysis of III is 33.6 M^{-1} sec^{-1} at 25.0° and that for the reaction of IV is 4.94×10^{-5} M^{-1} sec^{-1}. The five-membered cyclic sulfonate (III) thus hydrolyzes 6.8×10^5 times faster than its open-chain analog (IV), and this is the second observation of a very large rate enhancement for the hydrolysis of a five-membered cyclic sulfur-containing ester.*

The next problem which was attacked was to determine whether the great lability of the five-membered cyclic sulfur-containing esters was confined to this particular ring size. Therefore, the six-membered cyclic sulfonate (V) was prepared (9) and the rate of its alkaline hydrolysis determined.

At 25° the second-order rate constant for the alkaline hydrolysis of V is 1.45×10^{-3} M^{-1} sec^{-1}. Although this is somewhat larger than the

$$\text{(V)} \qquad + \text{OH}^- \longrightarrow \qquad \qquad (5)$$

* A comparison of the phosphorus and sulfur systems reveals the following interesting trend: the ratios of the rates for the cyclic esters compared to their acyclic analogs are somewhat lower when a methylene group is directly attached to the heteroatom (phostonates and sulfones) than those which have been observed for the phosphates and sulfates.

rate constant for the reaction of the open-chain compound (IV), it is much smaller than that for the five-membered cyclic ester (III) and demonstrates that the latter ring system is indeed uniquely labile (10).

As discussed earlier, attack by hydroxide ion at the aromatic carbon atoms of the ring is improbable, and the pathway for the hydrolysis of catechol cyclic sulfate should involve reaction by the nucleophile at the sulfur atoms. However, in the case of the five-membered sultone (III), in addition to attack at sulfur, alternative pathways for reaction must be considered, since mechanisms involving a sulfene intermediate can be written. Four mechanisms which can be suggested for the hydrolysis of III are shown in equations 6–9.

$$\tag{6}$$

$$\tag{7}$$

$$\tag{8}$$

$$\tag{9}$$

Equation 6 represents a direct displacement by hydroxide ion at sulfur, and in equation 7 the formation of a pentacovalent intermediate is postulated. Equation 8 indicates how the hydrolysis could proceed through a sulfene formed by a concerted elimination reaction, and equation 9 shows a carbanion mechanism for the production of the sulfene. These mechanisms can be subjected to a variety of experimental tests, and such studies are in progress. A prediction which can be made if the scheme given in equation 8 applies is that if the reaction were run in D_2O the resultant sulfonic acid should have one deuterium atom in the methylene group (11).

(The hydrolysis can be run under conditions where the hydrogens of the methylene group of the sulfonic acid do not exchange with the deuterium of the solvent D_2O.) However, when the hydrolysis of III was conducted in D_2O—OD^- solution in which the sultone was in excess over OD^-, and III could be recovered after all the OD^- was consumed, the sultone was found to have undergone extensive exchange of deuterium into the methylene group (12). From this observation it is clear that a carbanion is in equilibrium with the sultone in basic solution, and a conclusion cannot be reached from the D_2O experiment as to whether or not a sulfene intermediate is formed. Although the possible importance of a sulfene mechanism for the hydrolysis of III cannot be assessed as yet, a large rate of hydrolysis has been observed for a sultone, VI, which cannot react by way of a sulfene since it has no methylene group (10). Our measurements show that VI hydrolyzes in alkali at a rate comparable to that of III (10). This result does not bear upon the occurrence or nonoccurrence of a sulfene in the hydrolysis of III, but it demonstrates at least that a sulfene pathway is not obligatory for the rapid hydrolysis of a five-membered sultone.

$$O——SO_2$$

(VI)

Many other aspects of the hydrolyses of the reactive five-membered cyclic esters of sulfur-containing acids are being explored, but to maintain the moderate length of this review a discussion of our findings must be deferred. Nevertheless, it should be mentioned that we are completing investigations of the reactions of various different nucleophiles (imidazole, N-methylimidazole, etc.) with the sulfur-containing esters (10), and that we have found these esters to be interesting substrates for the action of several enzymes. For example, we have discovered that the sultone (VII) is hydrolyzed by bovine carbonic anhydrase with a very large second-order rate constant, 1.27×10^6 liters $mole^{-1}$ min^{-1} at pH 7.5 and 25°, and appears to be the most reactive ester substrate of this enzyme known (13). Also, both III and VII are intriguing new substrates for the action of α-chymotrypsin, and a detailed investigation of their enzymatic reactions will be reported in the near future (14).

$$O_2N——\begin{array}{c} CH_2 \\ SO_2 \\ O \end{array}$$

(VII)

Acknowledgments

In concluding this review the author would like to thank his co-workers, O. R. Zaborsky, T. F. Wulfers, K. Kudo, I. R. Katz, K. W. Lo, and J. H. Heidema for their valuable contributions to the work discussed. The support of the National Science Foundation and the American Cancer Society is gratefully acknowledged.

References

1. J. Kumamoto, J. R. Cox, Jr., and F. H. Westheimer, *J. Am. Chem. Soc.*, **78**, 4858 (1956).
2. A. Eberhard and F. H. Westheimer, *J. Am. Chem. Soc.*, **87**, 253 (1965).
3. P. C. Haake and F. H. Westheimer, *J. Am. Chem. Soc.*, **83**, 1102 (1961).
4. C. A. Bunton, D. R. Llewellyn, K. G. Oldham, and C. A. Vernon, *J. Chem. Soc.*, **1958**, 3574.
5. E. T. Kaiser, M. Panar, and F. H. Westheimer, *J. Am. Chem. Soc.*, **85**, 602 (1963).
6. E. T. Kaiser, I. R. Katz, and T. F. Wulfers, *J. Am. Chem. Soc.*, **87**, 3781 (1965)
7. P. De la Mare, J. Tillett, and H. van Woerden, *J. Chem. Soc.*, **1962** 4888.
8. O. R. Zaborsky and E. T. Kaiser, *J. Am. Chem. Soc.*, **88**, 3084 (1966).
9. W. E. Truce and F. D. Hoerger, *J. Am. Chem. Soc.*, **76**, 5357 (1954).
10. E. T. Kaiser, K. Kudo, and O. R. Zaborsky, *J. Am. Chem. Soc.*, **89**, 1393 (1967); K. Kudo, unpublished observations.
11. J. F. King and T. Durst, *J. Am. Chem. Soc.*, **87**, 5684 (1966).
12. O. R. Zaborsky, unpublished observations.
13. K. W. Lo and E. T. Kaiser, *Chem. Commun.*, **1966**, 834.
14. J. H. Heidema and E. T. Kaiser, *J. Am. Chem. Soc.*, **89**, 460 (1967); J. H. Heidema, unpublished observations.

The Reactivity of Some Sulfur-Containing Compounds of Biological Interest with One-Electron Equivalent Reagents

GABRIEL STEIN*

Salk Institute for Biological Studies, La Jolla, California

Some substances of biological interest, for example DPN^+

$$DPN^+ + H^- \rightleftharpoons DPNH$$

or ribonuclease

$$\underset{S-S}{\overset{\ulcorner R \urcorner}{}} \quad 2H \rightleftharpoons \underset{SH \ HS}{\overset{\ulcorner R \urcorner}{}}$$

may pass from one stable state to another by two-electron equivalent reversible oxidation–reduction processes. Some years ago, we showed in the case of DPN^+ and its model compounds that forcing one-electron equivalent changes on it and thus forming intermediate free radicals, results in biologically inactive products (1).

Ionizing radiations act through compulsory one-electron equivalent changes by a free-radical mechanism. One of the reactive intermediates in the case of ionizing radiation in aqueous solutions is atomic hydrogen. We evolved a method for the reproducible quantitative investigation of the reactions of atomic hydrogen in aqueous solution (2). The results may be compared with specific rate constants and reaction mechanisms of hydrogen atoms from radiation chemistry. Studying sulfur-containing compounds of biological interest, we found that ferricytochrome c, which contains in its protein divalent sulfur (but no disulfide bridges) and in which the ferric form is reduced by one-electron equivalent reduction to the ferrous, is not inactivated by atomic hydrogen as long as the ferric form is present (3). The electron is conveyed by radical transfer from the protein to the iron.

By contrast, trypsine (4) (and chrymotrypsine (5)) are very effectively inactivated by atomic hydrogen. A specific correlation was found between aromatic and sulfur-containing amino acids affected in the protein.

* Permanent address: Department of Physical Chemistry, Hebrew University, Jerusalem, Israel.

Particularly striking is H_2S evolution from these proteins compared with the behavior of cysteine and glutathione under the action of H atoms (6).

Ribonuclease was chosen for special study and it was shown (7) that a specific correlation exists between the action of atomic hydrogen on the inactivation of this enzyme and the chemical changes observed in the aromatic amino acids (tyrosine and phenylalanine) on the one hand, and the divalent sulfur amino acids (methionine and cysteine). These aromatic and sulfur-containing amino acids are selectively affected. All other amino acids remain intact.

It appears that the sulfur-containing amino acids are reduced and the aromatic oxidized in a linked process by free-radical reaction resulting on the addition of H atoms. In this process the d orbitals of divalent sulfur can act as a very effective electron acceptor.

This view is supported by two specific features of divalent sulfur: (*a*) the formation of the radical ion H_2S^- in the interaction of solvated electrons with H_2S in the frozen state, and (*b*) the exceptionally fast rate constant of the reaction of H_2S in aqueous solutions with the hydrated electron, according to $e_{aq}^- + H_2S \rightarrow HS^- + H^0$, to yield atomic hydrogen.

This reaction may be shown (8) to proceed by two parallel mechanisms:

$$S\overset{\displaystyle H}{\underset{\displaystyle H}{\big<}} + e_{aq}^- \longrightarrow {}^-SH + H \qquad \text{(Brønsted type proton transfer)} \qquad (1)$$

$$e_{aq}^- + S\overset{\displaystyle H}{\underset{\displaystyle H}{\big<}} \longrightarrow {}^-SH + H \qquad \text{(primary addition to } d \text{ orbitals)} \qquad (2)$$

Acknowledgment

This research was supported by the U.S. Atomic Energy Commission, Biology Division.

References

1. G. Stein and A. J. Swallow, *Nature*, **173**, 937 (1954); *J. Chem. Soc.*, **1958**, 306; Y. Paiss and G. Stein, *ibid.*, **1958**, 2905.
2. For a summary and previous references cf. G. Navon and G. Stein, *J. Phys. Chem.*, **69**, 1384, 1390 (1965); G. Stein, *Discussions Faraday Soc.*, **29**, 235 (1960).
3. G. Czapski, N. Frohwirth, and G. Stein, *Nature*, **207**, 1191 (1965).
4. L. K. Mee, G. Navon, and G. Stein, *Biochim. Biophys. Acta*, **104**, 151 (1965).
5. L. K. Mee, G. Navon, and G. Stein, *Nature*, **204**, 1056 (1964).
6. G. Navon and G. Stein, *Israel J. Chem.*, **2**, 151 (1964); and to be published.
7. B. E. Holmes, G. Navon, and G. Stein, *Nature*, **213**, 1087 (1967).
8. G. Stein, to be published.

Author Index

Numbers in parentheses are reference numbers and show that an author's work is referred to although his name is not mentioned in the text. Numbers in *italics* indicate the pages on which the full references appear.

A

Abrahams, S. C., 46(8), *58*, 65, *72*
Adamek, S., 150(42), 152, 154(42), *155*
Allen, T. L., 62(2), *72*
Alston, T. G., 109(21), *110*
Ambler, D. P., 242
Ames, D. P., 46(14), *58*
Anderson, A. W., 134, 135(13), *144*
Anfinsen, C. B., 242
Appel, R., 5(8), *7*
Ariyan, Z. S., 106, 107(11), *110*
Arnon, D., 242
Ashley, J. R., 55(42), *59*
Astbury, W. T., 197, *203*
Avramenko, L. I., 23(2), *43*
Aynsley, E. E., 5(9), *7*

B

Backer, H. J., 53, *58*, 73(2), *81*
Bacon, R. F., 10, 18(8), *21*
Bacon, R. G. R., *110*
Bacskai, R., 125(2), *131*
Banes, F. W., 114, *123*
Barney, A. L., 207(7), *210*
Barron, E. S. G., 157, 158, *163*
Bartlett, P. D., 46(7,9) 50(25), 51(25,33), *58*
Barton, B. C., 181(19), *183*
Bateman, L., 173(16), 174(16), 181(16), *183*
Beckwith, A. J., 109(26), *110*
Beevers, C. A., 46(6), *58*
Bendit, E. G., 186(9,10), *202*
Benesch, R., 52(34), *58*
Benesch, R. E., 52(34), *58*
Bennett, G. M., 146(9), *154*
Benson, R. S., *104*

Berbalk, H., 106(9), *110*
Berenbaum, M. B., *144*, 145, 146(10), *154*, 221
Bertozzi, E., 191(34), *202*, 223, *228*
Bethune, J. L., 242
Birch, S. F., 62, *72*, 126(16), *131*
Blau, N. F., 119(7), *123*
Block, E., 73(4), 74(4), *81*
Bloomfield, G. F., 62, *72*
Blumenfeld, O. O., 251
Boberg, F., 108(13), *110*
Boček, K., 88, *103*, *104*
Boileau, S., 148, 151, *155*
Bost, R. W., 141(36), *144*
Boyd, A. W., *155*
Brauckhoff, H., 197(40), *202*
Braun, J. v., 237, *255*
Brindell, G., 75(8), *81*
Brode, G. L., 125(6) 126(6), *131*, 133, 138(31,32), 140, *144*
Broderick, E., 146(10), *154*
Brown, E. J., 109(20), *110*
Bruce, J. M., Jr., 207(7), *210*
Buckler, S. A., 70(19), *72*
Bunton, C. A., 257(4), *262*
Burg, K. H., 159(16), *163*
Burley, R. W., 185, *202*
Burness, D. M., 66(15), *72*
Busfield, W. K., 133(1,2), 137(1), *144*

C

Cahnmann, H. J., 242
Caldwell, J. B., 185(5,6), *202*
Callear, A. B., 23(4), 34(4), 35(4), 40(4), *43*
Campaigne, E., 87, *103*
Campbell, D. S., 167(22), *183*
Campbell, T. W., 126(12), *131*

Campbell, W. A., 5(9), *7*
Cannon, B. K., 157(3), *163*
Capecchi, M. R., 255(15), *256*
Carazzolo, G., 147(21), 152, *154*
Caron, A., 46(8), *58*
Carruthers, W., 109, *110*
Carter, F. L., 38(16), *43*
Cava, M. P., 137(22), *144*
Cecil, R., 46(16), 47, *58*
Champtetier, G., 148(32), *155*
Chapman, D., 6, *7*
Cheshko, R. S., 91(9–11), *103*
Christina, R. C., 146(10), *154*
Cilento, G., 84, 103, *103*
Cleland, W. W., 252(14), *256*
Clendenning, R. A., 137(18,19), *144*
Coffey, D. S., 158(13b), *163*
Coffman, D. D., 147(15), *154*
Cohen, A., 46(13), 47(2,3), 50(26), *58*
Cohen, B., 5(10), *7*
Cohen, L. A., 236(5), *255*
Coker, J. N., 207(7), *210*
Colodny, P. C., 225, *228*
Conn, M. W., 141(36), *144*
Cook, R. E., 133(9), *144*
Coran, A. Y., 169(8), *182*
Cordes, A. W., 3(3), *7*
Corey, E. J., 73, 74(4), *81*, 236(5), *255*
Coste, J., 148(31), *155*
Cotton, F. A., 159(15), *163*
Coughanower, D. R., 55(41), *59*
Coulson, C. A., 103(24), *104*
Cox, E., 51(33), *58*
Cox, J. R., Jr., 257(1), *262*
Crafts, J. M., 137(20), *144*, 146, *154*
Cram, D. J., 133(7), *144*
Credali, L., 146(12), *154*
Crewther, W. G., 185(2), *202*
Cristol, S. J., 75(8), *81*
Csizmadia, I. G., 24(7), *43*
Cullum, T. V., 62(11), *72*
Cunningham, G. L., *155*
Cvetanovic, R. J., 23(1), 34(1), 35(1), *43*
Czapski, G., 263(3), *264*

D

Dainton, F. S., 126(17), 128(17), *131*, 133, 134(10–12), 135, *144*

Daly, W. H., 159(16), *163*
Dan, K., 231(1), *233*
Dansizer, C., 185(7), 187(21), 191(7,35), 197(42), 198(35), *202, 203*
Darwent, B. De B., 133(6), *144*
Davis, F. O., 138(8), *144*, 145(1), 146(1), *154*, 191(34), *202*, 223, *228*
Davis, O. C. M., 5(6), *7*
Davis, R. E., 45, 46(7,9,11,13), 47(2,3), 48(20,21), 49(20,23), 50(25–28), 51 (25,27,33), 53, 54(20), 55(20), *58*, 70, *72*, 258
Dean, R. A., 62(11), *72*, 126(16), *131*
DeChecchi, C., 146(12), 147(22), *154, 155*
Dedio, E. L., 34(15), *43*
De la Mare, P., 258(7), *262*
Demarcay, E., 3(1), *7*
Dermer, O. C., 145(2), 148, *154*
Dixon, G. S., 235(1), *255*
Dörges, J., 109(17), *110*
Dole, M., 52(35), *58*
Donohue, J., 46(8), *58*
Dow Chemical Co., 146(13,14), *154*
Dowling, L. M., 185(2), *202*
Downs, A. J., 205(6), *210*
Drana, A. A., 137(22), *144*
Drews, H., 136, *144*
Dunn, J. R., 172(14), *182*
Du Pont de Nemours, E. I., & Co., 146 (11), 147(15), *154*
Durst, T., 260(11), *262*
Dyatlovitskava, S. V., 150(44), *155*

E

Eaton, D. R., *104*
Eberhard, A., 257(2), *262*
Ebsworth, E. A. V., 205(6), *210*
Edwards, J. O., 50, *58*
Ehrenburg, E. G., 227(5), *228*
Eisenberg, A., 15, 17, *21*, 71(26), *72*
Eland, J. H. D., 109(20), *110*
Empen, J. A., 125, *131*, 148(27), 150(27), *155*
Engelbertz, G., 237(7), *255*
Erwin, M. J., 158(13a), *163*
Eyring, E., 191(32), *202*

F

Fairbrother, F., 70(22), *72*
Fanelli, R., 9, 10, 14, 18(1,8), *21*
Farbwerke Hoechst, 147(19), *154*
Farmer, R. H., *103*
Farnham, A. G., 137(18,19), *144*
Farnworth, H. D., 186(20), 200(45), *202*, *203*
Faucher, J. A., 128(19), *131*
Fava, A., 46(15), *58*
Feher, F., 62(4), *72*
Fenton, G. W., 133(3), 136(16), *144*
Ferguson, L. N., *103*
Ferm, R. J., 24(8), *43*
Fernando, J., 47(19), 48(19), *58*
Ferraro, J. J., 157(11,12), *163*
Fettes, E. M., 133(8), *144*, 145(1), 146 (1), *154*, 191, *202*, 223, 227, *228*
Feughelman, M., 186(11–14,18,19), 187 (19), 190(19), 191(28,36), 197(18,39), *202*
Fields, E. K., 136, *144*
Finke, M. L., *155*
Fisher, E., 147(19), *154*
Foldi, V. S., 125(5), 126(6), *131*, 141, *144*
Foppl, H., 46(17), *58*
Foss, O., 45(5), 46(5,10), 50, *58*
Foster, R. E., 66(15), *72*
Fowles, P., 27(12), *43*
Fraenkel, G. K., 71(27), *72*
Frampton, V. L., 38(16), *43*
Francis, R., 159(15), *163*
Franklin, J. L., 71(23), *72*
Frohwirth, N., 263(3), *264*
Fryling, C. F., 115, *123*
Furukawa, J., 126(8–10), *131*, 149, *155*
Fuson, R. C., 66, *72*
Fuzita, Y., 149(41), *155*

G

Gardner, D. M., 71(27), *72*
Gawron, O., 47, 48(19), *58*
Gee, G., 70, *72*
Ghersetti, S., 103(25), *104*
Gibbs, J. H., 86, *103*
Gibbs, W. E., 113(1), *123*
Gipstein, E., 135, 136(15), *144*, 147(18), *154*

Glemser, O., 5(11), *7*
Glockler, G., 45(4), 47, *58*
Gobran, R. H., 145, *154*
Goehring, M., 3(2), 5(8), *7*
Gold, R. J., 157(5), *163*
Golub, M. A., 115, *123*
Goodman, L., 103(26), *104*
Gordon, E. K., 3(3), *7*
Gordon, J. T., 109(21), *110*
Grant, D., 62, *72*
Graven, G. R., 242
Gray, J., 231(2), *233*
Gregory, H., 242
Greidanus, J. W., 83
Grellman, K.-H., 109(20), *110*
Gritter, R. J., 109(24), *110*
Gross, E., 235, 236(4), 244(9), 248(11), 252(13), *255*, *256*
Gross, M. E., *155*
Gruber, R. J., 73(3), 74(3), *81*
Guenthner, M. C., 49(23), *58*
Gunning, H. E., 23, 24(6,7), 26(9–11), 27(9,12), 29(11,13), 30(14), 34(15), *43*
Guryanova, E. N., 66, *72*
Gutschik, E., 106, *110*
Guy, R. G., *110*
Gwinn, W. D., *155*

H

Haake, P. C., 257(3), *262*
Hadler, H. I., 158(13a), *163*
Haefele, L. F., 236(5), *255*
Haines, W. E., 109(23), *110*
Hale, W. F., 137, *144*
Hall, H. K., 126(12), *131*
Haly, A. R., 186(11–14,19), 187(19), 190(19), 197(39,41), *202*, *203*
Hampson, G. C., *103*
Hardy, D. M., 242
Harmon, J., 146(11), *154*
Harris, J. F., Jr., 106, 108, *110*
Harris, L. J., 157(1), *163*
Harris, P., 231(3,4), 232(14), *233*
Hart, E. J., 181(19), *183*
Hatchard, W. R., 66(15), *72*
Hayes, H. R., 126(15), *131*, 140(35), *144*
Heidema, J. H., 261(14), *262*
Hellerman, L., 158(13b), *163*

Higgins, G. M. C., 169(7), 178(18), *182,*
 183
Hikida, T., 29(13), *43*
Hildebrand, D., 199(44), *203*
Hinz, G., 126(13), 128(13), *131*
Hiramoto, Y., 231(5–7), *233*
Hobrick, B. G., 71, *72*
Hodges, C. T., 10(3), *21*
Hodgson, W. G., 70, *72*
Hoerger, F. D., 259(9), *262*
Hoffman, P., 126(13), 128(13), *131*
Hofmeister, E., 107(12), *110*
Hogeveen, H., 89, 90, 103, *103*
Hohenschutz, H., 5(8), *7*
Holmberg, B., 114, *123*
Holmes, B. E., 264(7), *264*
Hooper, T. R., 5(10), *7*
Hopkins, T. E., 5, *7*
Hordnik, A., 45(5), 46(5,10), *58*
Horner, L., 69, *72*, 109, *110*
Howard, E. G., 205(1,4), *210*
Hugell, D., 5(10), *7*
Hulbard, W. N., *155*
Hunter, N. J., 126(16), *131*
Huyser, E. S., 137(26), *144*
Hyne, J. B., 20(11), *21*, 83

I

Imai, H., 126(8–10), *131*
Ingold, C. K., 133(3), 136(16), *144*
Irwin, R. S., *110*
Ishii, Y., 149(41), *155*
Ivin, K. J., 126(17), 128(17), *131*, 133, 134
 (10–12), 135,137(1), *144*

J

Jacobson, H. W., 205(2), 207(7), *210*
Jacox, M. E., 38(17), *43*
Jaffé, H., 88, *103*
Jagger, L., 186(17), *202*
Jensen, L. H., 46(16), 47(16), *58*
Jessup, R. S., 38(19), *43*
Johnson, C. R., 75(7), *81*
Johnson, J. W., 119(7), *123*
Johnson, R. N., 137, *144*
Jolly, W. L., 3, 4(4), 5(12), 6(14), *7*

Jones, D. S., 242
Jones, S. O., 62, *72*
Josey, A. D., *104*

K

Kagokawa, G., 149(34), *155*
Kaiser, E. T., 109(27), *110*, 257, 258(5,6),
 259(8), 260(10), 261(10,13,14), *262*
Kalnitsky, G., 157(9), *163*
Kampmeier, J. A., 107(12), 108, *110*
Kane, R. E., 231(8), *233*
Karabinos, G., 159(14a), *163*
Katz, C., *155*
Katz, I. R., 258(6), *262*
Katz, S. M., 191(29), *202*
Kaufman, F., 23(3), *43*
Kawaoka, Y., 170(10), *182*
Kawasaki, A., 149(33), *155*
Kebarle, P., 23(5), *43*
Kende, I., 62(6), 63(6), 65(6), 71(25), *72*
Kenner, G. W., 242
Kharasch, N., 105. 106, 107(11), 108,
 109, *110*
Khodair, A. I., 105, 108, 109, *110*
Kice, J. L., 65, *72*, 133(4), *144*
Kiefer, B., 232(9), *233*
King, J. F., 260(11), *262*
Kingsbury, C. A., 133(7), *144*
Kiser, R. W., 71, *72*
Kloosterziel, H., 105, 106, *110*
Knight, A. R., 26(9–11), 27(9), 29(11), *43*
Kolesnikova, B. M., 91(9), *103*
Kolesnikova, R. V., 23(2), *43*
Kondo, A., 148, *155*
Koppel, L. B., 55(41), *59*
Koshland, D. E., Jr., 239(8), *256*
Kotch, A., 140(34), *144*
Krespan, C. G., 211
Kroning, E., 126(13), 128(13), *131*
Kruh, R. F., 3(3), *7*
Kubu, E. T., 191(30,31), *202*
Kudo, K., 260(10), 261(10), *262*
Kullmar, K., 147(19), *154*
Kumamoto, J., 257(1), *262*
Kunitz, F. W., 185(4), 199(4,44), *202, 203*
Kutch, E. L., 149(39), *155*
Kuzina, L. S., 66(16), *72*
Kuznetzov, T. S., 251(12), *256*

L

La Combe, E. M., 137(24), *144*
Lal, J., 125(1), *131*, 150(45), *155*
Lamfrom, H., 157(8), *163*
Landau, J. V., 231(12), *233*
Lando, J. B., 147(20), 152, *154*
Langford, R. B., 108(16), *110*
Lardy, H. A., 158(13a), *163*
Lautenschlaeger, F., 73, 74(5,6), *81*
Lauterbur, P. C., 76(9), *81*
Lawson, W. B., 236(4), *255*
Leach, S. J., 185(5,6), *202*
Ledbetter, M. C., 232, *233*
Leonard, E. C., 137(23), *144*
Leussing, D. L., 157(5,7), *163*
Levin, I. S., 150(44), *155*
Lewis, H. B., 109(21), *110*
Li, C. H., 235, *255*
Lindquist, L. C., 109(21), *110*
Linschitz, H., 109(20), *110*
Lipscomb, R. D., 66(15), *72*
Litvinenko, L. M., 91, *103*
Liu, W. K., 235(1), *255*
Llewellyn, D. R., 257(4), *262*
Lo, K. W., 261(13), *262*
Loewig, C., 146, *154*
Logan, N., 3(4), 4(4), *7*
Louis, J. B., 46(13), 47(2,3), *58*
Lown, E. M., 30(14), 34(15), *43*
Lüdemann, H., 5(11), *7*
Lumpkin, H. E., 71(23), *72*
Lutz, E. F., 126(15), *131*, 140(35), *144*

M

Macallum, A. D., 146(13), *154*
McCants, D., 75(7), *81*
McCullough, J. P., *155*
McDonald, R. N., 38(18), *43*
McGlynn, S. P., 109(22), *110*
Machon, J. P., 149(38), 152, *155*
McIntosh, C. L., 109(25), *110*
McIntosh, J. J., 87, 98, 100, *104*
Mackle, H., 62, *72*, 133(2), *144*, 147, 148, *155*
MacKnight, W. J., 61(1), *72*, 194(37), 196(37), *202*, 226(3), *228*
McMillan, D., 90, 91, *104*
McPhee, J. R., 46(16), 47, *58*

Mahbobb, S., 47(19), 48(19), *58*
Mahon, J. J., 159(14b), *163*
Mallory, F. B., 109(21), *110*
Malm, S. M., 26(10), *43*
Mammi, M., 147(21,22), 152, *154*, *155*
Mangini, A., 86–88, 92, 103(27–29), *103*, *104*
Marcus, S. H., 93, 99, *104*
Mark, H., 227, *228*
Markhart, A. H., 147(17), *154*
Marsland, D. A., 231(11,12), *233*
Marvel, C. S., 125(4), *131*, 133(5), 134, 140(34), *144*, 147, *154*
Mason, P., 186(14), *202*
Massey, A. G., 6, *7*
Matson, R. F., 10(3), *21*
Mayo, P. de, 109(25), *110*
Mayrich, R. G., 62(3), *72*
Mazia, D., 231(4,13), 232(9,14), *233*
Medina, H., 232(14), *233*
Mee, L. K., 263(4,5) *264*
Meerwein, H., 126(13), 128(13), *131*
Meichelbeck, H., 185(4), 199(4), *202*
Meinzer, R. A., 6, *7*
Meise, W., 205(3), *210*
Mels, W. H. v., 53, *58*
Merall, G. T.. 70(22), *72*
Merriam, C. N., 137(18), *144*
Meschers, A., 185(5), *202*
Messerly, J. F., *155*
Meyer, G. E., 113, *123*
Meyer, V., 146, *154*
Meyer, W. W., 88, *103*
Meyers, C. A., 91, *104*
Meyerson, S., 136, *144*
Michaelis, L., 157(2), *163*
Middleton, W. J., 205(1,2,4), *210*
Miller, S. I., 93, 99(16), *104*
Miller, Z. B., 157(9), *163*
Milligan, B., 70, *72*, 169(69), 170(9), *182*, 185(5,6), *202*
Milligan, D. F., 38(17), *43*
Mislan, J. P., 157(5), *163*
Mitchell, T. W., 186(18), 197(18), *202*
Mitchison, J. M., 231(15,22), 232(14), *233*
Mochulsky, M., 190(23), 191(23), *202*
Montgomery, D. J., 191(31), *202*
Moore, C. G., 167(1–5), 170(11,12), 172(12,15), 173(16), 174(16), 181(16,20), *182*, *183*

Moore, J. A., 157
Morell, J. L., 244(9), 252(13), *256*
Mortellaro, L., 146(12), 147(22), *154, 155*
Morton, M., 122
Müller, E., 106, *110*
Muller, E., 20(11), *21*
Mullins, L., 167(1), *182*
Murphy, T., 90, 91, *104*
Myers, R. J., 6, 7, *155*

N

Nakshbendi, H., 53, *58*, 70, *72*
Naples, F. J., 113(1), *123*
Nasonova, T. P., 227(5), *228*
Navon, G., 263(2,4,5), 264(6,7), *264*
Naylor, M. A., 134, 135(13), *144*
Nelson, R. A., 38(19), *43*
Newman, L., 157(7), *163*
Nicolaides, N., 138(28), *144*
Nielsen, S. O., 157(8), *163*
Nier, A. O., 55(40), *59*
Noether, H. D., 141, *144*
Norell, J. R., 137, *144*
Noshay, A., 125(3), *131*, 149(40), *155*
Novalena, G. G., 251(12), *256*

O

Oae, S., 84, 103, *104*
Obara, M., 149(41), *155*
O'Callaghan, W. B., 23(5), *43*
O'Hare, P. A. G., 133(2), *144*, 147, *155*
Ohi, R., 148, *155*
Ohsugi, S., 126(10), *131*
Ohta, M., 148, *155*
Oldham, K. G., 257(4), *262*
Orttung, F. W., 157(11), *163*
Osborn, S. W., 145, 149(39), *155*
Otsuji, K., 88, *103*
Otto, R., 137(21), *144*
Overberger, C. G., *144*, 157, 159(16), *163*

P

Paiss, Y., 263(1), *264*
Pajaro, G., 46(15), *58*

Panar, M., 257(5), 258(5), *262*
Passerini, R., 86(13,14), *103*
Pasto, D. J., 90, 91, 103, *104*
Patchornik, A., 236(4,6), *255*
Pawlowski, N. E., 66, *72*
Peacock, R. D., 5(10), *7*
Pearson, R. G., 50(32), *58*
Pell, A. S., 126(18), *131*
Pennington, R. E., *155*
Perlmann, G. E., 251
Peters, G., 70(19), *72*
Peterson, J., 46(16), 47(16), *58*
Pfeil, E., 126(13), 128(13), *131*
Phillips, W. D., *104*
Pickering, T. L., 61, 62(6), 63(6), 65(6), 71, *72*
Pierson, R. M., 113(1), *123*
Pilcher, G., 126(18), *131*
Piskareva, E. P., 227(5), *228*
Plato, C. H., 244(9), *256*
Porter, K. R., 232, *233*
Porter, M., 165, 173(16), 174(16), 178 (18), 181(16,20), *183*
Posner, J., 114, *123*
Post, B., 151(30), *155*
Pratt, D. W., 6(14), *7*
Prey, V., 106, *110*
Price, C. C., 66(15), *72*, 84, 103, *104*, 125 (3), *131*, 149(40), *155*
Pritchard, J. G., 76(9), *81*
Pryor, W., 137(25), *144*
Putnam, R. E., 205(2), *210*
Pye, D. G., 205(2), *210*

R

Ramakrishnan, V., 109(22), *110*
Ratner, S., 55(39), *58*
Ray, S. K., 6(14), *7*
Ray, W. J., Jr., 239(8), *256*
Raynal, J., 148(31), *155*
Rebenfeld, L., 185, 187(21), 191(7,35), 197(42), 198(35), *202, 203*
Reding, E. P., 128(19), *131*
Reese, C. E., 191(32), *202*
Reid, E. E., 42(20), *43*, 62, *72*
Reimann, S. P., 55(40), *59*
Reynolds, W. F., 93, 99(16), *104*
Rice, H. M., 113(1), *123*

Richards, F. M., 248(10), *256*
Richardson, G. W., 157(3), *163*
Rigby, B. J., 186(19), 187(19), 190(19), 191(27,28), *202*
Rittenberg, D., 55(39,40), *58*, *59*
Roberts, C. S., 147(16), *154*
Rubero, P. A., 19(10), *21*
Russo, M., 146(12), 147(22), *154*, *155*

S

Saegusa, T., 126(8–10), *131*, 149, *155*
Sakai, H., 231, 232(9,16,17,19–21), *233*
Sakai, N., 38(17), *43*
Sakata, R., 149(33,35), *155*
Saltman, W. M., 113(1), *123*
Sander, M., 145(3), 150(43), *154*, *155*
Saunders, K. J., 61
Saville, B., 70(21), *72*, 167(5,22), 169(7), 170(11), 173(16), 174(16), 181(16), *182*, *183*
Savitz, M. L., 109(21), *110*
Scanlan, J., 172(14), *183*
Scheele, W., 170(13), *183*
Scherf, K., 69, *72*
Schmadebeck, J. H., 73(1), *81*
Schmidbaur, H., 20, *21*
Schmidt, E. W., 106, *110*
Schmidt, M., 20(12), *21*
Schmir, G. L., 236(5), *255*
Schön, W., 236(3), *255*
Schoenheimer, R., 55(39), *58*
Schrock, R. W., 113(1), *123*
Schubert, M., 157(4), *163*
Schwab, P. A., 38(18), *43*
Scott, C. B., 50(24), *58*
Scott, D. W., *155*
Searles, S., 126(15), *131*, 138, 140, *144*
See, L. B., 109(26), *110*
Sehon, A. H., 133(6), *144*
Sela, M., 242
Senbold, F. H., 138(30), *144*
Senning, A., 108(13), *110*
Serniuk, G. E., 114, *123*
Shaetiel, S., 236(6), *255*
Shah, S. Y., 191(25), *202*
Sharkey, W. H., 133(5), *144*, 205, 207(7), *210*

Sharma, R. K., 105(1), 108, *110*
Sheppard, R. C., 242
Sherman, G. M., 109(20), *110*
Shida, S., 38(17), *43*
Shlyakhter, R. A., 227, *228*
Sidhu, K. S., 24(7), 30(14), *43*
Siebert, W., 20(12), *21*
Sigwalt, P., 145(4), 148, 149(38), 151, 152, *154*, *155*
Sims, D., 126(11), *131*
Skertchly, A. R. B., 186(15), *202*
Skinner, T. D., 181(21), *183*
Smith, H. A., 146(14), *154*
Smith, K. J., 73(3), 74(3), *81*
Snaith, J. W., 197(39,41), *202*, *203*
Solari, A. J., 232(9), *233*
Sorgo, M. de, 27(12), *43*
Speakman, J. B., 185(8), 186(16,17), 191, 200(45,46), *202*, *203*
Stannett, V., 147(20), 152, *154*
Steers, E., Jr., 242
Stegemeyer, H., 109, *110*
Stein, G., 263, 264(6–8), *264*
Steinrauf, L. K., 46(16), 47(16), *58*
Stepanov, V. M., 251(12), *256*
Stern, M. D., 190(24), 191(24), *202*
Stewart, B., 137(24), *144*
Stille, J. K., 38(18), *43*, 125, *131*, 148(27), 150(27), *155*
Strating, J., 73(2), *81*
Stratta, J. J., 128(19), *131*
Strausz, O. P., 23, 24(67), 26(9–11), 27 (9,12), 29(11,13), 30(14), 34(15), *43*
Strumeyer, D. H., 239(8) *256*
Stuckwisch, C. G., 119(7), *123*
Sundermeyer, W., 205(3), *210*
Sutton, L. E., *103*
Swain, C. G., 50(24), *58*
Swallow, A. J., 263(1), *264*
Swan, J. M., 70(21), *72*
Swaney, M. W., 114, *123*
Swann, M. M., 231(22), *233*
Sweeney, W., 125(5), 126(5), *131*, 141, *144*
Sweeting, O. J., 135, 136(15), *144*, 147 (18), *154*
Swift, P. M., 167(1), *182*
Szmant, H. H., 87, 98, 100, *104*

T

Taft, R. W., 103(26), *104*
Takahashi, M., 191(37), 196(37), *202*, 226 (3), *228*
Taliaferro, J. D., 137(26), *144*
Tamelen, E. E. van, 126(14), *131*
Taylor, J. E., 157(6), *163*
Taylor, P. G., 46(6), *58*
Templeton, D. H., 5, *7*
Terao, T., 38(17), *43*
Teter, L. A., 16, *21*
Tewksbury, L. B., 113(1), 121, *123*
Thiokol Chemical Corp., 146(10), 149 (36,37), 152(37), *154*, *155*
Thompson, S. D., 109(22), *110*
Tillett, J., 258(7), *262*
Tobolsky, A. V., 15, 17, *21*, 61, 62(6), 63(6), 65(6), 71(25,26), *72*, 190(22–24), 191, 194, 196(37,38), *202*, 221, 225, 226, *228*
Touro, F. J., 9, 14, 15(6), 18(9), *21*
Trego, B. R., 167(3–5), *182*
Trick, G. S., 113(1), *123*
Truce, W. E., 137, *144*, 259(9), *262*
Tsukerman, S. V., 91(9,10), *103*
Tsurugi, J., 87, *103*
Tsuruta, T., 149, *155*
Twiss, D., 62, 66, *72*
Tyerman, W. J. R., 23(4,5), 34(4), 35(4), 40(4), *43*

U

Uishima, T., 126(9), *131*
Urry, W. H., 138(28), *144*

V

Valle, G., 147(22), *155*
Van Wazer, J. R., 62, *72*
Vasil'eva, A. S., 205(5), *210*
Vasilyeva, V. N., 66(16), *72*
Vernon, C. A., 257(4), *262*
Vithayathil, P. J., 248(10), *256*

W

Waddington, G., *155*
Wagner, C., 53, *58*
Wagner, E. S., 47, 48, 49(20,23), 54(20), 55(20), *58*
Wallace, T. S., 159(14b), *163*
Walling, C., 68, *72*
Walmsley, D. A. G., 126(17), 128(17), *131*
Walter, H. C., 205(2), *210*
Wang, J., 157(6), *163*
Watson, A. A., 170(11,12), 172(12,15), 176(17), 177(17), 181(21), *182*, *183*
Weidmann, S., 146, *154*
Weigmann, H.-D., 185, 187(21), 191(7, 35), 197(42), 198(35), *202*, *203*
Weil, E. D., 73, 74(3), *81*, 125(4), *131* 134
Weiss, J., 3(3), *7*
Weissermel, K., 147(19), *154*
Wellisch, E., 135, 136, *144*, 147(18), *154*
Wells, T. F., 149(39), *155*
Westheimer, F. H., 257(1–3,5), 258(5), *262*
Whitehurst, D. D., 38(18), *43*
Whittaker, V. P., 157, *163*
Wiebe, H. A., 26(11), 29(11), *43*
Wieland, Th., 236(3), *255*
Wiewiorowski, T. K., 9, 14, 15(6), 18(9), 20(11), *21*
Willard, J. E., 46(14), *58*
Wilson, E. B., 232, *233*
Wilson, D. W., 55(40), *59*
Winkhaus, G., 62(4), *72*
Witkop, B., 235(2), 236(4,5), 244(9), 248 (11), *255*, *256*
Wittbecker, E. L., 126(12), *131*
Wölbling, H., 5(7), *7*
Woerden, H. van, 258(7), *262*
Wolf, W., 105(1), *110*
Wood, B. B. J., 150(42), *152*, 154(42), *155*
Wood, C. S., 109(21), *110*
Wood, G. C., 191(26), *202*
Woodhams, R. T., 150(42), 152, 154(42), *155*
Woods, H. J., 197, *203*
Wulfers, T. F., 109(27), *110*, 258(6), *262*
Wynne, K. J., 5(12), *7*

Y

Yan, J. F., 157(6), *163*
Yannios, S., 159(14a), *163*
Yarovenko, N. N., 205(5), *210*
Yarwood, A. J., 27(12), *43*
Yip, R. W., 109(27), *110*
Yuriev, Y. K., 150(44), *155*

Z

Zaborsky, O. R., 259(8), 260(10), 261
 (10,12), *262*
Zachariasen, W. H., 46(12), *58*
Zahn, H., 185(4), 197(40), 199(4,44), *202,*
 203
Zahradnik, R., 88, *103, 104*
Zalkin, A., 5, *7*
Zauli, C., 103(24), *104*

Subject Index

A

Absorption bands, temperature dependence of, 12

Acid strengths, electronic effect transmission through —S— bridges and, 89

Activation energy, of disulfide interchange reaction in wool fibers, 194

Active sulfurating agent, formation of, in vulcanization of rubber, 169

Adduct rubber, preparation of, 113
    properties of, 117

Allylic rearrangement, during vulcanization, 176

Alpha–beta transformation, in wool fibers, 186

B

Benzene sulfonyl halides, photolysis of, 108

Biphenyl, 108

Bis(pentachlorophenyl) disulfide, 106

Bis(pentachlorophenyl) sulfide, 108

Bis(trichloromethyl) disulfide, synthesis of, 106

Bond dissociation energy, of S—S bonds, 61

Bond lengths, of various C—X bonds, 126

Bunte salts, 48

Butadiene episulfide, 36

2-Butene episulfide, *cis* and *trans*, 30

1-Butene-3-thiol, 30

1-Butene-4-thiol, 30

2-Butene-1-thiol, 30

s-Butyl selenomercaptan, 42

t-Butyl selenomercaptan, 42

C

Catalyst, in mercaptan oxidation, ferric ion as, 159
    in polymerization, Lewis acids as, 126, 140, 148

metals alkyls as, 148

mineral acids as, 125, 148

trimethyloxonium fluoroborate as, 126

in polymerization of cyclic sulfides, 125

CBS (*N*-cyclohexylbenzothiazole-2-sulfenamide), 180

Chain length, in thermal decomposition of dimethyl tri- and tetrasulfide, 65, 68

Chemical relaxation time, 194

Chemical shift, effect of neighboring sulfur atoms on, 77

Compression set, of polysulfide polymers, 225

Condensation reaction, chemistry of, in polysulfide polymer preparation, 223

Contractile protein, 232

Copolymers, random, preparation by interchange of polysulfide homopolymers, 223
    ˜of thiocarbonyl fluoride and olefins, 208

Crosslinking efficiency, definition of, 166

Crosslinks, nature of, in vulcanized rubber, 165

Cyanogen bromide, as reagent for nonenzymatic cleavage of certain peptide bonds, 237

Cyclobutylselenomercaptan, 42

Cyclohexene sulfide, polymerization of, 126

Cyclohexylpentafluorophenyl sulfide, 106

Cyclopentene thiols, 32

Cyclopropene, 38

Cyclopropyl mercaptan, synthesis of, 28

Cyclopropylselenomercaptan, 42

D

Decomposition of sulfones, by beta elimination, 133
    by homolytic bond cleavage, 133

275

Deformation, reversibility of, keratin fibers, 197
Degree of polymerization, control of in polysulfide preparation, 222
Desulfuration, of polysulfide crosslinks in vulcanization, 176, 179
1,1-Difluoroethylene-2-thiol, 34
Difluoroethylene episulfide, *cis* and *trans*, 34
Dimethyl sulfate, hydrolysis of, 257
Dimethyl tetrasulfide, thermal decomposition of, 62
3,3-Dimethyl thietane, polymerization of, 126
Dimethyl thiophene, 39
Dimethyl trisulfide, thermal decomposition of, 67
Diphenyl sulfide, photolysis of, 108
Diphenyl sulfone, photolysis of, 108
Diphenyl sulfoxide, photolysis of, 108
Disulfide interchange, catalysis of, by mercaptans, 185
  by ZMBT complexes, 176
  in wool fibers, 185

E

Electronic configuration, of oxygen group elements, 24, 83
Electronic effect, transmission of, by sulfur atoms, 83
Electrophilic character, of $S(^1D)$ and $S(^3P)$ atoms, 35
Episelenides, 40
Episulfides. *See* Thiiranes *or look under specific compound names, e.g.,* Propylene episulfide.
Episulfonium ion, in reactions of sulfur dichloride with olefins, 79
Equilibration, of polysulfide bonds in alkaline media, 224
ESR spectra, of sulfur nitride anions, 6
Ethylene sulfate, hydrolysis of, 257

F

Free radical displacement reaction at carbon, 216

H

Hammett σ values, correlation of NMR chemical shift differences with, in aromatic sulfides, 102
Heat of polymerization, of thiirane, 148
Heat of solution, of hydrogen monosulfide in molten sulfur, 13
2,6-Heptane dithiol, oxidation of, 158
Hexamethylbenzene, 39
2,5-Hexane dithiol, oxidation of, 158
Hydrogen monosulfide, infrared spectrum of, 11
Hydrogen polysulfides, infrared spectra of, 11
  NMR spectra of, 20
Hydrolysis of cyclic sulfates, rate enhancement in, 257
o-Hydroxy-α-toluene sulfonic acid sultone, hydrolysis of, 259

I

Infrared spectra, of fluorothiocarbonyl compounds, 206
  of hydrogen polysulfides. *See* Hydrogen polysulfides.
Infrared spectroscopy, use in determination of rates of addition of mercaptans to polyolefins, 118
  use in determination of transmission effects in aromatic sulfides, 88
  use of molten sulfur in, 9
Inhibition, of thermal decomposition of dimethyl trisulfide, 67
Inhibition time, in decomposition of dimethyl tetrasulfide, 64
Interchange reaction, of polysulfide bonds, 224, 226
Ionization potential of olefins, correlation between the rate of addition of triplet sulfur atoms to olefins and, 35
Isobutylene episulfide, 30
Isomerization, of stereoregular polymers by mercaptans, 115
Isotope effect, for insertion of sulfur atoms into C—H bonds, 27
  in the reaction of cystine with sulfite ion, 48

Isovoltage, in sulfite–thiosulfate system, 51

L

Ladder polymers, formation of, from 1,2-polybutadiene, 122

M

MBT (mercaptobenzothiazole), 181
MBTS (mercaptobenzothiazoyl disulfide), 181
Methyl mercaptan, free radical addition of, to polybutadiene, 113, 115
2-Methyl-1-propene-1-thiol, 30
2-Methyl-1-propene-3-thiol, 30
Mitotic apparatus, protein components of, 232
Monosulfide polymers. *See* Polythioethers *or look under specific polymer names, e.g.*, Polymethylene sulfide.

N

NEMI (*N*-ethyl maleimide), use of as a blocking agent for mercapto groups, 187
NMR spectra, of dimethyl polysulfides, 62
of fluorothiocarbonyl compounds, 206
of hydrogen polysulfides. *See* Hydrogen polysulfides.
of polysulfide polymers, 141
of products from sulfur dichloride–olefin reactions, 75–77
of sulfur–hydrogen sulfide systems, 20
of sulfur–nitrogen compounds, 3, 4
NMR spectroscopy, use in determination of transmission effects in aromatic sulfides, 92
NMR spectrum, of tetrafluoro-1,2,3,4-tetrathiane, 212
Nucleophilic attack, by hydroxide on sulfur in hydrolysis of sulfate esters, 258
Nucleophilic displacement, by mercaptide ions on cyclic tetrasulfides, 214
by mercaptide ions on polysulfide bonds, 222

O

Octachlorobenzothiophene, 107
Octachlorothianthrene, 107
Octafluoro-1,4-dithiane, 216
One-electron reagents, reaction of sulfur compounds with, 263
d Orbitals, involvements of, in sulfur compounds, 83
Oxibase scale, 50
application to the cystine sulfite ion system, 52
Oxidation, of polyvinyl mercaptan, 157
of thiol-terminated polysulfide liquid polymers, 225
Oxidation–reduction, of thiol groups during cell division, 232
Oxidative dimerization potential, 50

P

Pentachlorobenzenesulfenyl chloride, photolysis of, 106
2,4-Pentane dithiol, oxidation of, 158
Peptide bonds, nonenzymatic cleavage of, 235
Perfluorotetramethyl thiophene, 40
Permanent set, in wool fibers, 197
Phalloidin, nonenzymatic fragmentation of, 236
Phenyl-α-toluenesulfonate, hydrolysis of, 259
Photolysis, of carbon disulfide, 26
of carbonyl selenide, 40
of carbonyl sulfide, 24
Photochemical synthesis. *See* Synthesis, photochemical.
Piperdinium propane-2-thiolate, use as a specific reagent for cleavage of polysulfide linkages, 167
Polyethylene sulfide, 148
properties of, 151
Polymethylene sulfide, properties of, 152
Polypropylene sulfide, properties of, 152
Polysulfide crosslinks, factors controlling the structure of, in rubber, 179
precursors of, in vulcanization, 168
Polysulfide elastomers, 145, 221, 225

Polysulfide polymers, fluorinated, properties of, 217
  properties of, 129
  synthesis of, 221
  thiol terminated, 225
Polysulfone polymers, properties of, 130, 139
Polythioethers, preparation, by addition of thiols to olefins, 146
  by condensation polymerization, 138, 145
  by ring opening polymerization, 140, 147
  properties of, 150, 205
Propene-1-thiol, *cis* and *trans*, synthesis of, 30
Propene-3-thiol, synthesis of, 30
Propylene episulfide, synthesis of, 30

Q

Quenching, of $S(^1D)$ atoms by CO_2, 32

R

Radiative lifetime, of COS, 24
Rank of polysulfide solutions, 224
Relaxation rate of polysulfide polymers, effect of mercaptide–disulfide interchange on, 226
Resonance stabilization, of sulfur radicals, 71
Rubber bound intermediate, formation of and conversion into crosslinks, in vulcanization, 170, 172

S

S_4N_3 ion, 3
Selectivity, in insertion reactions of sulfur atoms, 27
Selenium, atomic, addition and insertion reactions of, 40
  insertion into C—H and Si—H bonds, 42
S_N2 displacement, by sulfite ion on cystine, 48

Sodium di-*n*-butyl phosphite, use as a specific reagent for di- and polysulfide linkages, 167
Spectroscopic states, of S_2, 25
  of sulfur atoms, 24
S—S bonds, relation between activation energy for cleavage of and length of, 45
Stereoregularity, in polypropylene sulfide polymers, 150
Stereospecificity, of reaction of singlet and triplet sulfur atoms with difluoroethylene, 33
  of singlet and triplet sulfur atom additions to olefins, 30
Strain energy, of cyclic sulfides, 128, 147
Stress relaxation, chemical, in polysulfide rubbers, 221
  effect of ionic bonds on chemical, 226
  of keratin fibers, 191
  scission of disulfide bonds as mechanism of, in wool fibers, 191
Stress–strain behavior, of wool fibers, 185
Stripping, of polysulfide polymers, 227
Sulfene, possible formation of, in hydrolysis of sulfate esters, 260
Sulfenyl halides, photolysis of, 105
Sulfone polymers, preparation by condensation methods, 138
Sulfonium salts, formation of, in cleavage of peptides by cyanogen bromide, 239
Sulfur, atomic, insertion into C—H bonds, 27, 35
  insertion into Si—H and B—H bonds, 28
  reaction with alkynes, 37
  reaction with olefins, 29
  reaction with paraffins, 26
  relative rates of reaction of singlet and triplet, with olefins, 34
  sources of singlet and triplet, 24
  spectroscopic excited states, 24
  spectroscopic ground state, 24
Sulfur dichloride, addition of, to diolefins, 73
Sulfur, elemental, reaction of with fluoroolefins, 211
  solutions of, in amines, 70

Sulfur–hydrogen sulfide solutions, equilibria in, 16
Sulfur, molten, equilibria in, 15
Sulfur nitride, Lewis acid adducts of, 5
paramagnetic anions of, 6
Sulfur–nitrogen–chlorine compounds, 3
Synthesis, photochemical, of unsaturated mercaptans, 29, 36

T

Tetrachlorobenzyne, possible formation of, in photolysis of pentachloro-benzenesulfenyl halide, 107
Tetrafluoro-1,2,3,4-thiane, polymerization of, 213
preparation of, 212
Tetrafluorothiirane, polymerization of, 215
preparation of, 213, 215
Tetrafluoro-1,2,3-trithiolane, preparation of, 212
1,3,5,7-Tetrathiacyclooctane, polymerization of, 147
Thermal decomposition, of polysulfide crosslinks in vulcanized rubber, 179
Thermal stability, of dimethyl tetrasulfide, 65
of neopentyl-based sulfide and sulfone monomers and polymers, 138, 143
Thermochemical bond energy, of S—S bonds, 61
6-Thiabicyclo [3.1.1] heptane, polymerization of, 126
Thiacyclopropenes, 37, 38
Thiatrimethylene biradical, reaction with olefins, 31
Thietane, 147
polymerization of, 126
Thiirane, 147
Thiiranes, gas-phase photochemical synthesis of, 29, 36
polymerization of, 125, 148

Thiocarbonyl fluoride, anionic polymerization of, 205
free radical polymerization of, 207
Thioethers, stability of, 121
Thiophene, 31
tetramethyl, 39
Thiophilicity, of various nucleophiles, 50, 51
Thiothiyl radicals, reaction with alkyl polysulfides, 64
Thiyl radicals, reaction with tetrafluoro-ethylene, 212
TMTD (tetramethylthiuram disulfide), 170
Trialkylborane/oxygen system, as low temperature free radical initiator, 207
Trichloromethanesulfonyl chloride, photolysis of, 108
Trimethyl benzene, 39
Trimethylene sulfate, hydrolysis of, 257
sym-Trithiane, polymerization of, 147

U

Ultraviolet spectroscopy, use of to determine transmission effects in aromatic sulfides, 86
Unsaturation, residual, in adduct rubber, 118

V

Vinyl mercaptan, synthesis of, 29
Vinylthiacyclopropane, 31
Vulcanization, of rubber, course of, 168
structure of the initial polysulfide crosslinks formed in, 175
structural units formed in, 165

Z

ZDC (zinc dialkyldithiocarbamate), 169
ZMBT (zinc benzothiazole-2-thiolate), 169